MST224

Mathematical methods

Book 4

Advanced topics

Cover image: This shows a simulation of the patterns formed by smoke particles moving in air, which is itself in turbulent motion. The positions of the particles are described by relatively simple differential equations, yet the patterns that they form are complex and intriguing. Similar patterns are also relevant to understanding how clouds produce rain, and are a subject of ongoing research at The Open University.

This publication forms part of an Open University module. Details of this and other Open University modules can be obtained from the Student Registration and Enquiry Service, The Open University, PO Box 197, Milton Keynes MK7 6BJ, United Kingdom (tel. +44 (0)845 300 6090; email general-enquiries@open.ac.uk).

Alternatively, you may visit the Open University website at www.open.ac.uk where you can learn more about the wide range of modules and packs offered at all levels by The Open University.

To purchase a selection of Open University materials visit www.ouw.co.uk, or contact Open University Worldwide, Walton Hall, Milton Keynes MK7 6AA, United Kingdom for a brochure (tel. +44 (0)1908 858779; fax +44 (0)1908 858787; email ouw-customer-services@open.ac.uk).

The Open University has had Woodland Carbon Code Pending Issuance Units assigned from Doddington North forest creation project (IHS ID103/26819) that will, as the trees grow, compensate for the greenhouse gas emissions from the manufacture of the paper in MST224 *Block 4*. More information can be found at https://www.woodlandcarboncode.org.uk/

The Open University, Walton Hall, Milton Keynes, MK7 6AA.

First published 2013.

Edited, designed and typeset by The Open University, using the Open University TeX System.

Printed in the United Kingdom by Halstan & Co. Ltd, Amersham, Bucks.

ISBN 978 1 7800 7482 5

1.1

Contents

Contents

Fourier series

Introduction

This unit is concerned with *periodic functions*. A simple example is provided by the cosine function shown in Figure 1.

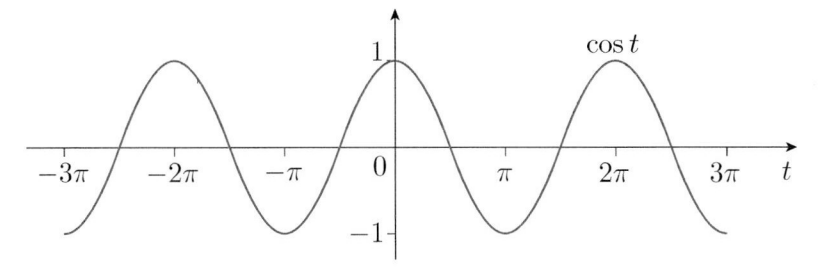

Figure 1 The cosine function $\cos t$, which has period 2π

This is a periodic function that repeats itself over every 2π interval of its domain. That is, if we plot the function for $0 \leq t \leq 2\pi$, and translate that piece of the function by $\pm 2\pi, \pm 4\pi, \ldots$ along the horizontal t-axis, then we recover the entire function. The same is true, of course, if we plot the function over any other domain interval of length 2π. A more mathematical way of expressing this fact is to say that $\cos t$ and $\cos(t + 2\pi)$ have the same value for all t. We write

$$\cos(t + 2\pi) = \cos(t) \quad \text{for all } t,$$

and say that $\cos t$ has *period* 2π.

Figures 2–4 show three more examples of periodic functions.

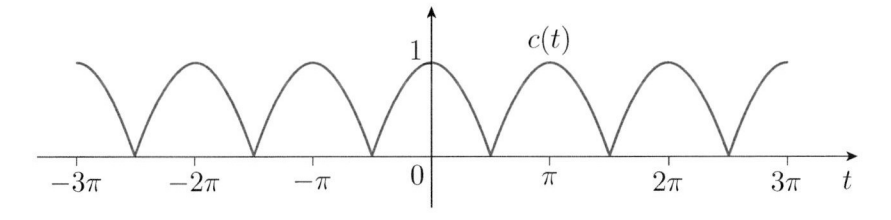

Figure 2 The function $c(t) = |\cos t|$, with period π

The function $c(t)$ shown in Figure 2 is the modulus of the cosine function, defined by

$$c(t) = |\cos t|.$$

This function repeats itself every domain interval of length π. Its period is π, and we write

$$c(t + \pi) = c(t) \quad \text{for all } t.$$

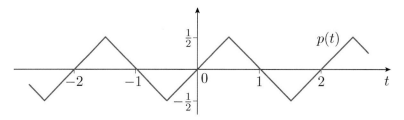

Figure 3   A sawtooth function $p(t)$, with period 2

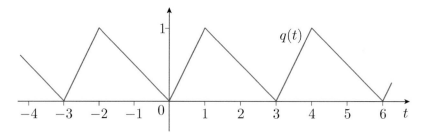

Figure 4   A sawtooth function $q(t)$, with period 3

The functions $p(t)$ and $q(t)$ shown in Figures 3 and 4 are of a type known as **sawtooth functions** because their graphs are similar in shape to the teeth of a saw. There are no simple one-line formulas for functions like this, but you will see how they can be specified in Section 1. The graph of $p(t)$ in Figure 3 repeats itself over every domain interval of length 2. Its period is 2, and we write

$$p(t + 2) = p(t) \quad \text{for all } t.$$

The graph of $q(t)$ in Figure 4 repeats itself over every domain interval of length 3. Its period is 3, and we write

$$q(t + 3) = q(t) \quad \text{for all } t.$$

Periodicity and hence periodic functions arise naturally in a wide variety of contexts. They may describe a regular oscillation in time or a regular variation in space. For the most part we will ignore the physical setting and just think about periodic functions of an independent variable.

The importance of periodic functions

A familiar example of a periodic function arises when an undamped pendulum or an undamped harmonic oscillator (of the type discussed in Unit 3) moves to and fro; in this case, the displacement is a periodic function of time. Many musical instruments are mechanical oscillators: for example, you can see the vibrating motion of the strings of a guitar or a piano. Other musical instruments, such as an organ or a flute, create oscillations of pressure in the air.

Periodic functions are often a consequence of circular or cyclic motion. For example, the number of hours of daylight in London varies periodically with a period of one year (with a maximum around 21 June and a minimum around 21 December). This periodic variation is a consequence of the orbit of the Earth around the Sun. Other examples of approximately periodic functions of time, such as the rise and fall of the tides, can be traced to the orbits of astronomical bodies. (In the case of tides, the effect is predominantly due to the gravitational influence of the Moon.)

Many mechanical systems naturally give rise to periodic functions of time. An example is the steam locomotive shown in Figure 5, where the periodic motion of a piston inside a cylinder drives the rotation of a set of wheels through a connecting rod. A very similar arrangement for converting the periodic motion of a piston to circular motion is used in almost all car engines.

In science and engineering, we encounter periodic functions of position as well as time. A very important example is the arrangement of atoms in a crystal, where the atoms form a regular arrangement on a three-dimensional lattice, such as that illustrated in Figure 6. Here the density of electrons in the crystal is described by a periodic function of three spatial variables. However, this is beyond the scope of this unit, which considers only periodic functions of a single variable.

Figure 5 Periodic and cyclical motions are often closely related: for example, periodic motion of a piston in a cylinder, driven by escaping steam, is converted to a circular motion of a set of wheels on this locomotive

Obviously sines and cosines are periodic functions. However, it turns out that (almost) all periodic functions can be written in a unified way: as a constant (which may be zero) plus an infinite sum over sines and cosines. In this way sines and cosines can be viewed as the 'fundamental' periodic functions, i.e. all others can be expressed as linear combinations of them.

For example, it can be shown that the function $c(t) = |\cos t|$ corresponds to the infinite sum

$$C(t) = \frac{4}{\pi} \left[\tfrac{1}{2} + \tfrac{1}{3}\cos(2t) - \tfrac{1}{15}\cos(4t) + \tfrac{1}{35}\cos(6t) - \cdots \right]. \tag{1}$$

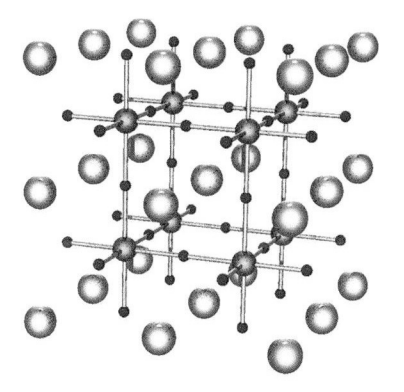

Figure 6 The atoms of many materials, such as this perovskite crystal, have a regular and periodic spacing; the electron density in such a crystal is a periodic function of position

This sum contains infinitely many terms. In the limiting case where all these terms are added together, the sum $C(t)$ becomes equal to the original function $c(t)$, allowing us to write

$$c(t) = C(t).$$

In a similar way, the sawtooth functions $p(t)$ and $q(t)$ introduced above correspond to the infinite sums

$$P(t) = \frac{4}{\pi^2} \left[\sin(\pi t) - \tfrac{1}{9}\sin(3\pi t) + \tfrac{1}{25}\sin(5\pi t) - \tfrac{1}{49}\sin(7\pi t) + \cdots \right], \tag{2}$$

$$Q(t) = \frac{1}{2} - \frac{27}{8\pi^2} \left[\cos\left(\tfrac{2\pi t}{3}\right) + \tfrac{1}{4}\cos\left(\tfrac{4\pi t}{3}\right) + \tfrac{1}{16}\cos\left(\tfrac{8\pi t}{3}\right) + \cdots \right]$$
$$+ \frac{9\sqrt{3}}{8\pi^2} \left[\sin\left(\tfrac{2\pi t}{3}\right) - \tfrac{1}{4}\sin\left(\tfrac{4\pi t}{3}\right) + \tfrac{1}{16}\sin(\tfrac{8\pi t}{3}) + \cdots \right]. \tag{3}$$

When all the terms in these sums are added together, we get $p(t) = P(t)$ and $q(t) = Q(t)$.

Infinite sums like these are called **Fourier series**, named after their discoverer Joseph Fourier. They have a common structure, which can be written as

$$F(t) = A_0 + \sum_{n=1}^{\infty} A_n \cos(\omega_n t) + \sum_{n=1}^{\infty} B_n \sin(\omega_n t),$$

where A_0, A_n, B_n and ω_n are real numbers, some of which may be equal to zero (details will be given in Subsection 2.1).

Notice that we distinguish the Fourier series from its corresponding function by using a capital letter, so that the Fourier series for $c(t)$ is denoted $C(t)$. For all the functions that we will consider, the function $f(t)$ and its Fourier series $F(t)$ have the same values, i.e. $f(t) = F(t)$ (except perhaps at isolated points), even though they may be completely different expressions.

There are some interesting differences between the Fourier series in equations (1)–(3). $C(t)$ is a constant plus a sum over cosines, $P(t)$ is a sum over sines, and $Q(t)$ is a constant plus a sum over both sines and cosines.

Since sines and cosines are periodic, it is perhaps not too surprising that $C(t)$, $P(t)$ and $Q(t)$ are also periodic. Note also that for successive terms in each sum, the argument of the sine or cosine increases, but the constant multiplying the term decreases. The sums are infinite in the sense that they do not stop after a finite number of terms, although in practice we take only enough terms to make the result as accurate as required. In this unit you will see how to calculate Fourier series. This means finding appropriate values for A_0, A_n, B_n and ω_n for any given periodic function.

To see how it is possible for a sum over sines and cosines to approach a given function, take a look at Figure 7.

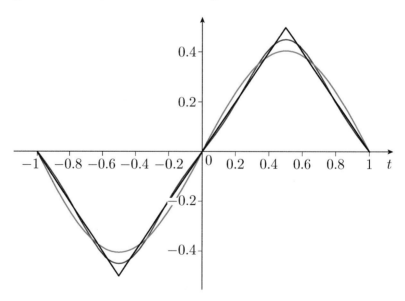

Figure 7 The function $p(t)$ (in black), together with the approximations $P_1(t)$ (in blue) and $P_2(t)$ (in red) representing the first term and the sum of the first two terms in equation (2), the Fourier series for $p(t)$

Here we compare the exact sawtooth function $p(t)$ of Figure 3 with the first two approximations to its Fourier series $P(t)$. The first approximation $P_1(t)$ is just the first term in $P(t)$, and the second approximation $P_2(t)$ is the sum of the first two terms:

$$P_1(t) = \frac{4}{\pi^2} \sin(\pi t),$$

$$P_2(t) = \frac{4}{\pi^2} \left[\sin(\pi t) - \tfrac{1}{9} \sin(3\pi t) \right].$$

You can see that P_2 (in red) is a better approximation than P_1 (in blue). More generally, as we add more terms to the Fourier series, it gradually approaches the original function. Each additional term improves the approximation. In fact, if we were to plot $P_{10}(t)$, the sum of the first 10 terms in the Fourier series, it would be hardly distinguishable from the original function. Adding all the terms in the Fourier series would give $p(t) = P(t)$ exactly.

Fourier series will be used in Unit 12. There you will be looking at the transverse vibrations of guitar strings and the conduction of heat along metal rods. In the case of a vibrating guitar string, it is not surprising that periodic functions are involved and that Fourier series are applicable. In fact, by describing the shape of a displaced guitar string by a Fourier series, we can represent the sound made by a guitar as a sum of a fundamental tone and a series of harmonics. However, it is not so obvious that solutions to the heat conduction problem can also be found as sums of sinusoidal terms. This was one of the many great discoveries of Joseph Fourier (Figure 8).

Figure 8 The French mathematician, physicist and historian Joseph Fourier (1768–1830)

Study guide

This unit shows you how to calculate the Fourier series for periodic and other functions, like those in equations (1)–(3). It assumes that you are familiar with *integration by parts* and *complex numbers* (see Unit 1).

Section 1 defines what periodic functions are and explains how to write down their formulas. Much of this may be familiar to you, but we recommend that you read it and attempt the exercises as the ideas are used throughout the rest of the unit.

Section 2 is the core section of this unit. It defines the Fourier series for a periodic function, and shows how such a series is calculated. It also explains how Fourier series can be used to represent non-periodic functions defined over a finite domain. Section 3 discusses the behaviour of Fourier series near discontinuities, and considers the differentiation of Fourier series.

The remainder of the unit consists of Section 4 and an Appendix. These parts of the unit are optional, but we strongly advise you to study them if you have time, because they develop ideas that are important in more advanced areas of mathematics and the physical sciences. Section 4 introduces an alternative form of the Fourier series, based on a sum of complex exponential functions. We illustrate the value of this form of the

Fourier series by showing how it can help us to solve a differential equation. Finally, the Appendix contains proofs of formulas used in the main text, and also develops the important idea of orthogonal functions.

1 Periodic functions

Before explaining how to calculate Fourier series, we first look at the definition and properties of periodic functions. We then briefly review the types of notation that are used to express periodic functions. Finally, we remind you about some properties of odd and even functions. Much of this material may already be familiar to you, but these subsections are short and the material contained in them is essential to what follows. So it is worth reading them and trying the exercises before moving on to Section 2.

1.1 The period of a function

In the Introduction we looked at some examples of periodic functions, and stated that they have the property that, when plotted, they *repeat themselves* over some interval. We now make this intuitive notion of periodicity precise.

Consider the function $\cos t$ shown in Figure 9.

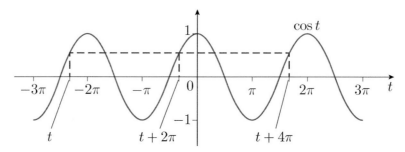

Figure 9   The periodicity of the cosine function:
$\cos t = \cos(t + 2\pi) = \cos(t + 4\pi) = \cos(t + 6\pi) = \ldots$

Notice that $\cos 0 = \cos 2\pi$. In fact, it is clear that $\cos t = \cos(t + 2\pi)$ for all values of t. Likewise, we can say that

$$\cos t = \cos(t + 2\pi) = \cos(t + 4\pi) = \cos(t + 6\pi) = \ldots \quad \text{for all } t.$$

So there is an infinite set of positive values $\tau = 2\pi, 4\pi, 6\pi, \ldots$ for which

$$\cos t = \cos(t + \tau) \quad \text{for all } t.$$

We call these values of τ the *periods* of $\cos t$. The smallest (non-zero) period is $\tau = 2\pi$, and this is called the *fundamental period* of $\cos t$. More generally, we make the following definitions.

Periodic functions and their periods

A function $f(t)$ is said to be **periodic** if for some *positive* number τ it satisfies

$$f(t) = f(t + \tau) \quad \text{for all } t.$$

The number τ is said to be a **period** of the function $f(t)$.

If τ is a period of $f(t)$, then so are 2τ, 3τ, and so on. By definition, all periods are positive, and the smallest period of $f(t)$ is called the **fundamental period**.

In applications, the fundamental period is far more important than the other periods. For this reason, many scientists use the term *period* as a shorthand for the fundamental period. For example, the fundamental period of a pendulum (the time it takes to swing to and fro) is usually called *the* period of the pendulum. We occasionally use this shorthand when there is no risk of confusion. If we talk about *the period* of a function, then we mean its fundamental period, but if we talk of the *set of periods* of a function, then we mean all of its periods, fundamental and not.

We sometimes need to find the period of a function such as $\cos(5t)$. In this case, we can argue as follows. The complete set of periods of the cosine function is $\tau = 2\pi, 4\pi, 6\pi, 8\pi, \dots$. For any of these values of τ, we have

$$\cos(5(t + \tau/5)) = \cos(5t + \tau) = \cos(5t).$$

This shows that $\tau/5$ is one of the periods of $\cos(5t)$. The smallest such period corresponds to the smallest of the above values of τ, which is 2π, so the fundamental period of $\cos(5t)$ is $2\pi/5$. More generally, the constant ω in the functions $\cos(\omega t)$ and $\sin(\omega t)$ is called the **angular frequency**, and the fundamental period of these functions is $2\pi/\omega$.

Example 1

What are the fundamental periods of the following functions?

(a) $\sin 5t$

(b) $\cos 3t$

(c) $3 \sin 5t + 7 \cos 3t$

Solution

(a) The function $\sin 5t$ has angular frequency $\omega = 5$ and therefore has fundamental period $\tau = 2\pi/\omega = 2\pi/5$.

(b) The function $\cos 3t$ has angular frequency $\omega = 3$ and therefore has fundamental period $\tau = 2\pi/\omega = 2\pi/3$.

(c) The function $3\sin 5t + 7\cos 3t$ is the sum of two functions: $3\sin 5t$ and $7\cos 3t$. The complete set of periods for $3\sin 5t$ is given by the positive integer multiples of $2\pi/5$, that is,

$$\frac{2\pi}{5}, \frac{4\pi}{5}, \frac{6\pi}{5}, \frac{8\pi}{5}, \frac{10\pi}{5}, \ldots.$$

The complete set of periods for $7\cos 3t$ is given by the positive integer multiples of $2\pi/3$, that is,

$$\frac{2\pi}{3}, \frac{4\pi}{3}, \frac{6\pi}{3}, \frac{8\pi}{3}, \frac{10\pi}{3}, \ldots.$$

The smallest period that these functions have in common is $10\pi/5 = 2\pi$ for $3\sin 5t$ and $6\pi/3 = 2\pi$ for $7\cos 3t$. So the fundamental period of $3\sin 5t + 7\cos 3t$ is 2π.

Example 2

Find $p(99)$ and $p(99.5)$ for the sawtooth function $p(t)$ in Figure 3.

Solution

The given function has period 2, so $p(t+2) = p(t)$. Hence

$$p(99) = p(97) = p(95) = \ldots = p(1) = 0,$$

where the final value is obtained by examination of Figure 3. Similarly,

$$p(99.5) = p(97.5) = p(95.5) = \ldots = p(1.5) = -\tfrac{1}{2}.$$

Exercise 1

What are the fundamental periods of the following functions?

(a) $\sin\left(\tfrac{1}{4}x\right)$ (b) $\cos\left(\tfrac{2}{5}x\right)$ (c) $\sin\left(\tfrac{1}{4}x\right) + 2\cos\left(\tfrac{2}{5}x\right)$

Exercise 2

Calculate $q(1000)$ and $q(-77)$, where $q(t)$ is the sawtooth function in Figure 4.

1.2 Piecewise functions

We have previously noted that the two sawtooth functions $p(t)$ and $q(t)$, sketched in Figures 3 and 4, cannot be described by simple one-line formulas. However, we can write down relatively simple formulas for these functions if we initially restrict attention to a finite interval and split this into two pieces.

First consider the function $p(t)$, whose graph is reproduced in Figure 10.

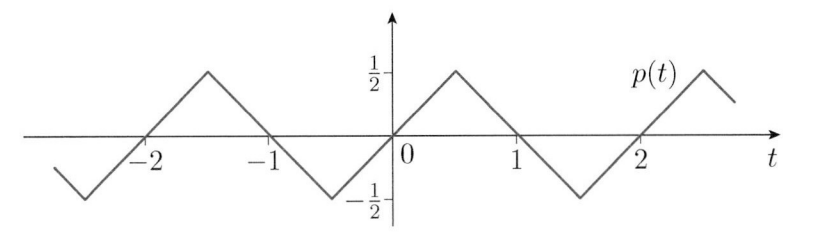

Figure 10   The function $p(t)$

Notice that if t lies in the interval $-\frac{1}{2} \leq t \leq \frac{1}{2}$, then $p(t) = t$. Also, if t lies in the interval $\frac{1}{2} \leq t \leq \frac{3}{2}$, then $p(t) = 1 - t$. This allows us to use the following notation to define $p(t)$ on the interval $-\frac{1}{2} \leq t \leq \frac{3}{2}$:

$$p(t) = \begin{cases} t & \text{for } -\frac{1}{2} \leq t \leq \frac{1}{2}, \\ 1 - t & \text{for } \frac{1}{2} < t \leq \frac{3}{2}. \end{cases}$$

In this expression, we have chosen to include the point $t = \frac{1}{2}$ in the first region, which is written as $-\frac{1}{2} \leq t \leq \frac{1}{2}$. There is then no need to include $t = \frac{1}{2}$ in the second region, so this is written as $\frac{1}{2} < t \leq \frac{3}{2}$.

Different choices are equally valid. For example, the two regions could be taken to be $-\frac{1}{2} \leq t < \frac{1}{2}$ and $\frac{1}{2} \leq t \leq \frac{3}{2}$.

Functions like this, which are defined on two or more pieces of their domain, are called **piecewise functions**. We now complete the definition of $p(t)$ for all t by adding the information that it is periodic with period 2, i.e. $p(t + 2) = p(t)$. So the full definition of $p(t)$ is

$$p(t) = \begin{cases} t & \text{for } -\frac{1}{2} \leq t \leq \frac{1}{2}, \\ 1 - t & \text{for } \frac{1}{2} < t \leq \frac{3}{2}, \end{cases} \tag{4}$$

$$p(t + 2) = p(t).$$

The condition $p(t + 2) = p(t)$ applies for all t.

The first part of this definition defines $p(t)$ on an interval of length $\tau = 2$. This interval is called the **fundamental interval** of the function. The second part tells us that the function has fundamental period $\tau = 2$.

Note that because $p(t)$ is periodic, it is quite permissible to define it on any other fundamental interval of length 2. For example,

$$p(t) = \begin{cases} t & \text{for } 0 \leq t \leq \frac{1}{2}, \\ 1 - t & \text{for } \frac{1}{2} < t \leq \frac{3}{2}, \\ t - 2 & \text{for } \frac{3}{2} < t \leq 2, \end{cases}$$

$$p(t + 2) = p(t)$$

is an equally valid, if less elegant, definition. In this case the fundamental interval is $0 \leq t \leq 2$, while in equation (4) the fundamental interval is $-\frac{1}{2} \leq t \leq \frac{3}{2}$.

Example 3

Give a piecewise definition of the function $q(t)$ in Figure 11, using the fundamental interval $0 \leq t \leq 3$.

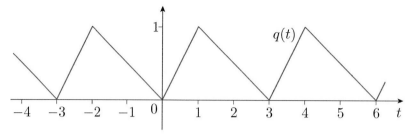

Figure 11   The function $q(t)$

Solution

We have $q(t) = t$ for $0 \leq t \leq 1$, and $q(t) = \frac{3}{2} - \frac{1}{2}t$ for $1 < t \leq 3$. Furthermore, $q(t)$ has period 3, so $q(t+3) = q(t)$ for all t. We can therefore define $q(t)$ as follows:

$$q(t) = \begin{cases} t & \text{for } 0 \leq t \leq 1, \\ \frac{3}{2} - \frac{1}{2}t & \text{for } 1 < t \leq 3, \end{cases}$$

$$q(t+3) = q(t).$$

Exercise 3

Write down the piecewise definition of the function $q(t)$ in Figure 11 over the fundamental interval $-\frac{3}{2} \leq t \leq \frac{3}{2}$.

Exercise 4

Sketch the following function over the range $-3 \leq x \leq 6$:

$$f(x) = \begin{cases} x & \text{for } 0 \leq x \leq 1, \\ 1 & \text{for } 1 < x \leq 2, \\ 3 - x & \text{for } 2 < x \leq 3, \end{cases}$$

$$f(x+3) = f(x).$$

1.3   Discontinuous functions

The function $\cos t$ shown in Figure 1 is both **continuous** and **smooth**. A *continuous* function can be sketched without lifting your pen from the paper – there are no abrupt changes in value. A *smooth* function has a graph with no sharp corners – there are no abrupt changes in slope. The functions $c(t)$, $p(t)$ and $q(t)$ in Figures 2–4 are all continuous, but they are not smooth because these graphs have sharp corners. In this subsection, we introduce functions that are not continuous.

Consider the function $h(t)$ shown in Figure 12.

The dashed lines are used to guide the eye; they are not part of the definition of the function.

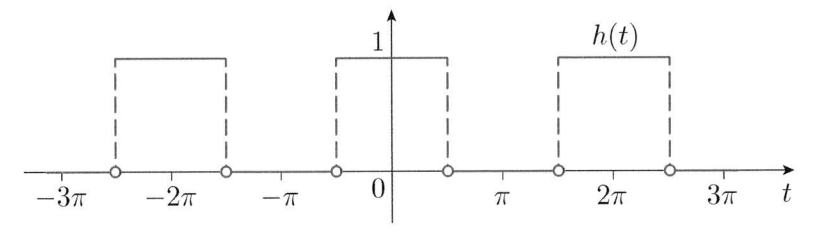

Figure 12   A square-wave function $h(t)$ with period 2π

This is a type of function known as a **square-wave function**, and the version considered here is defined by

$$h(t) = \begin{cases} 1 & \text{for } -\tfrac{1}{2}\pi \le t \le \tfrac{1}{2}\pi, \\ 0 & \text{for } \tfrac{1}{2}\pi < t < \tfrac{3}{2}\pi, \end{cases} \qquad (5)$$

$$h(t + 2\pi) = h(t).$$

The period of this function is 2π, and the fundamental interval used in the above definition is $-\tfrac{1}{2}\pi \le t < \tfrac{3}{2}\pi$. This function is *not* continuous since $h(t)$ has value 1 or 0 and there are abrupt changes in the function value at the points $t = \pm\tfrac{1}{2}\pi, \pm\tfrac{3}{2}\pi, \pm\tfrac{5}{2}\pi, \dots$. Such functions are said to be **discontinuous** or **non-continuous**.

As noted earlier, we sometimes use period to mean fundamental period.

In Figure 12, $h(t)$ is drawn using a convention that is sometimes used to specify a function at points of discontinuity. Intervals of the form $\tfrac{1}{2}\pi < t < \tfrac{3}{2}\pi$ are drawn with small open circles at the ends to denote the missing endpoints.

This convention is used in mathematics, but most science texts do not bother with it.

We need to be a little careful about piecewise function definitions when dealing with discontinuous functions. Remember that functions can take only *one* value for each point in their domain. That is why we have not included the point $t = \tfrac{1}{2}\pi$ in both halves of the function definition (5). In the first line of this definition, we have chosen to take $h = 1$ at $t = \tfrac{1}{2}\pi$; it would not be consistent to assign the value $h = 0$ at $t = \tfrac{1}{2}\pi$ in the second line of the definition. Also, we do not define the function value 0 at $t = \tfrac{3}{2}\pi$ because that would contradict the first line and the property of periodicity, which taken together give

$$h\left(\tfrac{3}{2}\pi\right) = h\left(-\tfrac{1}{2}\pi + 2\pi\right) = h\left(-\tfrac{1}{2}\pi\right) = 1.$$

We could equally well define a slightly different square-wave function $h(t)$, taking the value 0 at the points $\pm\tfrac{1}{2}\pi, \pm\tfrac{3}{2}\pi, \pm\tfrac{5}{2}\pi, \dots$. This would then be written as

Strictly speaking, we should use a different symbol for this function, but the change is so minor that we do not do so.

$$h(t) = \begin{cases} 1 & \text{for } -\tfrac{1}{2}\pi < t < \tfrac{1}{2}\pi, \\ 0 & \text{for } \tfrac{1}{2}\pi \le t \le \tfrac{3}{2}\pi, \end{cases} \qquad (6)$$

$$h(t + 2\pi) = h(t),$$

and drawn as shown in Figure 13.

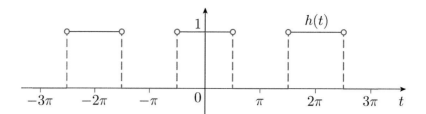

Figure 13   A slightly different definition of $h(t)$

You should check that this definition is internally consistent and does not attempt to give two different values at the same point.

> ### Discontinuities in graphs
>
> The real world almost always deals with continuous functions. In fact, discontinuous functions normally arise in science as convenient approximations to continuous functions. For this reason, scientists often take a relaxed attitude to the definitions and graphs of discontinuous functions, omitting the small open circles at points of discontinuity. We are more careful, but in the end this detail makes no *physical* difference.

You will see that discontinuous functions have Fourier series. For example, it turns out that the Fourier series for $h(t)$ is given by

$$H(t) = \frac{1}{2} + \frac{2}{\pi} \cos t - \frac{2}{3\pi} \cos 3t + \frac{2}{5\pi} \cos 5t - \frac{2}{7\pi} \cos 7t + \cdots . \tag{7}$$

This Fourier series applies whether $h(t)$ is defined by equation (5) or equation (6). This is because Fourier series *do not distinguish between functions that differ only at isolated points*. It is quite a remarkable result that a discontinuous function can be written as a sum of continuous and smooth functions, i.e. sines and cosines. We will have more to say about the Fourier series for discontinuous functions in Subsection 3.1.

Exercise 5

Sketch the following function over $-3\pi \leq t < 3\pi$:

$$f(t) = t \quad \text{for } -\pi \leq t < \pi,$$
$$f(t + 2\pi) = f(t).$$

Exercise 6

Consider the function $u(t)$ shown in the figure below.

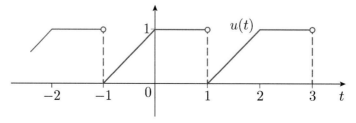

(a) State the positions of any discontinuities in the function, and give the value of its fundamental period.

(b) Write down the piecewise definition of the function, using the fundamental interval $-1 \leq t < 1$.

(c) What are the values of $u(99)$ and $u(100)$?

1.4   Even and odd functions

In the next section we will calculate Fourier series for periodic functions. In addition to being periodic, some of these functions will be even or odd, and this can simplify the calculations. It is therefore useful to review some properties of even and odd functions that were discussed in Unit 1. Recall that even and odd functions are defined as follows.

> **Definitions**
>
> A function $f(t)$ is said to be **even** if $f(-t) = f(t)$ for all t.
>
> A function $f(t)$ is said to be **odd** if $f(-t) = -f(t)$ for all t.

Most functions are neither even nor odd.

Typical examples of even functions are 1, x^2, $2x^2 + 4x^4$, $\cos x$ and $\exp(x^2)$.

Typical examples of odd functions are x, $x + 4x^5$, $\sin x$ and $x \exp(x^2)$.

It is easy to recognise even and odd functions from their graphs. An even function, such as that shown in Figure 14, takes the same values at corresponding points on either side of the vertical axis, so its graph remains unchanged when it is reflected in the vertical axis.

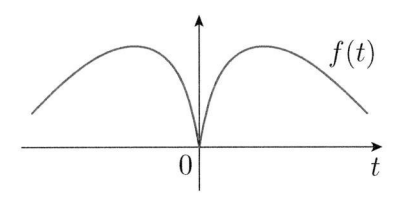

Figure 14   An even function

By contrast an odd function, such as that shown in Figure 15, has values of the same magnitude but opposite signs at corresponding points on either side of the vertical axis, so its graph changes sign when it is reflected in the vertical axis.

Returning to the functions considered at the beginning of the Introduction, we see that those in Figures 1 and 2 are even, while that in Figure 3 is odd. The function in Figure 4 is neither even nor odd.

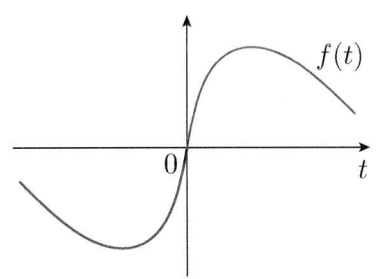

Figure 15   An odd function

When we calculate Fourier series, we will need to evaluate definite integrals. It is useful to note that simplifications occur when even and odd functions are integrated over a range that is symmetric about the origin.

Recall that if $f(t)$ is an odd function, then

$$\int_{-a}^{a} f(t)\, dt = 0.$$

The reason, illustrated in Figure 16, is that the area under $f(t)$ between $-a$ and 0 (in yellow) has the same magnitude but opposite sign to the area between 0 and a (in blue). So the total area between $-a$ and a vanishes.

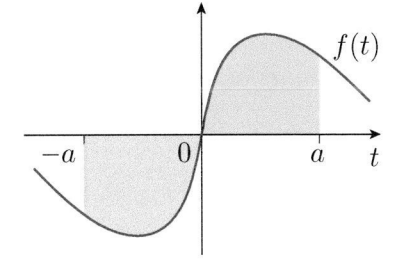

Figure 16   The integral of an odd function $f(t)$ over a range from $-a$ to a

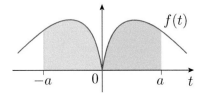

Figure 17　The integral of an even function $f(t)$ over a range from $-a$ to a

Now consider the integral of an even function $f(t)$ between $-a$ and a, as illustrated in Figure 17. Clearly the area under the function between $-a$ and a is just twice that between 0 and a. This means that

$$\int_{-a}^{a} f(t)\,dt = 2\int_{0}^{a} f(t)\,dt$$

for any even function $f(t)$.

We collect these results for later use.

Integrals of odd and even functions over symmetric ranges

If $f(x)$ is an *odd* function, then

$$\int_{-a}^{a} f(t)\,dt = 0. \tag{8}$$

If $f(x)$ is an *even* function, then

$$\int_{-a}^{a} f(t)\,dt = 2\int_{0}^{a} f(t)\,dt. \tag{9}$$

Example 4

Calculate the value of

$$I = \int_{-1}^{1} \sin(x^3)\cos(x^2)\,dx.$$

Solution

The integrand is $f(x) = \sin(x^3)\cos(x^2)$. This is odd because

$$\begin{aligned}
f(-x) &= \sin((-x)^3)\cos((-x)^2)\\
&= \sin(-x^3)\cos(x^2)\\
&= -\sin(x^3)\cos(x^2) = -f(x).
\end{aligned}$$

The range of integration is symmetric about the origin, so

$$I = \int_{-1}^{1} \sin(x^3)\cos(x^2)\,dx = 0.$$

In general, the product of an odd function and an even function is odd, and the product of two odd functions or two even functions is even. Also, the sum of two odd functions is odd, and the sum of two even functions is even.

Exercise 7

Determine whether the following functions are even, odd or neither.

(a) $x^3 - 3x$　　(b) $2\sin x + 3\sin(4x)$　　(c) $5 + 2\cos x + 7\cos(4x)$

(d) $4 - 2\sin x$　　(e) $2x\cos(3x)$

Exercise 8

Calculate the values of the following definite integrals.

(a) $\displaystyle\int_{-1}^{1} x^3 \cos(2x)\, dx$ (b) $\displaystyle\int_{-2}^{2} (3 + \sin(2x^3))\, dx$

---

2 Introducing Fourier series

This section contains the core material of this unit. It defines what is meant by a Fourier series and shows you the basic method for calculating the Fourier series for any periodic function. The process of finding the Fourier series for a function is given in Procedure 1. The three examples that follow apply this procedure to specific periodic functions. Subsection 2.2 shows how this procedure can be simplified if the periodic function is either even or odd. Finally, Subsection 2.3 shows how Fourier series can be calculated for non-periodic functions that are defined over a finite domain.

2.1 Fourier series for periodic functions

Suppose that we have a periodic function $f(t)$ with fundamental period τ. Then we *define* its Fourier series to have the form

$$
\begin{aligned}
F(t) = A_0 &+ \left(A_1 \cos\left(\frac{2\pi t}{\tau}\right) + A_2 \cos\left(\frac{4\pi t}{\tau}\right) + A_3 \cos\left(\frac{6\pi t}{\tau}\right) + \cdots \right) \\
&+ \left(B_1 \sin\left(\frac{2\pi t}{\tau}\right) + B_2 \sin\left(\frac{4\pi t}{\tau}\right) + B_3 \sin\left(\frac{6\pi t}{\tau}\right) + \cdots \right),
\end{aligned}
$$

where the sums may continue forever. More concisely, the Fourier series can be written as

$$
F(t) = A_0 + \sum_{n=1}^{\infty} A_n \cos\left(\frac{2n\pi t}{\tau}\right) + \sum_{n=1}^{\infty} B_n \sin\left(\frac{2n\pi t}{\tau}\right), \tag{10}
$$

or as

$$
F(t) = A_0 + \sum_{n=1}^{\infty} A_n \cos\left(\omega_n t\right) + \sum_{n=1}^{\infty} B_n \sin\left(\omega_n t\right), \tag{11}
$$

where

$$
\omega_n = \frac{2n\pi}{\tau} \quad (n = 1, 2, 3, \ldots).
$$

Each periodic function $f(t)$ of fundamental period τ has its own Fourier series $F(t)$, characterised by a particular set of constants A_0, A_n, B_n ($n = 1, 2, 3, \ldots$). These are called the **Fourier coefficients** for $f(t)$.

Finding the Fourier series for a function means finding its Fourier coefficients A_0, A_n, B_n for $n = 1, 2, 3, \ldots$.

As stated in the Introduction, a periodic function $f(t)$ and its Fourier series $F(t)$ are the same function, i.e. $f(t) = F(t)$ (except perhaps at isolated points), even though their formulas look quite different.

Since $f(t)$ has period τ, we know that $f(t + \tau) = f(t)$ for all t. Let us check that this property is also true for the Fourier series $F(t)$. We can do this by noting that $\cos(\omega t)$ and $\sin(\omega t)$ have angular frequency ω and fundamental period $\tau = 2\pi/\omega$. Similarly, $\cos(\omega_n t)$ and $\sin(\omega_n t)$ have angular frequency ω_n and fundamental period $2\pi/\omega_n = \tau/n$. Other periods of these functions are obtained by multiplying τ/n by any positive integer, so τ is one of the periods of $\cos(\omega_n t)$ and $\sin(\omega_n t)$. Since every term in the Fourier series of equation (11) has τ as one of its periods, we conclude that

$$F(t + \tau) = F(t) \quad \text{for all } t,$$

as required.

To illustrate the meaning of equations (10) and (11), let us return to the examples given in the Introduction. The function $c(t) = |\cos t|$, illustrated in Figure 2, has fundamental period $\tau = \pi$, so $\omega_n = 2n\pi/\pi = 2n$. We therefore expect this function to have a Fourier series of the form

$$C(t) = A_0 + \sum_{n=1}^{\infty} A_n \cos(2nt) + \sum_{n=1}^{\infty} B_n \sin(2nt).$$

However, the Introduction stated that the Fourier series for $c(t)$ is given by equation (1). You can see that these two equations are equivalent if the Fourier coefficients for $c(t)$ are given by

$$A_0 = \frac{2}{\pi}, \quad A_1 = \frac{4}{3\pi}, \quad A_2 = -\frac{4}{15\pi}, \quad A_3 = \frac{4}{35\pi}, \quad \ldots,$$

with $B_1 = B_2 = B_3 = \ldots = 0$.

Exercise 9

Deduce the Fourier coefficients A_0, A_1, A_2, A_3, A_4 and B_1, B_2, B_3, B_4 for the sawtooth function $p(t)$ in Figure 3, whose Fourier series is given by equation (2).

The key question, of course, is how do you deduce the Fourier coefficients for a general periodic function $f(t)$? To begin to answer this question, let us suppose that a function $f(t)$ with fundamental period τ has Fourier series $F(t)$. The function and its Fourier series are supposed to have identical values, so we can write equation (10) as

$$f(t) = A_0 + \sum_{n=1}^{\infty} A_n \cos\left(\frac{2n\pi t}{\tau}\right) + \sum_{n=1}^{\infty} B_n \sin\left(\frac{2n\pi t}{\tau}\right). \tag{12}$$

We can get some useful information by integrating both sides of this equation with respect to t over a complete period of $f(t)$, from $t = -\tau/2$ to $t = \tau/2$.

The expression on the right-hand side of equation (12) is a sum of terms, and its integral is found by integrating these terms one by one. In other words, we assume that the summation and integral signs can be interchanged, giving

$$\int_{-\tau/2}^{\tau/2} f(t)\,dt = \int_{-\tau/2}^{\tau/2} A_0\,dt + \sum_{n=1}^{\infty} A_n \int_{-\tau/2}^{\tau/2} \cos\left(\frac{2n\pi t}{\tau}\right) dt$$
$$+ \sum_{n=1}^{\infty} B_n \int_{-\tau/2}^{\tau/2} \sin\left(\frac{2n\pi t}{\tau}\right) dt. \qquad (13)$$

We can immediately see that the integrals of all the sine terms vanish. This is because $\sin(2n\pi t/\tau)$ is an odd function of t, and the range of integration is symmetric about the origin.

The integrals of the cosine terms also vanish, but for a different reason. In this case, we have

$$\int_{-\tau/2}^{\tau/2} \cos\left(\frac{2n\pi t}{\tau}\right) dt = \left[\frac{\tau}{2n\pi} \sin\left(\frac{2n\pi t}{\tau}\right)\right]_{-\tau/2}^{\tau/2}$$
$$= \frac{\tau}{2n\pi}\left(\sin(n\pi) - \sin(-n\pi)\right),$$

For any integer m, $\sin(m\pi) = 0$.

and this is equal to zero for $n = 1, 2, 3, \ldots$.

The only term that survives on the right-hand side of equation (13) is the integral of A_0, which is given by

$$\int_{-\tau/2}^{\tau/2} A_0\,dt = \left[A_0 t\right]_{-\tau/2}^{\tau/2} = A_0\tau.$$

We therefore conclude that

$$A_0 = \frac{1}{\tau} \int_{-\tau/2}^{\tau/2} f(t)\,dt. \qquad (14)$$

The coefficient A_0 in the Fourier series is therefore found by integrating $f(t)$ over its fundamental interval: this integral is the *average value* of $f(t)$.

Example 5

Use equation (14) to calculate the Fourier coefficient A_0 for the function $h(t)$ shown in Figure 13.

Solution

From Figure 13, it is clear that $h(t)$ has period $\tau = 2\pi$. Hence using equation (14) we have

$$A_0 = \frac{1}{\tau} \int_{-\tau/2}^{\tau/2} h(t)\,dt = \frac{1}{2\pi} \int_{-\pi}^{\pi} h(t)\,dt.$$

This integral represents the area under the graph of $h(t)$ between $-\pi$ and π. An examination of the figure shows that this is equal to π. Hence

$$A_0 = \tfrac{1}{2},$$

in agreement with the stated Fourier series in equation (7).

Exercise 10

Use equation (14) to calculate the Fourier coefficient A_0 for the function $c(t) = |\cos t|$ shown in Figure 2.

The above calculation of A_0 relies on the fact that the integrals of sines and cosines appearing in equation (13) are all equal to zero. Without doing any calculations, you can get an idea of why this happens. It is because the sine and cosine functions in equation (13) oscillate, taking both positive and negative values. The integral from $t = -\tau/2$ to $t = \tau/2$ takes us over a whole number of periods of $\cos(2n\pi t/\tau)$ or $\sin(2n\pi t/\tau)$, and over any such range, the positive and negative contributions cancel, giving zero integrals. An example of this (with $n = 2$) is shown in Figure 18.

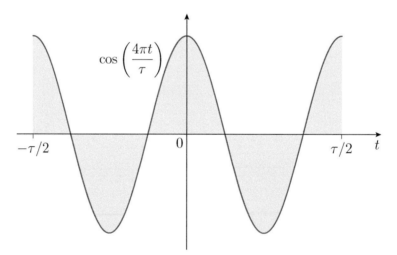

Figure 18   A graph of $\cos(4\pi t/\tau)$ from $-\tau/2$ to $\tau/2$

So far, we have found just one of the Fourier coefficients. The remaining coefficients can also be found by a process of integration. We will soon give formulas for them, and concentrate on the main task of calculating Fourier series for particular functions. The derivation of these formulas is given in the optional Appendix, but we give a sketch of the argument here, skimming over the fine details.

Suppose that we want to find the coefficient A_2. We note that the cosine that accompanies A_2 in the Fourier series is $\cos(4\pi t/\tau)$. The trick is then to multiply both sides of equation (12) by $\cos(4\pi t/\tau)$ *before* integrating over t from $-\tau/2$ to $\tau/2$. This gives a modified version of equation (13), but with an extra factor $\cos(4\pi t/\tau)$ inside each integral.

Now cosines are always even functions, so $\cos(4\pi t/\tau)\sin(2n\pi t/\tau)$ is an odd function. It follows that

$$B_n \int_{-\tau/2}^{\tau/2} \cos\left(\frac{4\pi t}{\tau}\right)\sin\left(\frac{2n\pi t}{\tau}\right) dt = 0.$$

We also have

$$A_0 \int_{-\tau/2}^{\tau/2} \cos\left(\frac{4\pi t}{\tau}\right) dt = 0,$$

for the reasons outlined above – we are integrating an oscillating cosine function over a complete number of its periods, so the positive and negative contributions to the integral cancel. Hence our modified version of equation (13) simplifies to

$$\int_{-\tau/2}^{\tau/2} f(t)\cos\left(\frac{4\pi t}{\tau}\right) dt = \sum_{n=1}^{\infty} A_n \int_{-\tau/2}^{\tau/2} \cos\left(\frac{4\pi t}{\tau}\right)\cos\left(\frac{2n\pi t}{\tau}\right) dt. \quad (15)$$

The integrals on the right-hand side can be evaluated by using the trigonometric identity $\cos A \cos B = \frac{1}{2}[\cos(A+B)+\cos(A-B)]$, which converts a product of two cosines into a sum of two cosines. We can use this identity to write

$$\cos\left(\frac{4\pi t}{\tau}\right)\cos\left(\frac{2n\pi t}{\tau}\right)$$
$$= \frac{1}{2}\left[\cos\left(\frac{(4+2n)\pi t}{\tau}\right) + \cos\left(\frac{(4-2n)\pi t}{\tau}\right)\right]. \quad (16)$$

We need to integrate this from $t = -\tau/2$ to $t = \tau/2$. Because n is an integer, we are integrating cosine functions over a whole number of their periods. As you have seen before, this means that the positive and negative contributions cancel, giving an integral that is equal to zero. This argument applies to almost every term on the right-hand side of equation (15), with just one exception. When $n = 2$, we have $4 - 2n = 0$ and one of the cosines in equation (16) is $\cos 0 = 1$. We therefore see that equation (15) reduces to

$$\int_{-\tau/2}^{\tau/2} f(t)\cos\left(\frac{4\pi t}{\tau}\right) dt = A_2 \int_{-\tau/2}^{\tau/2} \frac{1}{2} dt = \frac{\tau}{2}A_2,$$

which can be rearranged to give a formula for A_2:

$$A_2 = \frac{2}{\tau}\int_{-\tau/2}^{\tau/2} f(t)\cos\left(\frac{4\pi t}{\tau}\right) dt.$$

With more work this method can be extended, providing us with formulas for all the Fourier coefficients. The complete set of these formulas is

$$A_0 = \frac{1}{\tau} \int_{-\tau/2}^{\tau/2} f(t)\, dt,$$

$$A_n = \frac{2}{\tau} \int_{-\tau/2}^{\tau/2} f(t) \cos\left(\frac{2n\pi t}{\tau}\right) dt \quad (n = 1, 2, 3, \ldots),$$

$$B_n = \frac{2}{\tau} \int_{-\tau/2}^{\tau/2} f(t) \sin\left(\frac{2n\pi t}{\tau}\right) dt \quad (n = 1, 2, 3, \ldots).$$

Of course, we have only sketched the derivation of these results (further details can be found in the Appendix), but the really important thing is that these formulas exist and allow us to calculate the Fourier series for any periodic function $f(t)$.

Procedure 1   Fourier series for periodic functions

To find the Fourier series for a periodic function $f(t)$, proceed as follows.

1. Find the fundamental period τ.

2. Write down the Fourier series

$$F(t) = A_0 + \sum_{n=1}^{\infty} A_n \cos\left(\frac{2n\pi t}{\tau}\right) + \sum_{n=1}^{\infty} B_n \sin\left(\frac{2n\pi t}{\tau}\right), \quad (17)$$

where A_0 and the A_n and B_n are coefficients to be determined. Simplify the arguments of the sines and cosines where possible.

3. Use the following formulas to determine the Fourier coefficients:

$$A_0 = \frac{1}{\tau} \int_{-\tau/2}^{\tau/2} f(t)\, dt, \tag{18}$$

$$A_n = \frac{2}{\tau} \int_{-\tau/2}^{\tau/2} f(t) \cos\left(\frac{2n\pi t}{\tau}\right) dt \quad (n = 1, 2, 3, \ldots), \tag{19}$$

$$B_n = \frac{2}{\tau} \int_{-\tau/2}^{\tau/2} f(t) \sin\left(\frac{2n\pi t}{\tau}\right) dt \quad (n = 1, 2, 3, \ldots). \tag{20}$$

4. If desired, express the final Fourier series in a compact form with general formulas for its coefficients.

Because the Fourier series in equation (17) involves sines and cosines, we sometimes refer to it as the **trigonometric Fourier series**. This allows us distinguish it from the *exponential Fourier series*, which is discussed at the end of the unit. It is worth noting that the formula for A_0 contains the factor $1/\tau$, while the formulas for A_n and B_n contain the factor $2/\tau$.

Examples 6–8 below illustrate how to calculate the Fourier series for any periodic function. Sometimes the algebra gets a little tedious, and it is important to work with care and patience, but if you persevere you will have understood the main idea of this unit. Later we will show you some tricks that can simplify the calculations. In the last step of the procedure, the following values are often helpful.

Some useful values

If n is any integer, then we have

$$\cos(n\pi) = (-1)^n, \tag{21}$$

$$\sin(n\pi) = 0, \tag{22}$$

$$\cos\left(\frac{n\pi}{2}\right) = \begin{cases} (-1)^{n/2} & \text{for } n \text{ even}, \\ 0 & \text{for } n \text{ odd}, \end{cases} \tag{23}$$

$$\sin\left(\frac{n\pi}{2}\right) = \begin{cases} 0 & \text{for } n \text{ even}, \\ (-1)^{(n+3)/2} & \text{for } n \text{ odd}. \end{cases} \tag{24}$$

Example 6

Use Procedure 1 to find the Fourier series for the square-wave function

$$f(t) = \begin{cases} -1 & \text{for } -\frac{\pi}{2} < t < 0, \\ 1 & \text{for } 0 \le t \le \frac{\pi}{2}, \end{cases}$$

$$f(t + \pi) = f(t),$$

sketched in Figure 19.

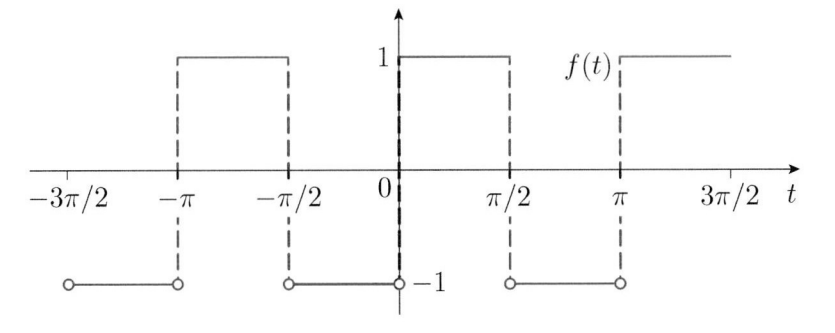

Figure 19   A particular type of square-wave function

Solution

The function $f(t)$ is odd and has fundamental period $\tau = \pi$. From equation (17), its Fourier series has the form

$$F(t) = A_0 + \sum_{n=1}^{\infty} A_n \cos(2nt) + \sum_{n=1}^{\infty} B_n \sin(2nt), \tag{25}$$

where A_0, A_n and B_n $(n = 1, 2, 3, \ldots)$ need to be determined.

We now calculate these Fourier coefficients. From equation (18) we get

$$A_0 = \frac{1}{\pi} \int_{-\pi/2}^{\pi/2} f(t)\, dt.$$

However, $f(t)$ is an odd function, and we know that the integral of an odd function over a range that is symmetric about the origin is equal to zero. Hence

$$A_0 = 0.$$

Using equation (19) we get

$$A_n = \frac{2}{\pi} \int_{-\pi/2}^{\pi/2} f(t) \cos(2nt)\, dt.$$

Again, $f(t) \cos(2nt)$ is an odd function of t because $f(t)$ is odd and $\cos(2nt)$ is even, so

$$A_n = 0 \quad \text{for all } n = 1, 2, 3, \ldots.$$

Finally, from equation (20) we get

$$B_n = \frac{2}{\pi} \int_{-\pi/2}^{\pi/2} f(t) \sin(2nt)\, dt.$$

Since both $f(t)$ and $\sin(2nt)$ are odd, $f(t) \sin(2nt)$ is even, so using equation (9) we have

$$B_n = \frac{4}{\pi} \int_{0}^{\pi/2} f(t) \sin(2nt)\, dt.$$

But $f(t) = 1$ for $0 \leq t \leq \pi/2$, so

$$B_n = \frac{4}{\pi} \int_{0}^{\pi/2} \sin(2nt)\, dt = \frac{4}{\pi} \left[-\frac{1}{2n} \cos(2nt) \right]_{0}^{\pi/2} = -\frac{2}{n\pi}(\cos(n\pi) - 1),$$

where we have used $\cos 0 = 1$. Also, from equation (21) we have $\cos(n\pi) = (-1)^n$, so

$$B_n = \frac{2}{n\pi}(1 - (-1)^n).$$

Substituting the values for A_0, A_n and B_n into equation (25) gives

$$F(t) = \sum_{n=1}^{\infty} \frac{2}{n\pi}(1 - (-1)^n) \sin(2nt). \tag{26}$$

This is the Fourier series for the function $f(t)$ given in the question.

The first few non-zero terms of the Fourier series in equation (26) look like

$$F(t) = \frac{2}{\pi}(1 - (-1)^1) \sin(2t) + \frac{2}{2\pi}(1 - (-1)^2) \sin(4t)$$
$$+ \frac{2}{3\pi}(1 - (-1)^3) \sin(6t) + \cdots$$
$$= \frac{4}{\pi} \sin(2t) + \frac{4}{3\pi} \sin(6t) + \frac{4}{5\pi} \sin(10t) + \cdots.$$

To see how many terms are needed to get a good approximation to the original function $f(t)$, let us take the **truncated Fourier series** $F_N(t)$ to be the sum of the first N terms of the Fourier series. In this case,

$$F_N(t) = \sum_{n=1}^{N} \frac{2}{n\pi}(1 - (-1)^n)\sin(2nt).$$

We would expect $F_N(t)$ to get closer and closer to $f(t)$ as N increases. This is borne out by Figure 20, which compares $F_5(t)$ (in blue) and $F_{20}(t)$ (in red) with the original function $f(t)$ (in black).

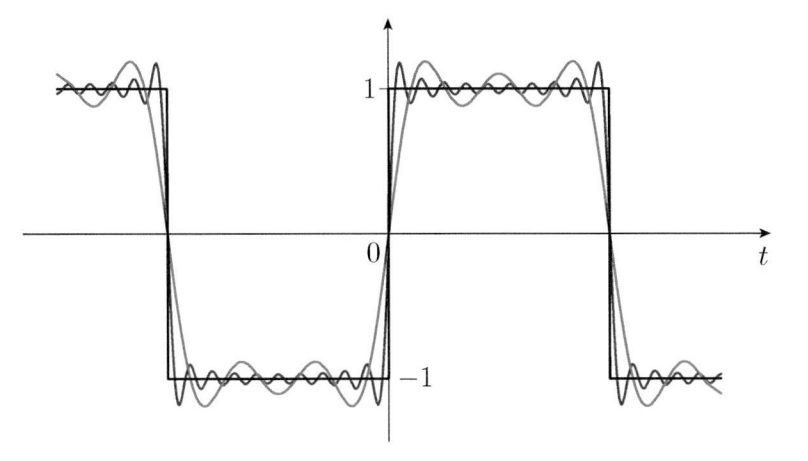

Figure 20   The square-wave function f (in black) together with its truncated Fourier series approximations F_5 (in blue) and F_{20} (in red)

In general, as the number of terms N increases, the truncated Fourier series $F_N(t)$ approaches the original function $f(t)$.

Fourier series can sometimes be written in alternative forms. Returning to equation (26), for example, we may notice that $1 - (-1)^n = 0$ when n is even, and $1 - (-1)^n = 2$ when n is odd. Hence the only values of n that contribute to this Fourier series are $n = 1, 3, 5, \ldots$. These values of n are given by $n = 2m - 1$ for $m = 1, 2, 3, \ldots$, so the Fourier series also can be expressed as

$$F(t) = \sum_{m=1}^{\infty} \frac{4}{(2m-1)\pi}\sin(2(2m-1)t). \tag{27}$$

Here m is just a label for different terms: you may replace it by n if you prefer.

Equations (26) and (27) are fully equivalent, and it doesn't matter which we use: both are the Fourier series for the function $f(t)$.

Let us pause for a moment to review what has been achieved. We assumed that the function $f(t)$ sketched in Figure 19 can be represented as a Fourier series of the form

$$F(t) = A_0 + \sum_{n=1}^{\infty} A_n \cos(2nt) + \sum_{n=1}^{\infty} B_n \sin(2nt).$$

This means that $f(t)$ is equal to $F(t)$, except possibly at isolated points, so almost everywhere we can write

$$f(t) = A_0 + \sum_{n=1}^{\infty} A_n \cos(2nt) + \sum_{n=1}^{\infty} B_n \sin(2nt), \qquad (28)$$

where A_0, A_n and B_n for $n = 1, 2, 3, \ldots$ are constants that are initially unknown. The major task of finding these constants was carried out using equations (18)–(20). For example,

$$A_n = \frac{2}{\pi} \int_{-\pi/2}^{\pi/2} f(t) \cos(2nt)\, dt \quad (n = 1, 2, 3, \ldots). \qquad (29)$$

A deep analogy

The task of finding Fourier coefficients has much in common with the task of finding vector components. Suppose that we are given a vector $\mathbf{v}$ in three-dimensional space. We may know the magnitude and direction of this vector, but not its components. Nevertheless, we can write

$$\mathbf{v} = v_x\,\mathbf{i} + v_y\,\mathbf{j} + v_z\,\mathbf{k}, \qquad (30)$$

where v_x, v_y and v_z are constants that are initially unknown, and $\mathbf{i}$, $\mathbf{j}$ and $\mathbf{k}$ are Cartesian unit vectors. The problem of finding the constants is solved by taking scalar products with the unit vectors, giving

Equations like this were discussed in Unit 4.

$$v_x = \mathbf{i} \cdot \mathbf{v}, \quad v_y = \mathbf{j} \cdot \mathbf{v}, \quad v_z = \mathbf{k} \cdot \mathbf{v}. \qquad (31)$$

Equations (28) and (30) are analogous because their right-hand sides are sums involving initially unknown constants. And equations (29) and (31) are analogous because they allow us to isolate individual constants from the sums. Most analogies are weak, and evaporate when we look at them in more detail. However, this analogy turns out to be deep and strong. Indeed, mathematicians often think of Fourier coefficients as being something like the components of vectors, and use language that further cements this kinship. More details of this fascinating viewpoint are given in the Appendix.

The most time-consuming task in calculating Fourier series is usually the evaluation of the integrals. In practice, scientists often use tables of integrals or computer algebra programs, and in this text we will give some standard integrals that can be used as shortcuts. The two results given below are often useful.

Two useful integrals

$$\int t \sin(at)\, dt = \frac{1}{a^2}\big(\sin(at) - at\cos(at)\big), \tag{32}$$

$$\int t \cos(at)\, dt = \frac{1}{a^2}\big(\cos(at) + at\sin(at)\big). \tag{33}$$

These results can be derived using integration by parts.

Example 7

Find the Fourier series for the sawtooth function

$$f(t) = \begin{cases} -t & \text{for } -1 \le t \le 0, \\ t & \text{for } 0 < t < 1, \end{cases}$$

$$f(t+2) = f(t),$$

sketched in Figure 21.

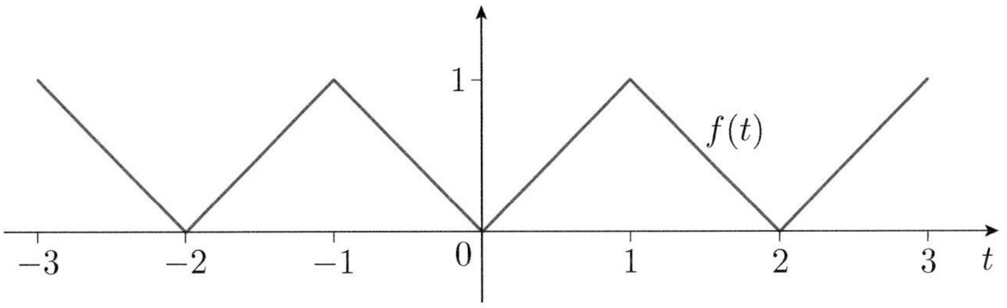

Figure 21 A sawtooth function

Solution

The function f is even and has fundamental period $\tau = 2$. Using equation (17), its Fourier series has the form

$$F(t) = A_0 + \sum_{n=1}^{\infty} A_n \cos(n\pi t) + \sum_{n=1}^{\infty} B_n \sin(n\pi t),$$

where A_0, A_n and B_n (for $n = 1, 2, 3, \ldots$) are the Fourier coefficients.

From equation (18) we get

$$A_0 = \frac{1}{2} \int_{-1}^{1} f(t)\, dt.$$

Since f is even, we can use equation (9) to write

$$A_0 = \int_{0}^{1} f(t)\, dt.$$

However, $f(t) = t$ for $0 < t < 1$, hence

$$A_0 = \int_{0}^{1} t\, dt = \left[\tfrac{1}{2}t^2\right]_0^1 = \tfrac{1}{2}.$$

We use a similar method to calculate the A_n:

$$A_n = \frac{2}{2} \int_{-1}^{1} f(t) \cos(n\pi t)\, dt$$

$$= 2 \int_{0}^{1} f(t) \cos(n\pi t)\, dt$$

$$= 2 \int_{0}^{1} t \cos(n\pi t)\, dt.$$

Using the standard integral in equation (33), we get

$$A_n = \frac{2}{(n\pi)^2} \big[\cos(n\pi t) + n\pi t \sin(n\pi t)\big]_0^1$$

$$= \frac{2}{(n\pi)^2} \big(\cos(n\pi) + n\pi \sin(n\pi) - 1\big).$$

But $\cos(n\pi) = (-1)^n$ and $\sin(n\pi) = 0$ for any integer n. So

These values are given in equations (21) and (22).

$$A_n = \frac{2}{(n\pi)^2}\big((-1)^n - 1\big) \quad (n = 1, 2, 3, \ldots).$$

The B_n are given by

$$B_n = \int_{-1}^{1} f(t) \sin(n\pi t)\, dt.$$

However, $\sin(n\pi t)$ is an odd function of t, and $f(t)$ is an even function of t, so the integrand $f(t)\sin(n\pi t)$ is an odd function of t. From Subsection 1.4 we know that the integral of an odd function over a range that is symmetric about the origin vanishes, so

$$B_n = 0 \quad (n = 1, 2, 3, \ldots).$$

Hence the Fourier series for $f(t)$ is given by

$$F(t) = \frac{1}{2} + \sum_{n=1}^{\infty} \frac{2}{(n\pi)^2}\big((-1)^n - 1\big) \cos(n\pi t). \tag{34}$$

The first few terms in equation (34) look like

$$F(t) = \frac{1}{2} - \frac{4}{\pi^2} \cos(\pi t) - \frac{4}{9\pi^2} \cos(3\pi t) - \frac{4}{25\pi^2} \cos(5\pi t) - \cdots.$$

To investigate how rapidly the right-hand side of this equation approaches the original function $f(t)$ as we add more and more terms, we introduce the truncated Fourier series $F_N(t)$ defined by

$$F_N(t) = \frac{1}{2} + \sum_{n=1}^{N} \frac{2}{(n\pi)^2}\big((-1)^n - 1\big) \cos(n\pi t).$$

Figure 22 compares F_3 (in blue) and F_5 (in red) with the original function f. We see that F_5 is already a very good approximation to f.

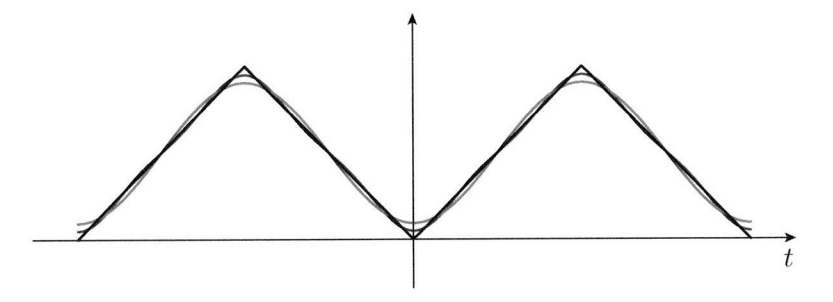

Figure 22 The sawtooth function f (in black) together with its truncated Fourier series approximations F_3 (in blue) and F_5 (in red)

It is also possible to express the Fourier series in a slightly different way. Noting that the non-zero terms in equation (34) occur only for odd values of n (i.e. for the values $n = 2m - 1$ with $m = 1, 2, 3, \ldots$), we can write the Fourier series as

$$F(t) = \frac{1}{2} - \sum_{m=1}^{\infty} \frac{4}{(2m-1)^2 \pi^2} \cos((2m-1)\pi t), \tag{35}$$

and this is entirely equivalent to equation (34).

Example 8

Find the Fourier series for the function

$$f(t) = \begin{cases} 0 & \text{for } -1 < t < 0, \\ t & \text{for } 0 \le t \le 1, \end{cases}$$

$$f(t + 2) = f(t),$$

sketched in Figure 23.

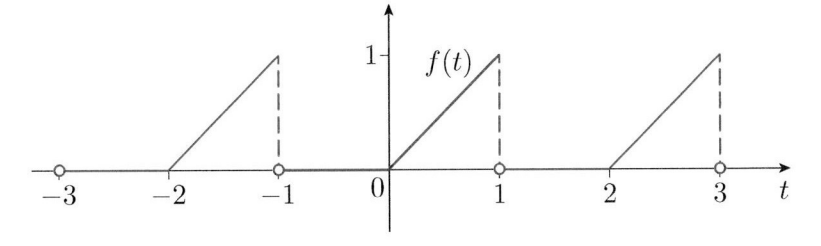

Figure 23 Graph of a function $f(t)$ that is neither even nor odd

Solution

The function $f(t)$ is neither even nor odd, and is discontinuous. It has fundamental period $\tau = 2$. So, using equation (17), its Fourier series takes the form

$$F(t) = A_0 + \sum_{n=1}^{\infty} A_n \cos(n\pi t) + \sum_{n=1}^{\infty} B_n \sin(n\pi t),$$

where the coefficients A_0, A_n and B_n ($n = 1, 2, 3, \ldots$) are to be determined.

From equation (18) we get

$$A_0 = \frac{1}{2} \int_{-1}^{1} f(t) \, dt.$$

To integrate a function defined on pieces, we simply integrate each piece in turn using the correct value of the function on each piece. So

$$A_0 = \frac{1}{2} \int_{-1}^{0} f(t) \, dt + \frac{1}{2} \int_{0}^{1} f(t) \, dt = \frac{1}{2} \int_{0}^{1} t \, dt = \left[\tfrac{1}{4} t^2 \right]_0^1 = \tfrac{1}{4},$$

where we have used the fact that $f(t) = 0$ for $-1 < t < 0$ and $f(t) = t$ for $0 \le t \le 1$.

Equation (19) gives

$$A_n = \frac{2}{2} \int_{-1}^{1} f(t) \cos(n\pi t) \, dt \quad (n = 1, 2, 3, \ldots).$$

Again, to integrate a function defined on pieces, we simply integrate on each piece in turn using the correct value of the function on each piece. This gives

$$A_n = \int_{-1}^{0} f(t) \cos(n\pi t) \, dt + \int_{0}^{1} f(t) \cos(n\pi t) \, dt$$

$$= \int_{0}^{1} t \cos(n\pi t) \, dt.$$

Using the standard integral given in equation (33), we get

$$A_n = \frac{1}{(n\pi)^2} \left[\cos(n\pi t) + n\pi t \sin(n\pi t) \right]_0^1$$

$$= \frac{1}{(n\pi)^2} \left(\cos(n\pi) + n\pi \sin(n\pi) - 1 \right).$$

These values are given in equations (21) and (22). But $\cos(n\pi) = (-1)^n$ and $\sin(n\pi) = 0$ for any integer n. So

$$A_n = \frac{1}{(n\pi)^2} \left((-1)^n - 1 \right) \quad (n = 1, 2, 3, \ldots).$$

The B_n are found using equation (20):

$$B_n = \int_{-1}^{1} f(t) \sin(n\pi t) \, dt$$

$$= \int_{-1}^{0} f(t) \sin(n\pi t) \, dt + \int_{0}^{1} f(t) \sin(n\pi t) \, dt$$

$$= \int_{0}^{1} t \sin(n\pi t) \, dt.$$

Now use the standard integral in equation (32). This gives

$$B_n = \frac{1}{(n\pi)^2} \left[\sin(n\pi t) - n\pi t \cos(n\pi t) \right]_0^1$$

$$= \frac{1}{(n\pi)^2} \left(\sin(n\pi) - n\pi \cos(n\pi) \right).$$

Since $\sin(n\pi) = 0$ and $\cos(n\pi) = (-1)^n$ for any integer n, we get

$$B_n = -\frac{(-1)^n}{n\pi} \quad (n = 1, 2, 3, \ldots).$$

Putting all these results together, the required Fourier series is

$$F(t) = \frac{1}{4} + \sum_{n=1}^{\infty} \frac{1}{(n\pi)^2}((-1)^n - 1)\cos(n\pi t) - \sum_{n=1}^{\infty} \frac{(-1)^n}{n\pi}\sin(n\pi t).$$

To see how the right-hand side of this equation for $F(t)$ approaches the original function $f(t)$ as we add more and more terms, we once again consider a truncated Fourier series:

$$F_N(t) = \frac{1}{4} + \sum_{n=1}^{N} \frac{1}{(n\pi)^2}((-1)^n - 1)\cos(n\pi t) - \sum_{n=1}^{N} \frac{(-1)^n}{n\pi}\sin(n\pi t).$$

Other definitions could be given for F_N, but this makes no difference to our general argument.

In Figure 24 we compare F_5 (in blue) and F_{20} (in red) with the original function f (in black).

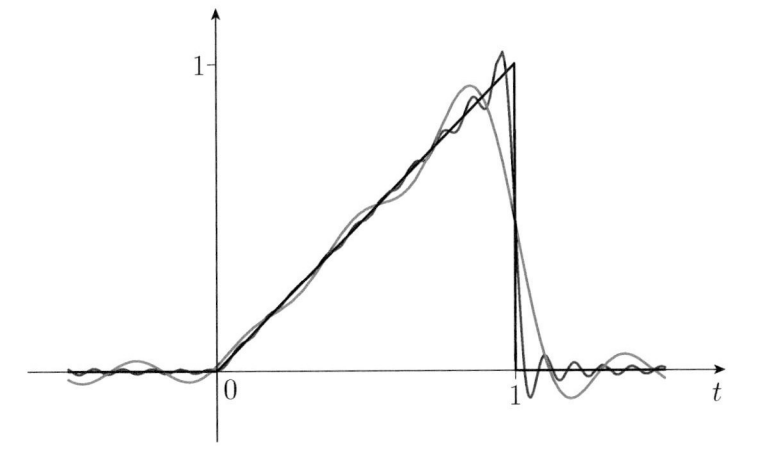

Figure 24   The function f (in black) together with the truncated Fourier series approximations F_5 (in blue) and F_{20} (in red)

Notice that in this case, we need to take $N = 20$ or more to get a reasonable approximation to this function at most points in its domain. A similar observation was made for the square-wave function in Example 6. However, the Fourier series for the continuous function discussed in Example 7 showed quite different behaviour; in that case a truncated Fourier series F_3 with only four terms is already a good approximation to the original function. In general, fewer terms of a Fourier series are needed to approximate a continuous function than a discontinuous one. We say that the Fourier series for a continuous function *converges* more rapidly than the Fourier series for a discontinuous function. We will return to this point in Subsection 3.1.

Fourier series and musical sounds

You can actually hear the difference between different Fourier series! A musical note corresponds to a rapid oscillation in the pressure of air, with a given fundamental period τ, and a corresponding fundamental angular frequency $\omega = 2\pi/\tau$. For example, middle C has a fundamental period of about 3.82 milliseconds. All musical instruments playing this note produce pressure variations that are periodic functions of time with this fundamental period. But the precise shapes of these periodic functions are *different* when produced by a piano, a guitar or a violin, and the corresponding Fourier series are different too.

The Fourier series for a musical note is a sum of sinusoidal functions with frequencies that are *harmonics*, that is, integer multiples of the fundamental angular frequency of the musical tone. The greater the contribution from the harmonics, the 'brighter' the tone of the musical instrument. For example, a violin produces a brighter tone than a guitar because the oscillation has a greater contribution from high harmonics of the fundamental frequency. The periodic function in Figure 24 contains harmonics that die away slowly as n increases. If this function represented a musical note of middle C, the effect would be unpleasantly rasping.

What can be analysed can also be synthesised. Figure 25 shows a Moog synthesiser, which was used in 1960s and 1970s pop music to construct complex musical tones from linear combinations of sinusoidal oscillations (Fourier series, in fact!).

Figure 25   The first commercial Moog synthesiser (1964)

Although it can be tedious, aim to be patient and careful when evaluating the integrals needed in Fourier series!

Exercise 11

Find the Fourier series for the function
$$f(t) = t \quad \text{for } -\pi \leq t < \pi,$$
$$f(t + 2\pi) = f(t).$$

Exercise 12

Find the Fourier series for the function
$$f(x) = \begin{cases} x + 1 & \text{for } -1 \leq x \leq 0, \\ 1 & \text{for } 0 < x < 1, \end{cases}$$
$$f(x + 2) = f(x).$$

2.2   Fourier series for odd and even functions

Examples 6–8 in the previous subsection displayed three different types of behaviour. In Example 6, the function was odd and the Fourier series contained only sine terms. In Example 7, the function was even and the Fourier series contained only constant and cosine terms. Finally, in Example 8, the function was neither odd nor even and its Fourier series contained constant, cosine and sine terms.

This pattern is easily explained. If the function $f(t)$ is odd, the integrals for A_0 and A_n in equations (18) and (19) involve odd integrands integrated over a range that is symmetric about the origin: such integrals are equal to zero, leaving only sine terms in the Fourier series. Similarly, if the function $f(t)$ is even, the integrals for B_n in equation (20) involve odd integrands integrated over a range that is symmetric about the origin: these integrals vanish, leaving only constant and cosine terms in the Fourier series. Taking note of these facts, the procedure for calculating the Fourier series for a function $f(t)$ can be simplified if $f(t)$ is either odd or even.

If $f(t)$ is an odd periodic function, with fundamental period τ, then all the Fourier coefficients A_0 and A_n vanish, and using equations (9) and (20), the integral for the B_n coefficients can be simplified slightly:

$$B_n = \frac{2}{\tau} \int_{-\tau/2}^{\tau/2} f(t) \sin\left(\frac{2n\pi t}{\tau}\right) dt = \frac{4}{\tau} \int_0^{\tau/2} f(t) \sin\left(\frac{2n\pi t}{\tau}\right) dt.$$

The second integral is often a little easier to evaluate than the first, but both lead to the same result.

Procedure 2   Fourier series for odd periodic functions

To find the Fourier series for an odd periodic function $f(t)$, proceed as follows.

1.   Identify $f(t)$ as being odd, and find its fundamental period τ.

2.   Write down the Fourier series

$$F(t) = \sum_{n=1}^{\infty} B_n \sin\left(\frac{2n\pi t}{\tau}\right). \tag{36}$$

3.   Find the coefficients by evaluating the definite integrals

$$B_n = \frac{4}{\tau} \int_0^{\tau/2} f(t) \sin\left(\frac{2n\pi t}{\tau}\right) dt \quad (n = 1, 2, 3, \ldots). \tag{37}$$

4.   If desired, express the final Fourier series in a compact form with general formulas for its coefficients.

A similar simplification occurs for even functions. In this case, the B_n coefficients vanish. Also, the integrands for A_0 and A_n are even, so these coefficients can be expressed as integrals from 0 to $\tau/2$.

Procedure 3   Fourier series for even periodic functions

To find the Fourier series for an even periodic function $f(t)$, proceed as follows.

1. Identify $f(t)$ as being even, and find its fundamental period τ.

2. Write down the Fourier series

$$F(t) = A_0 + \sum_{n=1}^{\infty} A_n \cos\left(\frac{2n\pi t}{\tau}\right). \tag{38}$$

3. Find the coefficients by evaluating the definite integrals

$$A_0 = \frac{2}{\tau} \int_0^{\tau/2} f(t)\, dt, \tag{39}$$

$$A_n = \frac{4}{\tau} \int_0^{\tau/2} f(t) \cos\left(\frac{2n\pi t}{\tau}\right) dt \quad (n = 1, 2, 3, \ldots). \tag{40}$$

4. If desired, express the final Fourier series in a compact form with general formulas for its coefficients.

To take advantage of the oddness and evenness of functions, we must take the fundamental interval to be symmetric about the origin, from $-\tau/2$ to $\tau/2$. However, a piecewise continuous periodic function may be given on some other fundamental interval. For example, the function $h(t)$ in Exercise 14 below is defined on $-\frac{1}{2}\pi \leq t < \frac{3}{2}\pi$, with a periodicity condition that gives the values of the function elsewhere. In cases like this, it is advisable to sketch a graph of the function – partly to check that it is odd or even, and partly to get the values that are needed in the range $-\tau/2 \leq t < \tau/2$.

Example 9

Use Procedure 2 to find the Fourier series for the sawtooth function

$$p(t) = \begin{cases} t & \text{for } -\frac{1}{2} \leq t \leq \frac{1}{2}, \\ 1-t & \text{for } \frac{1}{2} < t < \frac{3}{2}, \end{cases}$$

$$p(t+2) = p(t).$$

This function was sketched in Figure 3, which is reproduced in Figure 26.

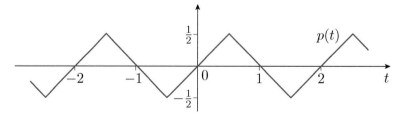

Figure 26   A sawtooth function

Solution

It is clear from Figure 26 that $p(t)$ is an odd function with fundamental period $\tau = 2$. Following Procedure 2, its Fourier series contains only sine terms and takes the form

$$P(t) = \sum_{n=1}^{\infty} B_n \sin(n\pi t).$$

The Fourier coefficients are given by

$$B_n = \frac{4}{2} \int_0^1 p(t) \sin(n\pi t) \, dt.$$

Within this range of integration, $p(t) = t$ for $0 \leq t \leq 1/2$, and $p(t) = 1 - t$ for $1/2 < t \leq 1$. So the integral splits into two pieces:

$$B_n = 2 \int_0^{1/2} t \sin(n\pi t) \, dt + 2 \int_{1/2}^1 (1 - t) \sin(n\pi t) \, dt.$$

Using the standard integral in equation (32), we obtain

$$B_n = \frac{2}{(n\pi)^2} \left[\sin(n\pi t) - n\pi t \cos(n\pi t) \right]_0^{1/2} + \frac{2}{n\pi} \left[-\cos(n\pi t) \right]_{1/2}^1$$

$$- \frac{2}{(n\pi)^2} \left[\sin(n\pi t) - n\pi t \cos(n\pi t) \right]_{1/2}^1.$$

Substituting in the limits, we get

$$B_n = \frac{2}{(n\pi)^2} \left(\sin\left(\frac{n\pi}{2}\right) - \frac{n\pi}{2} \cos\left(\frac{n\pi}{2}\right) \right)$$

$$+ \frac{2}{n\pi} \left(-\cos(n\pi) + \cos\left(\frac{n\pi}{2}\right) \right)$$

$$- \frac{2}{(n\pi)^2} \left(\sin(n\pi) - n\pi \cos(n\pi) - \sin\left(\frac{n\pi}{2}\right) + \frac{n\pi}{2} \cos\left(\frac{n\pi}{2}\right) \right).$$

Carefully combining terms, making cancellations, and using $\sin(n\pi) = 0$, this gives

$$B_n = \frac{4}{(n\pi)^2} \sin\left(\frac{n\pi}{2}\right).$$

The required Fourier series is therefore

$$P(t) = \frac{4}{\pi^2} \sum_{n=1}^{\infty} \frac{1}{n^2} \sin\left(\frac{n\pi}{2}\right) \sin(n\pi t).$$

For $n = 1, 2, 3, 4, 5, 6, 7$, the values of $\sin(n\pi/2)$ are $1, 0, -1, 0, 1, 0, -1$, so the first few terms in the Fourier series are

$$P(t) = \frac{4}{\pi^2} \left(\sin(\pi t) - \tfrac{1}{9} \sin(3\pi t) + \tfrac{1}{25} \sin(5\pi t) - \tfrac{1}{49} \sin(7\pi t) + \cdots \right),$$

as stated in equation (2) of the Introduction.

Only the odd values of n contribute to the Fourier series. Putting $n = 2m - 1$ and noting that equation (24) gives $\sin((2m-1)\pi/2) = (-1)^{m+1}$, this Fourier series can also be written in the alternative form

$$P(t) = \frac{4}{\pi^2} \sum_{m=1}^{\infty} \frac{(-1)^{m+1}}{(2m-1)^2} \sin((2m-1)\pi t).$$

Exercise 13

This function was discussed in Example 7, but the present calculation is more efficient.

Use Procedure 3 to find the Fourier series for the sawtooth function

$$f(t) = \begin{cases} -t & \text{for } -1 \leq t \leq 0, \\ t & \text{for } 0 < t < 1, \end{cases}$$

$$f(t+2) = f(t),$$

sketched in the figure below.

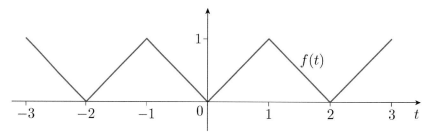

Exercise 14

Find the Fourier series for the square-wave function defined in equation (5) by

$$h(t) = \begin{cases} 1 & \text{for } -\frac{1}{2}\pi \leq t \leq \frac{1}{2}\pi, \\ 0 & \text{for } \frac{1}{2}\pi < t < \frac{3}{2}\pi, \end{cases}$$

$$h(t + 2\pi) = h(t).$$

Exercise 15

Find the Fourier series for the function $c(t)$ defined in the Introduction as

$$c(t) = |\cos t|,$$

and sketched in Figure 2.

You may use the standard integral

$$\int \cos(at)\cos(bt)\,dt = \frac{b\cos(at)\sin(bt) - a\cos(bt)\sin(at)}{b^2 - a^2} \quad (a \neq b).$$

2.3   Functions defined over a finite domain

So far you have seen how to calculate the Fourier series for any *periodic* function. However, this is not the whole story. It is also possible to calculate the Fourier series for (almost) *any* function, provided that it is defined over a finite domain. This idea will be particularly useful in the next unit.

Suppose that a function $f(t)$ is defined within the finite interval $0 \leq t \leq T$ of length T (see Figure 27). Furthermore, suppose that we do not care about what happens to the function outside this interval.

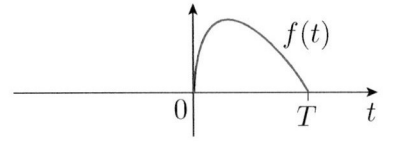

Figure 27   A function $f(t)$ defined on a finite interval $0 \leq t \leq T$

Then we can always define another function $f_{\text{ext}}(t)$ to be equal to $f(t)$ on the interval $0 \leq t \leq T$, and to be periodic with fundamental period T everywhere else. This function is called a **periodic extension** of $f(t)$ and is written as

$$f_{\text{ext}}(t) = f(t) \quad \text{for } 0 \leq t < T,$$
$$f_{\text{ext}}(t + T) = f_{\text{ext}}(t).$$

The graph of $f_{\text{ext}}(t)$ consists of copies of $f(t)$ shifted by T and by all positive and negative integer multiples of T, and is shown in Figure 28.

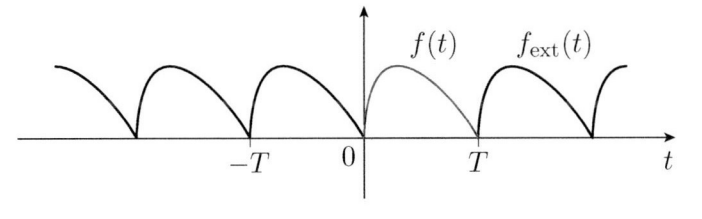

Figure 28   A periodic extension $f_{\text{ext}}(t)$ of $f(t)$

The periodic extension $f_{\text{ext}}(t)$ is a periodic function of fundamental period T, and we can find its Fourier series as normal. The resulting Fourier series will be equal to $f_{\text{ext}}(t)$ everywhere, and is equal to $f(t)$ for $0 \leq t \leq T$. So this Fourier series represents the non-periodic function $f(t)$ inside its domain of definition, $0 \leq t \leq T$. The periodic extension shown in Figure 28 is neither even nor odd, so the Fourier series contains both sine and cosine terms.

With a little preparation, we can use $f(t)$ to construct periodic functions that are either even or odd, before extending over all t. This is generally a sensible thing to do because the resulting Fourier series will be simpler. We make the following definitions.

Even and odd periodic extensions

Consider a function $f(t)$ defined over a finite domain $0 \le t \le T$.

The **even periodic extension** of $f(t)$ is given by

$$f_{\text{even}}(t) = \begin{cases} f(t) & \text{for } 0 \le t \le T, \\ f(-t) & \text{for } -T < t < 0, \end{cases}$$

$$f_{\text{even}}(t + 2T) = f_{\text{even}}(t).$$

An example of this extension is shown in Figure 29.

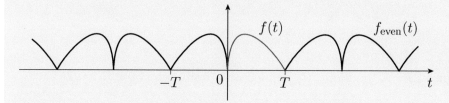

Figure 29   The even periodic extension $f_{\text{even}}(t)$ of $f(t)$

The **odd periodic extension** of $f(t)$ is given by

$$f_{\text{odd}}(t) = \begin{cases} f(t) & \text{for } 0 \le t \le T, \\ -f(-t) & \text{for } -T < t < 0, \end{cases}$$

$$f_{\text{odd}}(t + 2T) = f_{\text{odd}}(t).$$

An example of this extension is shown in Figure 30.

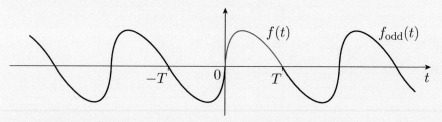

Figure 30   The odd periodic extension $f_{\text{odd}}(t)$ of $f(t)$

In general, both these functions have fundamental period $\tau = 2T$.

In exceptional cases, the even periodic extension may have fundamental period $\tau = T$ (see Exercise 17).

Example 10

Find the even and odd periodic extensions of the function

$$f(t) = t \quad \text{for } 0 \le t \le 1,$$

and sketch these two extensions.

Solution

The even periodic extension is given by

$$f_{\text{even}}(t) = \begin{cases} t & \text{for } 0 \leq t \leq 1, \\ -t & \text{for } -1 < t < 0, \end{cases}$$

$$f_{\text{even}}(t + 2) = f_{\text{even}}(t).$$

This function is sketched in Figure 31, with the original function shown in orange.

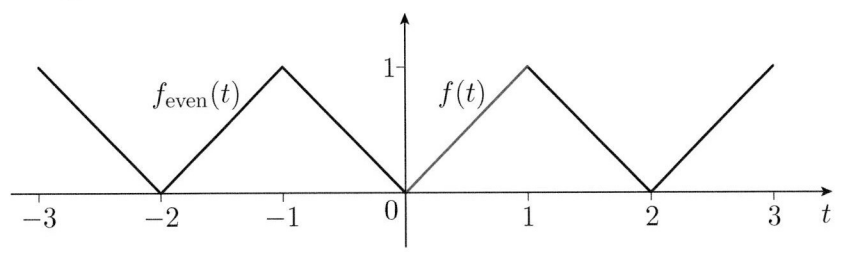

Figure 31 Even periodic extension

The odd periodic extension is given by

$$f_{\text{odd}}(t) = \begin{cases} t & \text{for } 0 \leq t \leq 1, \\ t & \text{for } -1 < t < 0, \end{cases}$$

$$f_{\text{odd}}(t + 2) = f_{\text{odd}}(t).$$

This function is sketched in Figure 32, with the original function shown in orange.

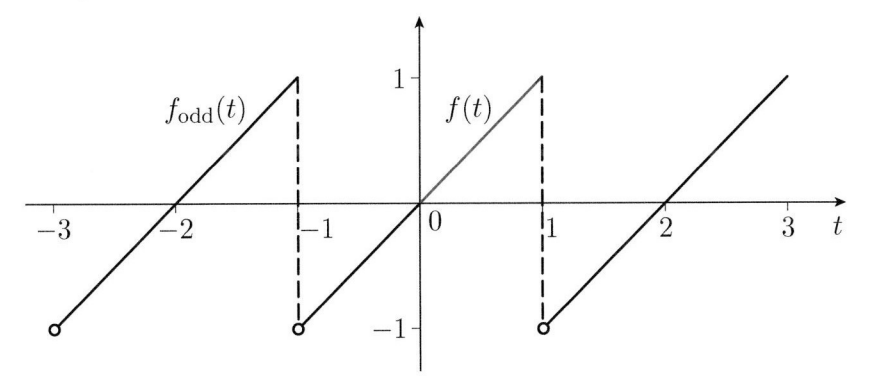

Figure 32 Odd periodic extension

In this particular case, both extensions can be expressed in alternative forms. The even periodic extension is

$$f_{\text{even}}(t) = |t| \quad \text{for } -1 < t \leq 1,$$
$$f_{\text{even}}(t + 2) = f_{\text{even}}(t),$$

and the odd periodic extension is

$$f_{\text{odd}}(t) = t \quad \text{for } -1 < t \leq 1,$$
$$f_{\text{odd}}(t + 2) = f_{\text{odd}}(t).$$

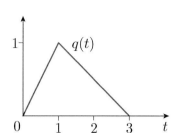

Exercise 16

Consider the function

$$q(t) = \begin{cases} t & \text{for } 0 \le t \le 1, \\ \frac{3}{2} - \frac{1}{2}t & \text{for } 1 < t \le 3, \end{cases}$$

sketched in the margin.

Define the even and odd periodic extensions of $q(t)$, simplifying the formulas if possible. State the fundamental periods, and sketch each extension over a range of three periods.

The following important example illustrates how a function defined on a finite interval can be represented by a Fourier series.

Example 11

The function

$$f(x) = \begin{cases} \dfrac{2d}{L}x & \text{for } 0 \le x \le L/2, \\ \dfrac{2d}{L}(L - x) & \text{for } L/2 < x \le L, \end{cases}$$

where d and L are positive constants, is defined on the finite interval $0 \le x \le L$. Express $f(x)$ as a Fourier series that involves only sine terms.

(*Hint:* With a change of variable to $u = x/L$, the integrals needed for the Fourier coefficients can be related to those calculated in Example 9.)

Solution

Because we are looking for a Fourier series that involves only sine terms, we need to consider the *odd* periodic extension of $f(x)$, denoted by $f_{\text{odd}}(x)$. This is sketched in Figure 33.

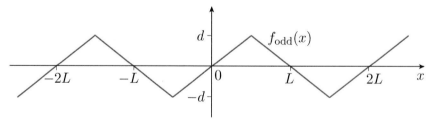

Figure 33　The odd periodic extension of the function $f(x)$

The function $f_{\text{odd}}(x)$ is odd and has period $\tau = 2L$, so its Fourier series takes the form

$$F_{\text{odd}}(x) = \sum_{n=1}^{\infty} B_n \sin\left(\frac{n\pi x}{L}\right),$$

where the Fourier coefficients B_n are given by

$$B_n = \frac{4}{2L} \int_0^L f_{\text{odd}}(x) \sin\left(\frac{n\pi x}{L}\right) dx.$$

But $f_{\text{odd}}(x) = f(x)$ on the interval $0 \le x \le L$, so

$$B_n = \frac{2}{L} \int_0^L f(x) \sin\left(\frac{n\pi x}{L}\right) dx.$$

Using the piecewise definition of $f(x)$ given in the question, we obtain

$$B_n = \frac{4d}{L^2} \left[\int_0^{L/2} x \sin\left(\frac{n\pi x}{L}\right) dx + \int_{L/2}^L (L-x) \sin\left(\frac{n\pi x}{L}\right) dx \right].$$

Making the suggested substitution $u = x/L$, we get

$$B_n = 4d \left[\int_0^{1/2} u \sin(n\pi u)\, du + \int_{1/2}^1 (1-u) \sin(n\pi u)\, du \right].$$

The required integrals have already been evaluated in Example 9. Comparing with the working in that example, we conclude that

$$B_n = \frac{8d}{(n\pi)^2} \sin\left(\frac{n\pi}{2}\right) \quad (n = 1, 2, 3, \ldots).$$

So

$$F_{\text{odd}}(x) = \frac{8d}{\pi^2} \sum_{n=1}^{\infty} \frac{1}{n^2} \sin\left(\frac{n\pi}{2}\right) \sin\left(\frac{n\pi x}{L}\right).$$

Since $f(x)$ and $f_{\text{odd}}(x)$ coincide on the interval $0 \le x \le L$, this is the required sine Fourier series $F(x)$ for $f(x)$.

For $n = 1, 2, 3, 4, 5, 6, 7$, the values of $\sin(n\pi/2)$ are $1, 0, -1, 0, 1, 0, -1$, so the first few terms in the Fourier series are

$$F(x) = \frac{8d}{\pi^2} \left(\sin\left(\frac{\pi x}{L}\right) - \frac{1}{3^2} \sin\left(\frac{3\pi x}{L}\right) + \frac{1}{5^2} \sin\left(\frac{5\pi x}{L}\right) \right.$$

$$\left. - \frac{1}{7^2} \sin\left(\frac{7\pi x}{L}\right) + \cdots \right).$$

Exercise 17

Consider the same function $f(x)$ as that discussed in Example 11. Within its domain of definition, $0 \le x \le L$, represent this function by a Fourier series that involves only constant and cosine functions.

To represent the original function $f(x)$ in Example 11 by a Fourier series, we can use the odd periodic extension, obtaining a series that contains only sine terms (as in Example 11), or we can use the even periodic extension, obtaining a series that contains only constant and cosine terms (as in Exercise 17).

Sometimes one choice is better than the other. In general, if we want to approximate a function by a truncated Fourier series, it is better to use a periodic extension that is continuous, rather than discontinuous. This is because, as pointed out earlier, the Fourier series for a continuous function converges more rapidly than that of a discontinuous function. So for the function discussed in Example 10 we would use the even periodic extension to obtain the Fourier series.

However, in the next unit we will use Fourier series to solve partial differential equations, and in that case our choice of an even or odd periodic extension is generally dictated by other factors, namely the boundary conditions.

Exercise 17 is an exceptional case in which the even periodic extension has fundamental period $\tau = L$ rather than $\tau = 2L$. This simplifies the calculations because we need integrals only over the range from 0 to $L/2$. If we were to treat the function in Exercise 17 as having period $2L$, then the usual formula would eventually give the *same* Fourier series, although the calculations would be longer. In general, making the mistake of using a non-fundamental period rather than the fundamental period will always give the same final Fourier series, but at the expense of more labour.

Exercise 18

Consider the function

$$f(t) = \begin{cases} 1 & \text{for } 0 \leq t \leq \frac{\pi}{2}, \\ -1 & \text{for } \frac{\pi}{2} < t \leq \pi. \end{cases}$$

(a) Define the even periodic extension, simplifying your answer as much possible. Sketch this function over $-3\pi/2 \leq t \leq 3\pi/2$, and state its fundamental period.

(b) Find the Fourier series for the even periodic extension.

(c) Define the odd periodic extension. Sketch this function over $-\pi \leq t \leq 3\pi$, and state its fundamental period.

(d) By slightly changing the definition of the odd extension at points of discontinuity, create a periodic extension that has fundamental period π, and hence find the Fourier series. (*Hint*: You may find the result of Example 6 useful.)

---

3 Working with Fourier series

This section contains a miscellany of topics related to Fourier series. First, it takes a closer look at the fact that the truncated Fourier series for discontinuous functions are slow to converge, especially near the points of discontinuity. It then goes on to look at some useful techniques for calculating and manipulating Fourier series, including differentiating them.

3.1   The Gibbs phenomenon

You saw in Section 2 that a continuous function can be closely approximated by the first few terms of its Fourier series. As more and more terms are added, the truncated Fourier series and the original function become practically identical in value everywhere. For example, a truncated Fourier series containing only a few terms gives a good approximation for the continuous function in Figure 22.

A different situation applies to discontinuous functions. For a given number of terms in the truncated Fourier series, the approximation is worse, especially around the points of discontinuity. In Figure 34(a) we give a comparison of $F_{20}(t)$ with a square-wave function, while in Figure 34(b) we magnify a portion of this graph near the discontinuous point $t = 0$. Note that F_{20} deviates from the original function by oscillating around it.

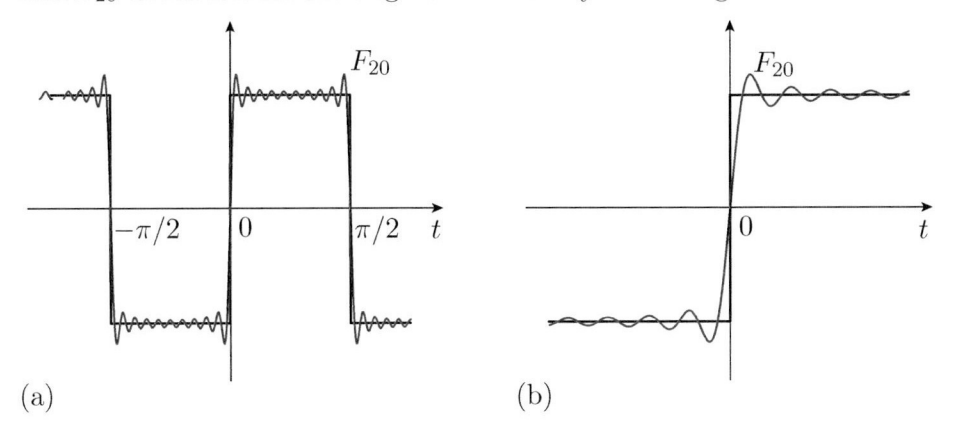

(a)   (b)

Figure 34   Comparison of a square-wave function (in black) with F_{20} (in red): (a) the first 20 terms in the Fourier series; (b) a magnification in the vicinity of a discontinuity

Such a deviation occurs in the vicinity of *any* discontinuous function and is known as the **Gibbs phenomenon**, after the American mathematical physicist Josiah Gibbs (Figure 35).

The main points of the Gibbs phenomenon are as follows. The truncated Fourier series $F_N(t)$ (with N terms, where N is large) provides a good approximation to $f(t)$ at points well away from any discontinuity. However, in the region of a discontinuity, F_N oscillates around f as shown in Figure 34. As N increases, F_N provides a better approximation to f, and the deviations are pushed into a region closer and closer to the discontinuity, but their amplitude does not diminish. Most importantly, at the point of discontinuity, as N tends to infinity, F_N always takes the average value of the function on either side of the discontinuity. We highlight this crucial point below.

Figure 35   Josiah Gibbs (1839–1903)

The value of a Fourier series at a point of discontinuity

If $f(t)$ is discontinuous at $t = t_0$, then the value of the corresponding Fourier series $F(t)$ at this point is the average of the function values immediately above and below the discontinuity. That is,

$$F(t_0) = \tfrac{1}{2}\left(f(t_0^+) + f(t_0^-)\right),$$

where $f(t_0^+)$ is the value of $f(t)$ just above t_0, and $f(t_0^-)$ is the value of $f(t)$ just below t_0.

In fact, this rule also works at points where f is continuous. If f is continuous at t_0, then $f(t_0^-) = f(t_0^+) = f(t_0)$ and hence

$$F(t_0) = \tfrac{1}{2}\left(f(t_0^+) + f(t_0^-)\right) = f(t_0),$$

so the Fourier series converges to $f(t_0)$ as expected.

This description closely follows C. Lanczos (1966) *Discourse on Fourier Series*, Oliver and Boyd.

Figure 36   Albert Michelson (1852–1931)

History of the Gibbs phenomenon

The American experimental physicist Albert Michelson (Figure 36) is primarily known for his 1887 experiment with Edward Morley, which showed that the speed of light is independent of the direction in which it is measured. This result undermined the concept of an ether, and prepared the ground for Einstein's special theory of relativity.

However, Michelson also invented many physical instruments of high precision. In 1898 he constructed a mechanical machine that could compute the first 80 Fourier coefficients for a function that was described numerically; the machine could also plot a graph of the truncated Fourier series and compare this with a graph of the original function. Michelson found that in most cases the input function and the truncated Fourier series agreed well everywhere. But for a discontinuous function, the truncated Fourier series agreed well *except near the point of discontinuity*. Michelson was puzzled and wrote to Gibbs, who explained the phenomenon mathematically and published his findings in Volume 59 of *Nature* (1898–9, pp. 200 and 606).

Although the phenomenon is named after Gibbs, it was first noticed and explained half a century earlier, in 1848, by the obscure English mathematician Henry Wilbraham. This work was unknown to Gibbs.

Example 12

What is the value of the Fourier series for the square-wave function $h(t)$ given in Exercise 14 (depicted here in Figure 37), at the point $t = \pi/2$?

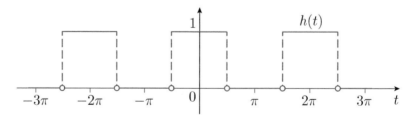

Figure 37   The square-wave function $h(t)$

Solution

The function $h(t)$ is discontinuous at $t = \pi/2$. Just below $t = \pi/2$, $h(t) = 1$, and just above $t = \pi/2$, $h(t) = 0$. Hence at $t = \pi/2$ the Fourier series converges to

$$H(\pi/2) = \tfrac{1}{2}(0 + 1) = \tfrac{1}{2}.$$

We can compare this result with the Fourier series derived in Exercise 14. There we showed that

$$H(t) = \frac{1}{2} + \frac{2}{\pi} \sum_{n=1}^{\infty} \frac{(-1)^{n+1}}{2n-1} \cos((2n-1)t).$$

But at $t = \pi/2$, $\cos((2n-1)t) = 0$ for n an integer, so $H(t) = \tfrac{1}{2}$, in agreement with the average value derived above.

Exercise 19

(a) What is the value of the Fourier series for the function $f(t)$ given in Example 8, at the point $t = 1$?

(b) By comparing with the Fourier series at $t = 1$, show that

$$\frac{\pi^2}{8} = \sum_{n=1}^{\infty} \frac{1}{(2n-1)^2}.$$

3.2   Shifting the range of integration

Suppose that we have a function $g(t)$ with period τ. Then the integral

$$I = \int_{-\tau/2}^{\tau/2} g(t)\, dt$$

is just the area under the graph of the function on the fundamental interval $-\tau/2 \le t \le \tau/2$, as shown in Figure 38. If we shift the interval to $-\tau/2 + a \le t \le \tau/2 + a$, as in Figure 39, we see that the area lost on the left is equal to the area gained on the right. Therefore

$$I = \int_{-\tau/2}^{\tau/2} g(t)\, dt = \int_{-\tau/2+a}^{\tau/2+a} g(t)\, dt.$$

In other words, when we integrate a function with period τ over an interval of length τ, it doesn't matter which interval of length τ we use.

In our formulas for the Fourier coefficients for a periodic function f with fundamental period τ (equations (18)–(20)), the integrand is always periodic with period τ. Hence those equations are equivalent to the following.

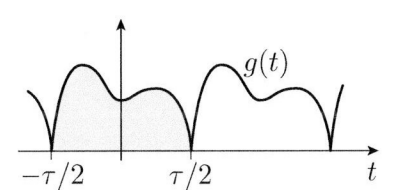

Figure 38   Area under g on the interval $-\tau/2 \le t \le \tau/2$

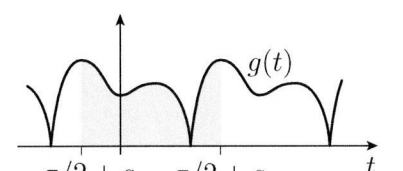

Figure 39   Area under g on the interval $-\tau/2 + a \le t \le \tau/2 + a$

Alternative formulas for Fourier coefficients

The Fourier coefficients for any function f with fundamental period τ are given by

$$A_0 = \frac{1}{\tau} \int_{t_0}^{t_0+\tau} f(t)\, dt, \tag{41}$$

$$A_n = \frac{2}{\tau} \int_{t_0}^{t_0+\tau} f(t) \cos\left(\frac{2n\pi t}{\tau}\right) dt \quad (n = 1, 2, 3, \ldots), \tag{42}$$

$$B_n = \frac{2}{\tau} \int_{t_0}^{t_0+\tau} f(t) \sin\left(\frac{2n\pi t}{\tau}\right) dt \quad (n = 1, 2, 3, \ldots), \tag{43}$$

where t_0 can take any value.

Equations (41)–(43) are sometimes easier to use than equations (18)–(20), as the following exercise illustrates.

Exercise 20

Show that the Fourier series for the function

$$f(x) = x \quad \text{for } \tfrac{1}{4} < x \leq \tfrac{3}{4},$$
$$f(x + 1) = f(x),$$

is given by

$$F(x) = \frac{1}{4} + \sum_{n=1}^{\infty} \frac{1}{n\pi} \left(\sin\left(\tfrac{3}{2}n\pi\right) \cos\left(2n\pi x\right) - \cos\left(\tfrac{3}{2}n\pi\right) \sin\left(2n\pi x\right) \right).$$

3.3 Differentiating Fourier series

Suppose that the continuous function $f(t)$ has the Fourier series

$$F(t) = A_0 + \sum_{n=1}^{\infty} A_n \cos(\omega_n t) + \sum_{n=1}^{\infty} B_n \sin(\omega_n t),$$

where A_0, A_n, B_n and ω_n are constants.

Then we can ask: what is the Fourier series for the derivative $f'(t) = df/dt$? The answer is obtained by differentiating each term in $F(t)$ in turn. So $f'(t)$ has the Fourier series

$$F'(t) = -\sum_{n=1}^{\infty} \omega_n A_n \sin(\omega_n t) + \sum_{n=1}^{\infty} \omega_n B_n \cos(\omega_n t).$$

Differentiation of Fourier series

The results in this subsection rely on the function being continuous.

If a *continuous* periodic function $f(t)$ with fundamental period τ has the Fourier series $F(t)$, then its derivative $f'(t)$ has the same fundamental period τ, and its Fourier series is given by $F'(t)$.

This allows us to deduce the Fourier series for $f'(t)$ from the Fourier series for $f(t)$. This may not always be useful because the Fourier series for $f'(t)$ is often easier to find than that for $f(t)$. However, we sometimes need both these Fourier series; in such a case, it is possible to save some time by calculating the Fourier series for $f(t)$ first, and then differentiating it.

Example 13

In equation (35) we showed that the function

$$f(t) = \begin{cases} -t & \text{for } -1 \leq t \leq 0, \\ t & \text{for } 0 < t < 1, \end{cases}$$

$$f(t + 2) = f(t),$$

has Fourier series

$$F(t) = \frac{1}{2} - \sum_{n=1}^{\infty} \frac{4}{(2n-1)^2 \pi^2} \cos((2n-1)\pi t).$$

This function is shown in Figure 40.

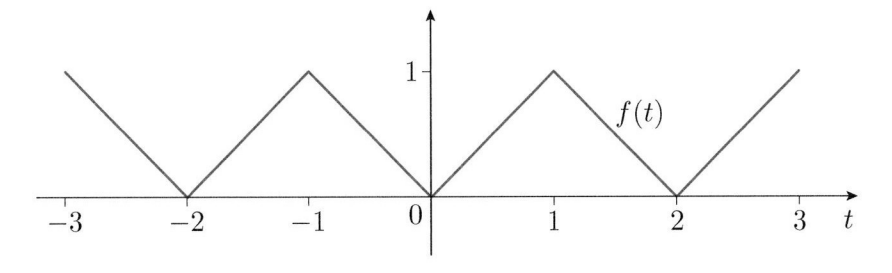

Figure 40   The function $f(t)$

Deduce the Fourier series for the function $f'(t)$, given by

$$f'(t) = \begin{cases} -1 & \text{for } -1 < t < 0, \\ 1 & \text{for } 0 < t < 1, \end{cases}$$

$$f'(t + 2) = f'(t),$$

and sketched in Figure 41.

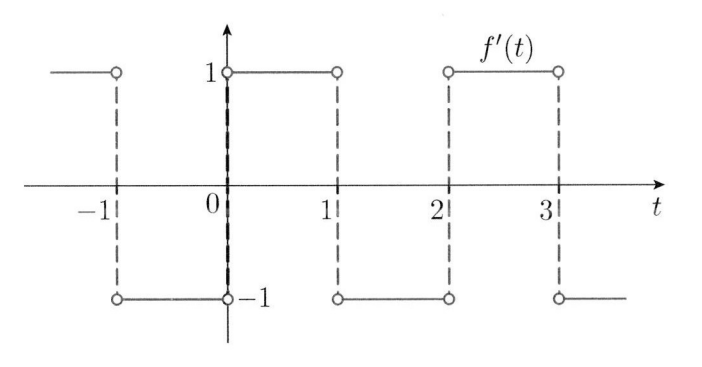

Figure 41   The function $f'(t)$

Solution

The function $f(t)$ is continuous, as can be seen from its graph, and $f'(t)$ is its derivative. The Fourier series for $f'(t)$ is given by the derivative of $F(t)$:

$$F'(t) = 0 - \sum_{n=1}^{\infty} \frac{4}{(2n-1)^2\pi^2} \frac{d}{dt}\left(\cos((2n-1)\pi t)\right)$$

$$= \sum_{n=1}^{\infty} \frac{4}{(2n-1)\pi} \sin((2n-1)\pi t).$$

In this case, $f'(t)$ is undefined at the points $t = 0, \pm 1, \pm 2, \dots$ because the slope of the function $f(t)$ changes abruptly there. This does not affect the evaluation of the Fourier series $F'(t)$, which converges to the average value of $f'(t)$ either side of these points (e.g. $F'(1) = F'(2) = \dots = 0$).

Exercise 21

The function $c(t) = |\cos t|$ can be defined as

$$c(t) = \cos t \quad \text{for } -\tfrac{\pi}{2} < t < \tfrac{\pi}{2},$$
$$c(t + \pi) = c(t).$$

From Exercise 15, this function has the Fourier series

$$C(t) = \frac{2}{\pi} + \frac{4}{\pi} \sum_{n=1}^{\infty} \frac{(-1)^{n+1}}{4n^2 - 1} \cos(2nt).$$

Deduce the Fourier series for the discontinuous function

$$s(t) = \sin t \quad \text{for } -\tfrac{\pi}{2} < t < \tfrac{\pi}{2},$$
$$s(t + \pi) = s(t).$$

If you are very short of time, you may omit the rest of this unit.

4 The exponential Fourier series

This section will not be assessed in the exam or in continuous assessment. However, you are advised to study it because it contains ideas that are very useful in the physical sciences.

4.1 The exponential Fourier series

There is another form of the Fourier series that is used extensively in mathematics and the physical sciences: this is the *exponential Fourier series*. It is fully equivalent to the *trigonometric Fourier series* discussed so far, but uses the (complex) exponential function instead of sines and cosines. This series has the advantage of being simpler and more concise than the trigonometric Fourier series, and it is often easier to evaluate its Fourier coefficients. Also, the exponential Fourier series is the starting point for *Fourier transforms*, an advanced topic that is used extensively in applied mathematics and science.

Recall that a function $f(t)$ with fundamental period τ has a trigonometric Fourier series $F(t)$ of the form

$$F(t) = A_0 + \sum_{n=1}^{\infty} A_n \cos(\omega_n t) + \sum_{n=1}^{\infty} B_n \sin(\omega_n t), \tag{44}$$

where A_0, A_n and B_n are constants, and $\omega_n = 2n\pi/\tau$ for $n = 1, 2, 3, \ldots$.

You know that Euler's formula relates the complex exponential function to cosines and sines, telling us that

$$e^{i\omega_n t} = \cos(\omega_n t) + i \sin(\omega_n t),$$

and conversely,

$$\cos(\omega_n t) = \frac{e^{i\omega_n t} + e^{-i\omega_n t}}{2}, \quad \sin(\omega_n t) = \frac{e^{i\omega_n t} - e^{-i\omega_n t}}{2i}.$$

Substituting these results into equation (44) gives

$$F(t) = A_0 + \sum_{n=1}^{\infty} \frac{A_n}{2} \left(e^{i\omega_n t} + e^{-i\omega_n t} \right) + \sum_{n=1}^{\infty} \frac{B_n}{2i} \left(e^{i\omega_n t} - e^{-i\omega_n t} \right),$$

and we can then collect terms to get

$$F(t) = A_0 + \sum_{n=1}^{\infty} \frac{A_n - iB_n}{2} e^{i\omega_n t} + \sum_{n=1}^{\infty} \frac{A_n + iB_n}{2} e^{-i\omega_n t}.$$

For $n = 0, 1, 2, 3, \ldots$, we then define the constants

$$C_0 = A_0, \quad C_n = \frac{A_n - iB_n}{2}, \quad C_{-n} = \frac{A_n + iB_n}{2}. \tag{45}$$

Notice that in the last of these definitions, the index used to label the constant C_{-n} is negative. For example, $C_{-1} = (A_1 + iB_1)/2$. Using this notation, the Fourier series can be written as

$$F(t) = C_0 + \sum_{n=1}^{\infty} C_n e^{i\omega_n t} + \sum_{n=1}^{\infty} C_{-n} e^{-i\omega_n t}.$$

Recalling that $\omega_n = 2n\pi/\tau$, this can also be expressed as

$$F(t) = C_0 + \sum_{n=1}^{\infty} C_n e^{2in\pi t/\tau} + \sum_{n=1}^{\infty} C_{-n} e^{-2in\pi t/\tau}. \tag{46}$$

The final sum on the right-hand side is a sum of terms

$$C_{-1} e^{-2i\pi t/\tau} + C_{-2} e^{-4i\pi t/\tau} + C_{-3} e^{-6i\pi t/\tau} + \cdots,$$

and this can be written as a sum over *negative* integers:

$$\sum_{n=-1}^{-\infty} C_n e^{2in\pi t/\tau}.$$

Hence we can combine all the terms in equation (46) to get

$$F(t) = \sum_{n=-\infty}^{\infty} C_n \, e^{2in\pi t/\tau}, \tag{47}$$

where the sum is now over all the integers – positive, zero and negative. This is called the **exponential Fourier series**, and the constants C_n are called *exponential Fourier coefficients*.

Equation (47) is more compact than equation (44), but a price has been paid. The sum now extends over all the integers, rather than just the positive integers, and the coefficients C_n are, in general, complex numbers (assuming that A_n and $B_n \neq 0$ are real). Nevertheless, the exponential Fourier series has some clear advantages. Given a function $f(t)$ with fundamental period τ, it turns out that the Fourier coefficients C_n are given by the formula

This result is proved in the Appendix.

$$C_n = \frac{1}{\tau} \int_{-\tau/2}^{\tau/2} f(t) \, e^{-2in\pi t/\tau} \, dt \quad (n = 0, \pm 1, \pm 2, \ldots).$$

This single formula compares favourably with the three separate integrals needed for A_0, A_n and B_n.

The results obtained above are summarised in the following box.

Exponential Fourier series for periodic functions

For a periodic function $f(t)$, with fundamental period τ, the exponential Fourier series is

$$F(t) = \sum_{n=-\infty}^{\infty} C_n \, e^{2in\pi t/\tau}. \tag{48}$$

The Fourier coefficients C_n are calculated from

$$C_n = \frac{1}{\tau} \int_{-\tau/2}^{\tau/2} f(t) \, e^{-2in\pi t/\tau} \, dt \quad (n = 0, \pm 1, \pm 2, \ldots). \tag{49}$$

Even if we ultimately want to find a *trigonometric* Fourier series, it can make sense to begin with the exponential Fourier series, using equation (49) to find the C_n, and then use the inverse of equations (45), namely

$$A_0 = C_0, \quad A_n = C_n + C_{-n}, \quad B_n = i(C_n - C_{-n}) \quad (n \geq 1), \tag{50}$$

to find A_0, A_n and B_n.

$\overline{f}$ denotes the complex conjugate of f.

If $f(t)$ is real, then we have $\overline{f}(t) = f(t)$ and equation (49) gives

$$\overline{C_n} = \frac{1}{\tau} \int_{-\tau/2}^{\tau/2} f(t) \, e^{+2in\pi t/\tau} \, dt = C_{-n}.$$

Combining this with equations (50), we obtain the following.

Fourier coefficients for real functions

$$A_0 = C_0, \quad A_n = 2\,\mathrm{Re}(C_n), \quad B_n = -2\,\mathrm{Im}(C_n) \quad (n \geq 1). \qquad (51)$$

Example 14

(a) Find the exponential Fourier series for the function

$$f(t) = t \quad \text{for } -\pi \leq t < \pi,$$
$$f(t + 2\pi) = f(t).$$

Hint: You may find the following standard integral useful:

$$\int x\, e^{ax}\, dx = \frac{1}{a^2}(ax - 1)e^{ax}.$$

(b) Use the exponential Fourier series derived in part (a) to derive the corresponding trigonometric Fourier series.

Solution

(a) $f(t)$ has fundamental period $\tau = 2\pi$. Using equation (48), its exponential Fourier series takes the form

$$F(t) = \sum_{n=-\infty}^{\infty} C_n\, e^{int}.$$

From equation (49), the Fourier coefficients are given by

$$C_n = \frac{1}{2\pi} \int_{-\pi}^{\pi} f(t)\, e^{-int}\, dt$$
$$= \frac{1}{2\pi} \int_{-\pi}^{\pi} t\, e^{-int}\, dt.$$

For $n = 0$, we have

$$C_0 = \frac{1}{2\pi} \int_{-\pi}^{\pi} t\, dt = 0$$

because the integrand is an odd function and the range of integration is symmetric about the origin.

For $n \neq 0$, the standard integral given in the question gives

$$C_n = \frac{1}{2\pi} \int_{-\pi}^{\pi} t\, e^{-int}\, dt$$
$$= \frac{1}{2\pi(-in)^2} \left[(-int - 1)\, e^{-int} \right]_{-\pi}^{\pi}$$
$$= -\frac{1}{2\pi n^2} \left((-in\pi - 1)\, e^{-in\pi} - (in\pi - 1)\, e^{in\pi} \right).$$

But

$$e^{\pm in\pi} = \cos(n\pi) \pm i\sin(n\pi)$$
$$= (-1)^n.$$

So

$$C_n = -\frac{(-1)^n}{2\pi n^2}(-2in\pi)$$
$$= \frac{i}{n}(-1)^n.$$

The exponential Fourier series is therefore

$$F(t) = \sum_{\substack{n=-\infty \\ n \neq 0}}^{\infty} \frac{i}{n}(-1)^n e^{int},$$

where the notation at the bottom of the summation symbol means that we sum n over all the integers except zero.

(b) Using equations (51), we get

$$A_0 = A_n = 0,$$
$$B_n = -2\,\mathrm{Im}(C_n) = -2\left[\frac{1}{n}(-1)^n\right] = \frac{2}{n}(-1)^{n+1}.$$

The corresponding trigonometric Fourier series is therefore

$$F(t) = \sum_{n=1}^{\infty} \frac{2}{n}(-1)^{n+1}\sin(nt).$$

This agrees with the trigonometric Fourier series found in Exercise 11.

Exercise 22

(a) Find the exponential Fourier series for the function

$$f(t) = e^{\alpha t} \quad \text{for } -1 \leq t < 1,$$
$$f(t+2) = f(t),$$

where α is a real but non-zero number.

(b) Use your answer to part (a) to find the corresponding trigonometric Fourier series for $f(t)$.

The fast Fourier transform in the modern world

The fast Fourier transform (FFT) is an algorithm for calculating the exponential Fourier coefficients for a function, when the function is specified at discrete points only. As a result it is particularly suited to implementation on a computer. Its importance lies in its speed of calculation. Previous to its discovery, the calculation of N Fourier coefficients took around N^2 arithmetic operations.

However, in 1965, James Cooley and John Tukey announced the discovery of the FFT, which could calculate N Fourier coefficients in around $N \ln N$ operations. This improvement in speed is crucial when it is necessary to compute millions or billions of Fourier coefficients. Subsequently, in 1984, it was discovered that the algorithm was already known to the great mathematician Carl Friedrich Gauss as early as 1805 – pre-dating even Fourier's work.

The FFT is of huge importance. It is used ubiquitously in the mathematical and computational sciences, in topics from solving differential equations to algorithms for quick multiplication of large integers and matrices. It also has wider applications in the modern world, where it is used billions of times a day:

- for analysing and detecting signals
- for coding and decoding audio and speech signals, e.g. MP3 encoding
- for digital TV (DVB) and digital audio radio (DAB) broadcasting
- for background noise reduction in mobile telephony.

In fact, you couldn't log on to a Wi-Fi network or make a call on your mobile phone without the FFT. The FFT has rightly been described as 'the most important numerical algorithm of our lifetime' (Gilbert Strang).

4.2   An application to differential equations

Here we illustrate how an exponential Fourier series can be used to construct the solution of a differential equation.

As motivation, consider the following problem. If a tyre fails on the wheel of a vehicle (Figure 42), the wheel may no longer be circular, and the suspension of the vehicle will be subject to a periodic force, with period τ. The manufacturer wishes to estimate the effect of this periodic force on the body of the vehicle.

Figure 42   Can an aircraft survive landing on this damaged tyre? Fourier series can solve the relevant differential equation.

The motion of the body of the vehicle can be modelled by a damped, driven harmonic oscillator, of the type considered in Unit 3, with a periodic driving term. The differential equation that must be solved is

$$\ddot{x} + 2\Gamma\dot{x} + \omega_0^2 x = f(t), \tag{52}$$

where the driving term $f(t)$ is a given periodic function, with fundamental period τ. Here, Γ is proportional to the damping constant, and ω_0 is the angular frequency of the harmonic oscillator in the absence of damping or external forces; this is called the **natural angular frequency**.

In this model, x represents the vertical displacement of the body of the vehicle, relative to its equilibrium position. $f(t)$ depends on the properties of the burst tyre, and τ depends on the speed of the vehicle and the diameter of the tyre.

We can solve the differential equation in the usual way: first find the complementary function $x_c(t)$ that satisfies the auxiliary equation $\ddot{x}_c + 2\Gamma\dot{x}_c + \omega_0^2 x_c = 0$; then find a particular solution x; finally, construct the general solution $x_g = x + x_c$. Finding the complementary function is straightforward, but this term dies away as time increases, so the motion is eventually closely approximated by the particular solution, and that is what we concentrate on finding here.

Since the driving term $f(t)$ is a given periodic function, with fundamental period τ, we can compute its exponential Fourier series:

$$f(t) = \sum_{n=-\infty}^{\infty} f_n \exp\left(\frac{2in\pi t}{\tau}\right) = \sum_{n=-\infty}^{\infty} f_n e^{in\omega t}, \tag{53}$$

where the f_n are the Fourier coefficients for $f(t)$ for $n = 1, 2, 3 \ldots$, and $\omega = 2\pi/\tau$ is the *angular frequency* of the driving force (not to be confused with the natural angular frequency of the system, ω_0).

Let us seek a particular solution $x(t)$ of equation (52) that is also a periodic function with period τ. Then we can also express $x(t)$ as a Fourier series, with Fourier coefficients x_n:

$$x(t) = \sum_{n=-\infty}^{\infty} x_n e^{in\omega t}. \tag{54}$$

If we are able to determine the Fourier coefficients x_n, then equation (54) will give us the required particular solution of equation (52).

The differential equation involves the derivatives $\dot{x}$ and $\ddot{x}$, and we can get expressions for these by differentiating equation (54) term by term:

$$\dot{x}(t) = \sum_{n=-\infty}^{\infty} in\omega\, x_n e^{in\omega t}, \tag{55}$$

$$\ddot{x}(t) = \sum_{n=-\infty}^{\infty} (in\omega)^2 x_n e^{in\omega t} = \sum_{n=-\infty}^{\infty} (-n^2\omega^2) x_n e^{in\omega t}. \tag{56}$$

These are the exponential Fourier series for $\dot{x}$ and $\ddot{x}$.

Substituting equations (53)–(56) into equation (52), we obtain

$$\sum_{n=-\infty}^{\infty} (-n^2\omega^2 + 2\Gamma in\omega + \omega_0^2) x_n e^{in\omega t} = \sum_{n=-\infty}^{\infty} f_n e^{in\omega t}.$$

The sums on both sides of this equation are Fourier series. They can be equal only if all of their coefficients are equal, so

$$x_n = \frac{1}{(\omega_0^2 - n^2\omega^2) + 2\Gamma in\omega} f_n. \tag{57}$$

The particular solution that we seek is therefore

$$x(t) = \sum_{n=-\infty}^{\infty} \frac{1}{(\omega_0^2 - n^2\omega^2) + 2\Gamma in\omega} f_n e^{in\omega t}. \tag{58}$$

Using equations (51), this could also be expressed as a Fourier series involving sines and cosines, but we will not do this here.

For small values of the damping parameter, $\Gamma \simeq 0$, we get

$$x_n \simeq \frac{1}{\omega_0^2 - n^2\omega^2}\, f_n.$$

So if $f_n \neq 0$, the Fourier coefficient x_n can be very large when $\omega_0 \simeq n\omega$, for $n = 0, 1, 2, \ldots$, i.e. whenever the natural angular frequency is an integer multiple of the angular frequency of the driving force. This is a generalisation of the phenomenon of resonance discussed in Section 5 of Unit 3.

Example 15

Find a particular solution of the differential equation

$$\ddot{x} + 2\Gamma\dot{x} + \omega_0^2 x = f(t),$$

where the driving term $f(t)$ is the function discussed in Example 14.

Solution

From Example 14, we have $\tau = 2\pi$ so $\omega = 2\pi/\tau = 1$, and the exponential Fourier series for f is given by

$$F(t) = \sum_{n=-\infty}^{\infty} f_n e^{int},$$

where

$$f_0 = 0 \quad \text{and} \quad f_n = \frac{i}{n}(-1)^n \quad (n \neq 0).$$

From equation (57) we see that the differential equation has a particular solution

$$x(t) = \sum_{n=-\infty}^{\infty} x_n e^{int},$$

where

$$x_0 = 0 \quad \text{and} \quad x_n = \frac{i(-1)^n}{n} \frac{1}{(\omega_0^2 - n^2\omega^2) + 2\Gamma in\omega} \quad (n \neq 0).$$

The expression for x_n ($n \neq 0$) can be simplified by the usual trick of multiplying the top and bottom by the complex conjugate of the bottom (see Unit 1). In the present case, the top and bottom are multiplied by $(\omega_0^2 - n^2\omega^2) - 2\Gamma in\omega$. Rearranging, and substituting the Fourier coefficients back into the exponential Fourier series, we conclude that

$$x(t) = \sum_{\substack{n=-\infty \\ n \neq 0}}^{\infty} \frac{i(-1)^n}{n} \frac{(\omega_0^2 - n^2\omega^2) - 2\Gamma in\omega}{(\omega_0^2 - n^2\omega^2)^2 + (2\Gamma in\omega)^2}\, e^{int}$$

$$= \sum_{\substack{n=-\infty \\ n \neq 0}}^{\infty} \frac{(-1)^n}{n} \frac{2\Gamma n\omega + i(\omega_0^2 - n^2\omega^2)}{(\omega_0^2 - n^2\omega^2)^2 - 4\Gamma^2 n^2\omega^2} \big(\cos(nt) + i\sin(nt)\big).$$

It is easy to see that the imaginary terms in the sum are odd functions of n. The imaginary part of $x(t)$ is therefore equal to 0 because the contributions with $n > 0$ exactly cancel those with $n < 0$.

Learning outcomes

After studying this unit, you should be able to do the following.

- Understand the terms angular frequency, period, fundamental period and fundamental interval, and be able to obtain their values for a periodic function.

- Give correct specifications of piecewise defined functions.

- Determine whether a function is even or odd, and use evenness and oddness to simplify definite integrals over a range that is symmetric about the origin.

- Calculate the trigonometric Fourier series for any periodic function, taking advantage of evenness or oddness where appropriate.

- Understand how to modify a function defined on a finite interval to give its even or odd periodic extension, and hence represent the function by a trigonometric Fourier series.

- Calculate the value of a Fourier series at a point of discontinuity.

- Where appropriate, simplify the calculation of Fourier coefficients by shifting the range of integration.

- Differentiate Fourier series to obtain new Fourier series from old.

Appendix: proofs and orthogonality

> This Appendix is optional and will not be assessed. It justifies the equations used to calculate Fourier coefficients and, more importantly, casts further light on the analogy between Fourier series and vectors. This analogy is frequently used in areas of advanced mathematics and in subjects like quantum mechanics.

Formulas for trigonometric Fourier coefficients

Given a function $f(t)$ with fundamental period τ, its trigonometric Fourier series is defined to be

$$F(t) = A_0 + \sum_{n=1}^{\infty} A_n \cos\left(\frac{2n\pi t}{\tau}\right) + \sum_{n=1}^{\infty} B_n \sin\left(\frac{2n\pi t}{\tau}\right), \qquad (59)$$

where A_0, A_n and B_n are the Fourier coefficients for $f(t)$ for $n = 1, 2, 3, \ldots$. This series is equal to the original function $f(t)$ (except at isolated points where $f(t)$ is discontinuous). So we write

$$f(t) = F(t).$$

The main text showed how to calculate A_0 by integrating both sides of equation (59) from $-\tau/2$ to $\tau/2$. The integrals of the sine functions vanish because their integrands are odd. The integrals of the cosine functions also vanish because we are integrating over a whole number of their periods. Explicitly, if $n \neq 0$ is an integer,

$$\int_{-\tau/2}^{\tau/2} \cos\left(\frac{2n\pi t}{\tau}\right) dt = \left[\frac{\tau}{2n\pi} \sin\left(\frac{2n\pi t}{\tau}\right)\right]_{-\tau/2}^{\tau/2}$$

$$= \frac{\tau}{2n\pi}\left(\sin(n\pi) - \sin(-n\pi)\right) = 0. \tag{60}$$

Hence integration of equation (59) from $-\tau/2$ to $\tau/2$ gives

$$\int_{-\tau/2}^{\tau/2} F(t)\, dt = A_0 \tau.$$

Using $f(t) = F(t)$, we obtain the following expression for A_0:

$$A_0 = \frac{1}{\tau}\int_{-\tau/2}^{\tau/2} f(t)\, dt.$$

The main text gave only a sketch of the derivation of the remaining Fourier coefficients, indicating how A_2 can be found. We now give more details. The key idea is as follows: we multiply both sides of equation (59) by a suitable function, chosen so that when we integrate from $-\tau/2$ to $\tau/2$, the integrals of all the terms vanish, except one. This remaining non-zero integral is multiplied by the Fourier coefficient that we want to find, and a simple rearrangement then gives a formula for that coefficient.

The calculation of A_0 is a trivial example of this idea, in which the multiplying function is the unit function, 1.

To implement this broad plan of action, we will use the following set of standard integrals, where n and m are any positive integers:

$$\int_{-\tau/2}^{\tau/2} \cos\left(\frac{2n\pi t}{\tau}\right) \sin\left(\frac{2m\pi t}{\tau}\right) dt = 0, \tag{61}$$

$$\int_{-\tau/2}^{\tau/2} \cos\left(\frac{2n\pi t}{\tau}\right) \cos\left(\frac{2m\pi t}{\tau}\right) dt = \begin{cases} \tau/2 & \text{for } n = m, \\ 0 & \text{for } n \neq m, \end{cases} \tag{62}$$

$$\int_{-\tau/2}^{\tau/2} \sin\left(\frac{2n\pi t}{\tau}\right) \sin\left(\frac{2m\pi t}{\tau}\right) dt = \begin{cases} \tau/2 & \text{for } n = m, \\ 0 & \text{for } n \neq m. \end{cases} \tag{63}$$

Equation (61) is obviously true. The sine function is odd and the cosine function is even, so their product is an odd function. This is integrated over a range that is symmetric about the origin, so the integral is equal to zero.

To establish equation (62), we use the trigonometric identity

$$\cos A \cos B = \tfrac{1}{2}[\cos(A - B) + \cos(A + B)],$$

which gives

$$\cos\left(\frac{2n\pi t}{\tau}\right) \cos\left(\frac{2m\pi t}{\tau}\right) = \frac{1}{2}\left[\cos\left(\frac{2(n-m)\pi t}{\tau}\right) + \cos\left(\frac{2(n+m)\pi t}{\tau}\right)\right].$$

Let us assume for the moment that $n \neq m$. Then, since n and m are positive integers, $n - m$ and $n + m$ are non-zero integers. We can therefore use the result of equation (60) (with n replaced by $n \pm m$) to show that the integral in equation (62) is equal to zero when $n \neq m$. This leaves the case $n = m$, for which the above trigonometric identity gives

$$\cos\left(\frac{2n\pi t}{\tau}\right)\cos\left(\frac{2n\pi t}{\tau}\right) = \frac{1}{2}\left[1 + \cos\left(\frac{4n\pi t}{\tau}\right)\right].$$

Again, the integral from $-\tau/2$ to $\tau/2$ of the cosine term gives zero, and we are left with

$$\int_{-\tau/2}^{\tau/2} \cos\left(\frac{2n\pi t}{\tau}\right)\cos\left(\frac{2n\pi t}{\tau}\right) dt = \int_{-\tau/2}^{\tau/2} \frac{1}{2}\, dt = \frac{\tau}{2}.$$

This completes the proof of equation (62).

Equation (63) is proved in a similar way, using the trigonometric identity

$$\sin A \sin B = \tfrac{1}{2}[\cos(A - B) - \cos(A + B)],$$

which gives

$$\sin\left(\frac{2n\pi t}{\tau}\right)\sin\left(\frac{2m\pi t}{\tau}\right) = \frac{1}{2}\left[\cos\left(\frac{2(n-m)\pi t}{\tau}\right) - \cos\left(\frac{2(n+m)\pi t}{\tau}\right)\right].$$

For exactly the same reasons as above, the integrals from $-\tau/2$ to $\tau/2$ of these terms are equal to zero provided that $n \neq m$. For the special case $n = m$ we have

$$\sin\left(\frac{2n\pi t}{\tau}\right)\sin\left(\frac{2n\pi t}{\tau}\right) = \frac{1}{2}\left[1 - \cos\left(\frac{4n\pi t}{\tau}\right)\right].$$

The integral from $-\tau/2$ to $\tau/2$ of the cosine term again gives zero, so

$$\int_{-\tau/2}^{\tau/2} \sin\left(\frac{2n\pi t}{\tau}\right)\sin\left(\frac{2n\pi t}{\tau}\right) dt = \int_{-\tau/2}^{\tau/2} \frac{1}{2}\, dt = \frac{\tau}{2},$$

completing the proof of equation (63).

Equations (62) and (63) can be tidied up using a shorthand notation that is surprisingly useful. The **Kronecker delta symbol** is defined by

The Kronecker delta symbol is named after the German mathematician Leopold Kronecker (1823–1891).

$$\delta_{nm} = \begin{cases} 1 & \text{for } n = m, \\ 0 & \text{for } n \neq m. \end{cases}$$

Using this notation, the integrals that we need can be expressed as follows.

Integrals needed to find Fourier coefficients

$$\int_{-\tau/2}^{\tau/2} \cos\left(\frac{2n\pi t}{\tau}\right)\sin\left(\frac{2m\pi t}{\tau}\right) dt = 0, \tag{64}$$

$$\int_{-\tau/2}^{\tau/2} \cos\left(\frac{2n\pi t}{\tau}\right)\cos\left(\frac{2m\pi t}{\tau}\right) dt = \frac{\tau}{2}\delta_{nm}, \tag{65}$$

$$\int_{-\tau/2}^{\tau/2} \sin\left(\frac{2n\pi t}{\tau}\right)\sin\left(\frac{2m\pi t}{\tau}\right) dt = \frac{\tau}{2}\delta_{nm}. \tag{66}$$

Using these integrals, we can easily obtain formulas for the Fourier coefficients A_n and B_n for $n = 1, 2, 3, \ldots$.

Let us multiply both sides of equation (59) by $\cos(2m\pi t/\tau)$, where m is a positive integer, and then integrate from $-\tau/2$ to $\tau/2$. Integrating each term in turn and using equations (64) and (65), we get

$$\int_{-\tau/2}^{\tau/2} F(t) \cos\left(\frac{2m\pi t}{\tau}\right) dt = \sum_{n=1}^{\infty} A_n \frac{\tau}{2} \delta_{nm} + 0.$$

In the sum on the right-hand side, the Kronecker delta symbol ensures that practically all the terms are equal to zero. Only the term with $n = m$ survives. Using the fact that $F(t) = f(t)$, we therefore conclude that

$$A_m = \frac{2}{\tau} \int_{-\tau/2}^{\tau/2} f(t) \cos\left(\frac{2m\pi t}{\tau}\right) dt \quad (m = 1, 2, 3, \ldots). \tag{67}$$

Similarly, multiplying both sides of equation (59) by $\sin(2m\pi t/\tau)$, where m is a positive integer, and then integrating from $-\tau/2$ to $\tau/2$ gives

$$\int_{-\tau/2}^{\tau/2} F(t) \sin\left(\frac{2m\pi t}{\tau}\right) dt = 0 + \sum_{n=1}^{\infty} B_n \frac{\tau}{2} \delta_{nm} = \frac{\tau}{2} B_m.$$

So, using the fact that $F(t) = f(t)$, we get

$$B_m = \frac{2}{\tau} \int_{-\tau/2}^{\tau/2} f(t) \sin\left(\frac{2m\pi t}{\tau}\right) dt \quad (m = 1, 2, 3, \ldots). \tag{68}$$

Equations (67) and (68) give the Fourier coefficients A_m and B_m for $m = 1, 2, 3, \ldots$. We may, of course, replace the label m by n to recover equations (19) and (20).

Formulas for exponential Fourier coefficients

Very similar arguments apply to the exponential Fourier series for a function $f(t)$ with fundamental period τ. In this case, we define

$$F(t) = \sum_{n=-\infty}^{\infty} C_n\, e^{2in\pi t/\tau}. \tag{69}$$

This Fourier series is equal to the original function $f(t)$ (except at isolated points where $f(t)$ is discontinuous). So we can write

$$f(t) = F(t).$$

We can again 'pick off' the Fourier coefficients by multiplying both sides by a suitable function and integrating. In this case, the standard integral that unlocks the coefficients is as follows.

$$\int_{-\tau/2}^{\tau/2} e^{-2im\pi t/\tau} e^{2in\pi t/\tau} \, dt = \tau \delta_{nm}, \tag{70}$$

where n and m are integers and δ_{nm} is the Kronecker delta symbol.

This integral is quite easy to establish. Assuming that $n \neq m$ are integers, we get

$$\int_{-\tau/2}^{\tau/2} e^{-2im\pi t/\tau} e^{2in\pi t/\tau}\, dt = \int_{-\tau/2}^{\tau/2} e^{2i(n-m)\pi t/\tau}\, dt$$

$$= \frac{\tau}{2i(n-m)\pi} \left[e^{2i(n-m)\pi t/\tau} \right]_{-\tau/2}^{\tau/2}$$

$$= \frac{\tau}{2i(n-m)\pi} \left(e^{i(n-m)\pi} - e^{-i(n-m)\pi} \right)$$

$$= \frac{\tau}{(n-m)\pi} \sin((n-m)\pi) = 0.$$

Recall that $\sin x = \dfrac{e^x - e^{-x}}{2i}$.

On the other hand, if $n = m$, the integrand becomes equal to 1, so

$$\int_{-\tau/2}^{\tau/2} e^{-2in\pi t/\tau} e^{2in\pi t/\tau}\, dt = \int_{-\tau/2}^{\tau/2} 1\, dt = \tau,$$

which completes the proof of equation (70).

Given equation (70), it is easy to derive a formula for the Fourier coefficients. We just multiply both sides of equation (69) by the factor $e^{-2im\pi t/\tau}$ and integrate term by term from $-\tau/2$ to $\tau/2$. This gives

$$\int_{-\tau/2}^{\tau/2} F(t)\, e^{-2im\pi t/\tau}\, dt = \sum_{n=-\infty}^{\infty} C_n\, \tau\, \delta_{nm}.$$

Again, the Kronecker delta symbol ensures that the sum on the right-hand side reduces to the single term $C_m \tau$. Hence, using the fact that $F(t) = f(t)$, we get

$$C_m = \frac{1}{\tau} \int_{-\tau/2}^{\tau/2} f(t)\, e^{-2im\pi t/\tau}\, dt.$$

Replacing the arbitrary label m by n, we then recover equation (49).

Orthogonal functions

Finally, let us return to the analogy between Fourier series and vectors mentioned earlier in the text.

You know that a vector in three-dimensional space can be expressed as

$$\mathbf{v} = v_x\, \mathbf{i} + v_y\, \mathbf{j} + v_z\, \mathbf{k}, \tag{71}$$

where $\mathbf{i}$, $\mathbf{j}$ and $\mathbf{k}$ are Cartesian unit vectors, and v_x, v_y and v_z are the corresponding components of $\mathbf{v}$. A key property of these unit vectors is that they are mutually orthogonal. This means that their scalar products satisfy

$$\mathbf{i} \cdot \mathbf{j} = \mathbf{i} \cdot \mathbf{k} = \mathbf{j} \cdot \mathbf{k} = 0. \tag{72}$$

The unit vectors also have unit magnitude, so

$$\mathbf{i} \cdot \mathbf{i} = \mathbf{j} \cdot \mathbf{j} = \mathbf{k} \cdot \mathbf{k} = 1. \tag{73}$$

These properties allow us to isolate any one of the components of $\mathbf{v}$. For example, taking the scalar product of equation (71) with $\mathbf{i}$ and using equations (72) and (73), we get

$$\mathbf{i} \cdot \mathbf{v} = v_x \left(\mathbf{i} \cdot \mathbf{i} \right) + v_y \left(\mathbf{i} \cdot \mathbf{j} \right) + v_z \left(\mathbf{i} \cdot \mathbf{k} \right)$$
$$= v_x \left(1 \right) + v_y \left(0 \right) + v_z \left(0 \right)$$
$$= v_x.$$

Note that taking the scalar product of $\mathbf{i}$ with $\mathbf{v}$ is achieved by taking the scalar product of $\mathbf{i}$ with each of the terms on the right-hand side of equation (71). Technically, we say that the scalar product is distributive. The component v_x can then be isolated because the unit vectors are orthogonal.

Similar language can be used to describe the calculation of Fourier coefficients. In this case, equation (71) for a vector is replaced by the Fourier series for a periodic function (equation (59) or (69)). Instead of taking the scalar product with a unit vector, we multiply by a suitable function and integrate over the fundamental period τ. The process of integration is also distributive, meaning that we can integrate each term on the right-hand side of the Fourier series in turn. Corresponding to the orthogonality of the unit vectors, we then have the standard integrals in equations (64)–(66) and (70):

$$\int_{-\tau/2}^{\tau/2} \cos \left(\frac{2n\pi t}{\tau} \right) \sin \left(\frac{2m\pi t}{\tau} \right) dt = 0,$$

$$\int_{-\tau/2}^{\tau/2} \cos \left(\frac{2n\pi t}{\tau} \right) \cos \left(\frac{2m\pi t}{\tau} \right) dt = \frac{\tau}{2} \delta_{nm},$$

$$\int_{-\tau/2}^{\tau/2} \sin \left(\frac{2n\pi t}{\tau} \right) \sin \left(\frac{2m\pi t}{\tau} \right) dt = \frac{\tau}{2} \delta_{nm},$$

$$\int_{-\tau/2}^{\tau/2} e^{-2im\pi t/\tau} e^{2in\pi t/\tau} dt = \tau \delta_{nm}.$$

This is what allows us to pick off individual Fourier coefficients from the sum. Because of these analogies, we say that the functions

$$\cos \left(\frac{2n\pi t}{\tau} \right), \quad \cos \left(\frac{4n\pi t}{\tau} \right), \quad \cos \left(\frac{6n\pi t}{\tau} \right), \quad \ldots,$$

$$\sin \left(\frac{2n\pi t}{\tau} \right), \quad \sin \left(\frac{4n\pi t}{\tau} \right), \quad \sin \left(\frac{6n\pi t}{\tau} \right), \quad \ldots,$$

and the constant function 1 are **orthogonal functions**. Similarly, the functions

$$e^{2in\pi t/\tau}, \quad e^{4in\pi t/\tau}, \quad e^{6in\pi t/\tau}, \quad \ldots$$

are said to be orthogonal. In both cases, orthogonality refers to the fact that certain integrals of these functions (given in equations (64)–(66) and (70)) are equal to zero. These integrals are sometimes called **orthogonality integrals**.

A minor difference compared with vectors is that the orthogonality integrals do not give 1 when $n = m$, so we do not have an analogue for equation (73). This could easily be remedied by scaling the functions, but this is not needed for our purposes. The important point to take away is that you can visualise the process of calculating Fourier coefficients as being similar to the process of projecting a vector onto the coordinate axes to find its components.

Solutions to exercises

Solution to Exercise 1

(a) The function $\sin\left(\frac{1}{4}x\right)$ has angular frequency $\omega = \frac{1}{4}$, so its fundamental period is $\tau = 2\pi/\omega = 8\pi$.

(b) The function $\cos\left(\frac{2}{5}x\right)$ has angular frequency $\omega = \frac{2}{5}$, so its fundamental period is $\tau = 2\pi/\omega = 5\pi$.

(c) The function $\sin\left(\frac{1}{4}x\right) + 2\cos\left(\frac{2}{5}x\right)$ is the sum of two functions: $\sin\left(\frac{1}{4}x\right)$ and $2\cos\left(\frac{2}{5}x\right)$. The complete set of periods for $\sin\left(\frac{1}{4}x\right)$ is given by the positive integer multiples of 8π, that is,

$$8\pi, \ 16\pi, \ 24\pi, \ 32\pi, \ 40\pi, \ 48\pi, \ \ldots.$$

The complete set of periods for $2\cos\left(\frac{2}{5}x\right)$ is given by the positive integer multiples of 5π, that is,

$$5\pi, \ 10\pi, \ 15\pi, \ 20\pi, \ 25\pi, \ 30\pi, \ 35\pi, \ 40\pi, \ \ldots.$$

The smallest period that these functions have in common is 40π. This is the fundamental period of $\sin\left(\frac{1}{4}x\right) + 2\cos\left(\frac{2}{5}x\right)$.

Solution to Exercise 2

The given function has period 3, so $q(t + 3) = q(t)$. Hence

$$q(1000) = q(1 + 3 \times 333) = q(1) = 1,$$

where the final value is obtained by examination of Figure 4. Similarly,

$$q(-77) = q(1 - 78) = q(1 - 3 \times 26) = q(1) = 1.$$

Solution to Exercise 3

Looking at Figure 11, we see that $q(t) = -\frac{1}{2}t$ for $-2 \leq t \leq 0$. Also, $q(t) = t$ for $0 < t \leq 1$, and $q(t) = \frac{3}{2} - \frac{1}{2}t$ for $1 < t \leq 3$.

Hence over the fundamental interval $-\frac{3}{2} \leq t \leq \frac{3}{2}$, $q(t)$ can be defined by

$$q(t) = \begin{cases} -\frac{1}{2}t & \text{for } -\frac{3}{2} \leq t \leq 0, \\ t & \text{for } 0 < t \leq 1, \\ \frac{3}{2} - \frac{1}{2}t & \text{for } 1 < t \leq \frac{3}{2}, \end{cases}$$

$$q(t + 3) = q(t).$$

Solution to Exercise 4

A sketch of the function is shown below.

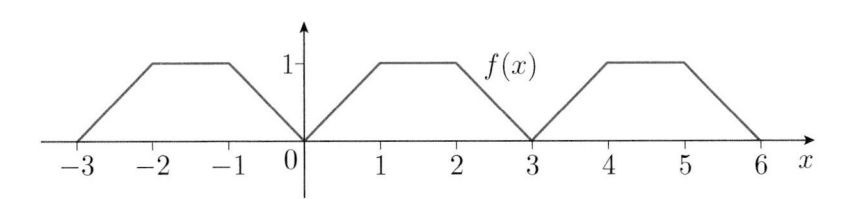

Solution to Exercise 5

This function is shown in the figure below. Note the positions of the open circles.

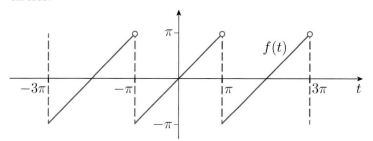

Solution to Exercise 6

(a) $u(t)$ has discontinuities at $t = \pm 1, \pm 3, \pm 5, \ldots$, i.e. at $t = 2n + 1$ for n an integer.

The fundamental period is $\tau = 2$.

(b) The piecewise definition is

$$u(t) = \begin{cases} t + 1 & \text{for } -1 \leq t \leq 0, \\ 1 & \text{for } 0 < t < 1, \end{cases}$$

$$u(t + 2) = u(t).$$

(c) Since $u(t + 2n) = u(t)$ for n an integer, $u(99) = u(-1) = 0$ and $u(100) = u(0) = 1$.

Solution to Exercise 7

(a) If $f(x) = x^3 - 3x$, then

$$f(-x) = (-x)^3 - 3(-x) = -(x^3 - 3x) = -f(x),$$

so this function is odd.

(b) The functions $\sin x$ and $\sin(4x)$ are both odd, so if $f(x) = 2\sin x + 3\sin(4x)$, then $f(x)$ is an odd function.

(c) Each term in the sum $5 + 2\cos x + 7\cos(4x)$ is even, so this function is even.

(d) The constant function 4 is even and $\sin x$ is odd, so if $f(x) = 4 - 2\sin x$, then $f(-x) = 4 + 2\sin x$. So $f(x)$ is neither even nor odd.

(e) If $f(x) = 2x\cos(3x)$, then

$$f(-x) = -2x\cos(-3x) = -2x\cos(3x) = -f(x),$$

so this function is odd.

Solution to Exercise 8

(a) The function x^3 is odd and the function $\cos(2x)$ is even, so the integrand is odd. The range of integration is symmetric about the origin, so the integral vanishes, i.e.

$$\int_{-1}^{1} x^3 \cos(2x)\, dx = 0.$$

(b) The function $\sin(2x^3)$ is odd and the constant function 3 is even. Since the range of integration is symmetric about the origin, we have

$$\int_{-2}^{2} (3 + \sin(2x^3))\, dx = \int_{-2}^{2} 3\, dx$$

$$= 6\int_{0}^{2} 1\, dx = \left[6x\right]_0^2 = 12.$$

We have used the fact that a constant is an even function, but this is an optional step.

Solution to Exercise 9

Looking at Figure 3, we see that $p(t)$ has fundamental period $\tau = 2$, therefore from equation (10), its Fourier series has the form

$$P(t) = A_0 + \sum_{n=1}^{\infty} A_n \cos(n\pi t) + \sum_{n=1}^{\infty} B_n \sin(n\pi t)$$

$$= A_0 + \left(A_1 \cos(\pi t) + A_2 \cos(2\pi t) + \cdots\right)$$
$$+ \left(B_1 \sin(\pi t) + B_2 \sin(2\pi t) + \cdots\right).$$

Comparing with equation (2), we see that $A_0 = A_1 = A_2 = A_3 = A_4 = 0$ and

$$B_1 = \frac{4}{\pi^2}, \quad B_2 = 0, \quad B_3 = -\frac{4}{9\pi^2}, \quad B_4 = 0.$$

Solution to Exercise 10

From Figure 2, it is clear that $|\cos t|$ has period $\tau = \pi$. Hence using equation (14) we have

$$A_0 = \frac{1}{\tau} \int_{-\tau/2}^{\tau/2} c(t)\, dt = \frac{1}{\pi} \int_{-\pi/2}^{\pi/2} |\cos t|\, dt = \frac{2}{\pi} \int_{0}^{\pi/2} |\cos t|\, dt,$$

where the last step follows because $|\cos t|$ is an even function.

But over the range $-\pi/2 \leq t \leq \pi/2$, $\cos t$ is positive, so $|\cos t| = \cos t$. Hence

$$A_0 = \frac{2}{\pi} \int_{0}^{\pi/2} \cos t\, dt$$

$$= \frac{2}{\pi} \left[\sin t\right]_0^{\pi/2}$$

$$= \frac{2}{\pi} \left(\sin(\pi/2) - \sin(0)\right) = \frac{2}{\pi},$$

in agreement with the stated Fourier series in equation (1).

Solution to Exercise 11

This function is sketched in the figure below.

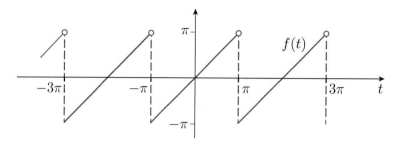

$f(t)$ is an odd function. It has fundamental period $\tau = 2\pi$, so its Fourier series (equation (17)) takes the form

$$F(t) = A_0 + \sum_{n=1}^{\infty} A_n \cos(nt) + \sum_{n=1}^{\infty} B_n \sin(nt).$$

From equation (18) we get

$$A_0 = \frac{1}{2\pi} \int_{-\pi}^{\pi} f(t)\,dt = 0,$$

because $f(t)$ is odd and the range of integration is symmetric about the origin.

From equation (19) we get

$$A_n = \frac{1}{\pi} \int_{-\pi}^{\pi} f(t) \cos(nt)\,dt \quad (n = 1, 2, 3, \ldots).$$

Because $f(t)$ is odd and $\cos(nt)$ is even, the integrand $f(t)\cos(nt)$ is an odd function, so when this is integrated from $t = -\pi$ to $t = \pi$, we get zero. Hence

$$A_n = 0 \quad (n = 1, 2, 3, \ldots).$$

Finally, from equation (20) we get

$$B_n = \frac{1}{\pi} \int_{-\pi}^{\pi} f(t) \sin(nt)\,dt = \frac{1}{\pi} \int_{-\pi}^{\pi} t \sin(nt)\,dt.$$

Using the standard integral in equation (32), we get

$$B_n = \frac{1}{n^2\pi} \left[\sin(nt) - nt\cos(nt) \right]_{-\pi}^{\pi}$$

$$= \frac{1}{n^2\pi} \left(\sin(n\pi) - n\pi\cos(n\pi) - (\sin(-n\pi) + n\pi\cos(-n\pi)) \right).$$

Since $\sin(n\pi) = 0$ and $\cos(n\pi) = (-1)^n$ for n an integer, this simplifies to

$$B_n = \frac{1}{n^2\pi}(-2n\pi(-1)^n) = \frac{2}{n}(-1)^{n+1} \quad (n = 1, 2, 3, \ldots).$$

Putting these results together, the required Fourier series is

$$F(t) = \sum_{n=1}^{\infty} \frac{2}{n}(-1)^{n+1} \sin(nt).$$

Solution to Exercise 12

The function is sketched in the figure below.

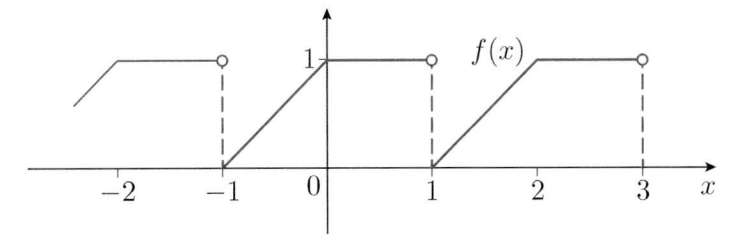

This function is neither even nor odd. It has fundamental period $\tau = 2$, so its Fourier series (equation (17)) has the form

$$F(x) = A_0 + \sum_{n=1}^{\infty} A_n \cos(n\pi x) + \sum_{n=1}^{\infty} B_n \sin(n\pi x).$$

From equation (18) we get

$$A_0 = \frac{1}{2} \int_{-1}^{1} f(x)\,dx.$$

To integrate a function defined on pieces, we integrate each piece in turn using the correct value of the function on each piece. So

$$A_0 = \tfrac{1}{2} \left(\int_{-1}^{0} (x+1)\,dx + \int_{0}^{1} 1\,dx \right)$$
$$= \tfrac{1}{2} \left(\left[\tfrac{1}{2}x^2 + x \right]_{-1}^{0} + \left[x \right]_{0}^{1} \right) = \tfrac{1}{2} \left(-(\tfrac{1}{2} - 1) + 1 \right) = \tfrac{3}{4}.$$

Similarly, equation (19) gives

$$A_n = \frac{2}{2} \int_{-1}^{1} f(x) \cos(n\pi x)\,dx \quad (n = 1, 2, 3, \ldots),$$

so

$$A_n = \int_{-1}^{0} (x+1) \cos(n\pi x)\,dx + \int_{0}^{1} \cos(n\pi x)\,dx.$$

For the integrals of $\cos(n\pi x)$, we can join the two integration ranges together. Hence

$$A_n = \int_{-1}^{0} x \cos(n\pi x)\,dx + \int_{-1}^{1} \cos(n\pi x)\,dx.$$

Using the standard integral in equation (33), we then get

$$A_n = \left[\frac{1}{(n\pi)^2} \left(\cos(n\pi x) + n\pi x \sin(n\pi x) \right) \right]_{-1}^{0} + \left[\frac{1}{n\pi} \sin(n\pi x) \right]_{-1}^{1}$$
$$= \frac{1}{(n\pi)^2} \left(\cos(0) - \cos(-n\pi) \right)$$
$$= \frac{1}{(n\pi)^2} \left(1 - (-1)^n \right) \quad (n = 1, 2, 3, \ldots),$$

where we have used $\sin(n\pi) = 0$ and $\cos(n\pi) = (-1)^n$ for n an integer.

Also, equation (20) gives

$$B_n = \frac{2}{2} \int_{-1}^{1} f(x)\sin(n\pi x)\,dx$$

$$= \int_{-1}^{0} (x+1)\sin(n\pi x)\,dx + \int_{0}^{1} \sin(n\pi x)\,dx$$

$$= \int_{-1}^{0} x\sin(n\pi x)\,dx + \int_{-1}^{1} \sin(n\pi x)\,dx.$$

Using the standard integral in equation (32), we get

$$B_n = \left[\frac{1}{(n\pi)^2} \big(\sin(n\pi x) - n\pi x\cos(n\pi x)\big) \right]_{-1}^{0} - \left[\frac{1}{n\pi}\cos(n\pi x) \right]_{-1}^{1}.$$

Since $\sin(n\pi) = 0$ and $\cos(n\pi) = (-1)^n$ for n an integer, we get

$$B_n = \frac{1}{(n\pi)^2}(0-0) - \frac{1}{(n\pi)^2}\big(\sin(-n\pi) + n\pi\cos(-n\pi)\big)$$

$$\quad - \frac{1}{n\pi}\big(\cos(n\pi) - \cos(-n\pi)\big)$$

$$= -\frac{1}{n\pi}(-1)^n \quad (n = 1,2,3,\ldots).$$

Putting all these results together, the required Fourier series is

$$F(x) = \frac{3}{4} + \frac{1}{\pi^2}\sum_{n=1}^{\infty}\frac{1}{n^2}(1-(-1)^n)\cos(n\pi x) - \frac{1}{\pi}\sum_{n=1}^{\infty}\frac{(-1)^n}{n}\sin(n\pi x).$$

The first few A_n are

$$A_1 = \frac{2}{1^2\pi^2}, \quad A_2 = 0, \quad A_3 = \frac{2}{3^2\pi^2}, \quad A_4 = 0, \quad A_5 = \frac{2}{5^2\pi^2}.$$

Hence the Fourier series can also be written as

$$F(x) = \frac{3}{4} + \frac{2}{\pi^2}\sum_{n=1}^{\infty}\frac{1}{(2n-1)^2}\cos((2n-1)\pi x) - \frac{1}{\pi}\sum_{n=1}^{\infty}\frac{(-1)^n}{n}\sin(n\pi x).$$

Solution to Exercise 13

It is clear from the figure given in the question that $f(t)$ is an even function with fundamental period $\tau = 2$. Following Procedure 3, its Fourier series involves only constant and cosine terms, and takes the form

$$F(t) = A_0 + \sum_{n=1}^{\infty} A_n \cos(n\pi t).$$

The constant term is

$$A_0 = \frac{2}{2}\int_{0}^{1} f(t)\,dt = \int_{0}^{1} t\,dt = \left[\frac{t^2}{2}\right]_{0}^{1} = \frac{1}{2}.$$

The remaining Fourier coefficients are

$$A_n = \frac{4}{2}\int_{0}^{1} f(t)\cos(n\pi t)\,dt = 2\int_{0}^{1} t\cos(n\pi t)\,dt.$$

This integral can be evaluated using equation (33). We get

$$A_n = \frac{2}{(n\pi)^2} \left[\cos(n\pi t) + n\pi t \sin(n\pi t)\right]_0^1$$

$$= \frac{2}{(n\pi)^2} \left(\cos(n\pi) - \cos(0)\right)$$

$$= \frac{2}{(n\pi)^2} \left((-1)^n - 1\right) \quad (n = 1, 2, 3, \ldots).$$

The Fourier series is therefore

$$F(t) = \frac{1}{2} + \sum_{n=1}^{\infty} \frac{2}{(n\pi)^2} \left((-1)^n - 1\right) \cos(n\pi t),$$

which agrees with the answer given in Example 7.

Solution to Exercise 14

The function $h(t)$ is sketched in the figure below.

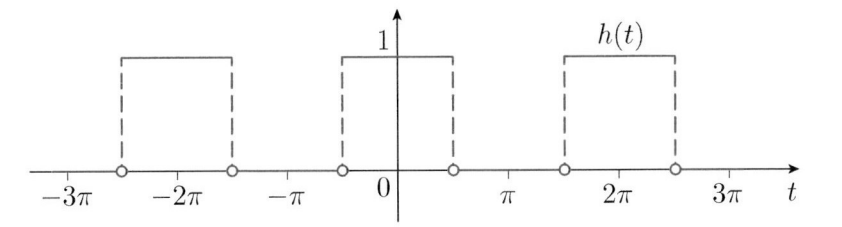

Clearly $h(t)$ is even and has fundamental period $\tau = 2\pi$. Following Procedure 3, its Fourier series involves only constant and cosine terms, and takes the form

$$H(t) = A_0 + \sum_{n=1}^{\infty} A_n \cos(nt).$$

The Fourier coefficients are evaluated as follows:

$$A_0 = \frac{1}{\pi} \int_0^{\pi} h(t)\, dt$$

$$= \frac{1}{\pi} \int_0^{\pi/2} 1\, dt + \frac{1}{\pi} \int_{\pi/2}^{\pi} 0\, dt$$

$$= \frac{1}{\pi} \left[t\right]_0^{\pi/2} = \frac{1}{2},$$

$$A_n = \frac{2}{\pi} \int_0^{\pi} h(t) \cos(nt)\, dt$$

$$= \frac{2}{\pi} \int_0^{\pi/2} \cos(nt)\, dt$$

$$= \frac{2}{n\pi} \left[\sin(nt)\right]_0^{\pi/2}$$

$$= \frac{2}{n\pi} \sin\left(\frac{n\pi}{2}\right) \quad (n = 1, 2, 3, \ldots).$$

Hence the Fourier series is given by

$$H(t) = \frac{1}{2} + \sum_{n=1}^{\infty} \frac{2}{n\pi} \sin\left(\frac{n\pi}{2}\right) \cos(nt).$$

For $n = 1, 2, 3, 4, 5$, the values of $\sin(n\pi/2)$ are $1, 0, -1, 0, 1$, so the first few terms of the Fourier series are

$$H(t) = \frac{1}{2} + \frac{2}{\pi} \cos(t) - \frac{2}{3\pi} \cos(3t) + \frac{2}{5\pi} \cos(5t) - \cdots,$$

in agreement with the Fourier series stated in equation (7).

Only the odd values of n contribute to the Fourier series. Putting $n = 2m - 1$ and noting that equation (24) gives

$$\sin((2m - 1)\pi/2) = (-1)^{m+1},$$

this Fourier series can also be written in the alternative form

$$H(t) = \frac{1}{2} + \frac{2}{\pi} \sum_{m=1}^{\infty} \frac{(-1)^{m+1}}{2m - 1} \cos((2m - 1)t).$$

Solution to Exercise 15

It is clear from Figure 2 that $c(t)$ is even and has fundamental period $\tau = \pi$. Following Procedure 3, its Fourier series involves only constant and cosine terms, and takes the form

$$C(t) = A_0 + \sum_{n=1}^{\infty} A_n \cos(2nt).$$

On the interval $0 \le t \le \pi/2$, we have $c(t) = \cos t$. Therefore

$$A_0 = \frac{2}{\pi} \int_0^{\pi/2} |\cos t| \, dt$$

$$= \frac{2}{\pi} \int_0^{\pi/2} \cos t \, dt$$

$$= \frac{2}{\pi} \left[\sin t\right]_0^{\pi/2} = \frac{2}{\pi}.$$

Similarly,

$$A_n = \frac{4}{\pi} \int_0^{\pi/2} \cos t \cos(2nt) \, dt.$$

Using the standard integral given in the question, with $a = 1$ and $b = 2n$, we then get

$$A_n = \frac{4}{\pi} \left[\frac{2n \cos t \sin(2nt) - \cos(2nt) \sin t}{4n^2 - 1}\right]_0^{\pi/2}$$

$$= \frac{4}{\pi} \left(\frac{2n \cos(\pi/2) \sin(n\pi) - \cos(n\pi) \sin(\pi/2)}{4n^2 - 1}\right)$$

$$= -\frac{4}{\pi} \frac{1}{4n^2 - 1} \cos(n\pi).$$

But $\cos(n\pi) = (-1)^n$, so

$$A_n = \frac{4}{\pi} \frac{(-1)^{n+1}}{4n^2 - 1} \quad (n = 1, 2, 3, \ldots).$$

Thus the Fourier series is

$$C(t) = \frac{2}{\pi} + \frac{4}{\pi} \sum_{n=1}^{\infty} \frac{(-1)^{n+1}}{4n^2 - 1} \cos(2nt).$$

The first few terms of this Fourier series are

$$C(t) = \frac{4}{\pi} \left(\tfrac{1}{2} + \tfrac{1}{3} \cos(2t) - \tfrac{1}{15} \cos(4t) + \tfrac{1}{35} \cos(6t) - \cdots \right),$$

in agreement with equation (1) in the Introduction.

Solution to Exercise 16

Using the definition of the even periodic extension, we have

$$q_{\text{even}}(t) = \begin{cases} t & \text{for } 0 \leq t \leq 1, \\ \tfrac{3}{2} - \tfrac{1}{2}t & \text{for } 1 < t \leq 3, \\ -t & \text{for } -1 \leq t < 0, \\ \tfrac{3}{2} + \tfrac{1}{2}t & \text{for } -3 < t < -1, \end{cases}$$

$$q_{\text{even}}(t + 6) = q_{\text{even}}(t).$$

This function has fundamental period $\tau = 6$, and its formula cannot be made much simpler. Its graph is sketched below.

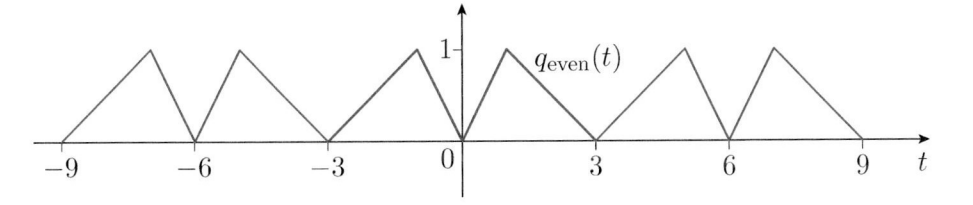

The odd periodic extension is given by

$$q_{\text{odd}}(t) = \begin{cases} t & \text{for } 0 \leq t \leq 1, \\ \tfrac{3}{2} - \tfrac{1}{2}t & \text{for } 1 < t \leq 3, \\ t & \text{for } -1 \leq t < 0, \\ -\tfrac{3}{2} - \tfrac{1}{2}t & \text{for } -3 < t < -1, \end{cases}$$

$$q_{\text{odd}}(t + 6) = q_{\text{odd}}(t).$$

This function has fundamental period $\tau = 6$, and its graph is sketched below.

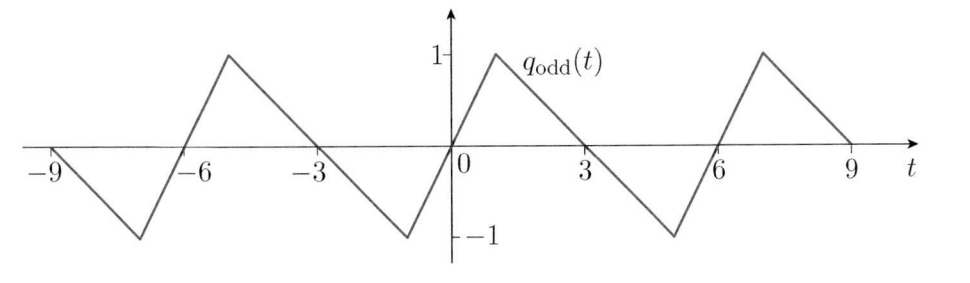

By examining this graph, we see that the formula can be simplified to

$$q_{\text{odd}}(t) = \begin{cases} t & \text{for } -1 < t \le 1, \\ \frac{3}{2} - \frac{1}{2}t & \text{for } 1 < t \le 5, \end{cases}$$

$$q_{\text{odd}}(t+6) = q_{\text{odd}}(t).$$

Solution to Exercise 17

Because we are looking for a Fourier series that involves only constant and cosine terms, we need to consider the *even* periodic extension of $f(x)$, denoted by $f_{\text{even}}(x)$. This is sketched in the figure below.

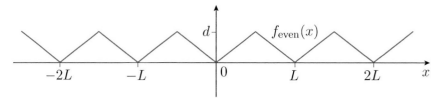

The function $f_{\text{even}}(x)$ is even, and from the above sketch has period $\tau = L$, so its Fourier series takes the form

$$F_{\text{even}}(x) = A_0 + \sum_{n=1}^{\infty} A_n \cos\left(\frac{2n\pi x}{L}\right),$$

where the Fourier coefficients A_0 and A_n are given by

$$A_0 = \frac{2}{L} \int_0^{L/2} f_{\text{even}}(x)\, dx,$$

$$A_n = \frac{4}{L} \int_0^{L/2} f_{\text{even}}(x) \cos\left(\frac{2n\pi x}{L}\right) dx \quad (n = 1, 2, 3, \ldots).$$

But on the interval $0 \le x \le L/2$,

$$f_{\text{even}}(x) = f(x) = \frac{2d}{L}x.$$

Hence

$$A_0 = \frac{4d}{L^2} \int_0^{L/2} x\, dx = \frac{4d}{L^2} \left[\frac{x^2}{2}\right]_0^{L/2} = \frac{d}{2}$$

and

$$A_n = \frac{8d}{L^2} \int_0^{L/2} x \cos\left(\frac{2n\pi x}{L}\right) dx \quad (n = 1, 2, 3, \ldots).$$

Using equation (33), we get

$$A_n = \frac{8d}{L^2}\left(\frac{L}{2n\pi}\right)^2 \left[\cos\left(\frac{2n\pi x}{L}\right) + \frac{2n\pi x}{L}\sin\left(\frac{2n\pi x}{L}\right)\right]_0^{L/2}$$

$$= \frac{2d}{n^2\pi^2}\left(\cos(n\pi) - \cos(0)\right)$$

$$= \frac{2d}{n^2\pi^2}\left((-1)^n - 1\right) \quad (n = 1, 2, 3, \ldots).$$

So

$$F_{\text{even}}(x) = \frac{d}{2} + \frac{2d}{\pi^2} \sum_{n=1}^{\infty} \frac{((-1)^n - 1)}{n^2} \cos\left(\frac{2n\pi x}{L}\right).$$

Since $f(x)$ and $f_{\text{even}}(x)$ coincide on the interval $0 \le x \le L$, this is the required cosine Fourier series $F(x)$ for $f(x)$.

The first few terms in the Fourier series are

$$F(x) = \frac{d}{2} - \frac{4d}{\pi^2} \left[\cos\left(\frac{2\pi x}{L}\right) + \frac{1}{3^2} \cos\left(\frac{6\pi x}{L}\right) + \frac{1}{5^2} \cos\left(\frac{10\pi x}{L}\right) + \cdots \right].$$

This agrees with the result of Exercise 13 in the special case $d = 1$, $L = 2$.

Solution to Exercise 18

(a) The even periodic extension is given by

$$f_{\text{even}}(t) = \begin{cases} 1 & \text{for } 0 \le t \le \frac{\pi}{2}, \\ -1 & \text{for } \frac{\pi}{2} < t \le \pi, \\ 1 & \text{for } -\frac{\pi}{2} \le t < 0, \\ -1 & \text{for } -\pi < t < -\frac{\pi}{2}, \end{cases}$$

$$f_{\text{even}}(t + 2\pi) = f_{\text{even}}(t),$$

and is drawn below.

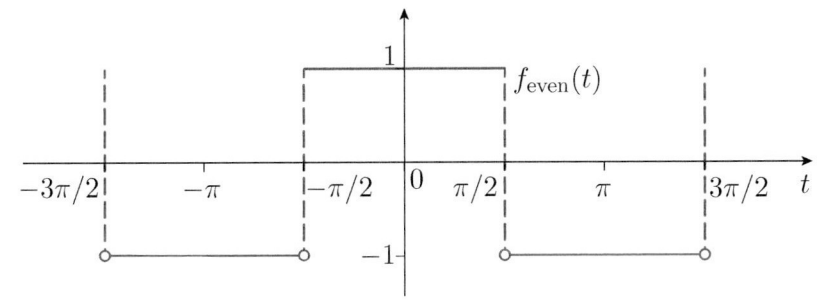

The fundamental period of this even extension is $\tau = 2\pi$, and its formula can be simplified to

$$f_{\text{even}}(t) = \begin{cases} 1 & \text{for } -\frac{1}{2}\pi \le t \le \frac{1}{2}\pi, \\ -1 & \text{for } \frac{1}{2}\pi < t < \frac{3}{2}\pi, \end{cases}$$

$$f_{\text{even}}(t + 2\pi) = f_{\text{even}}(t).$$

(b) Because the function $f_{\text{even}}(t)$ is even and has period $\tau = 2\pi$, its Fourier series takes the form

$$F_{\text{even}}(t) = A_0 + \sum_{n=1}^{\infty} A_n \cos(nt).$$

The coefficient A_0 is given by

$$A_0 = \frac{2}{2\pi} \int_0^{\pi} f_{\text{even}}(t)\, dt = \frac{1}{\pi} \left(\int_0^{\pi/2} 1\, dt + \int_{\pi/2}^{\pi} (-1)\, dt \right) = 0.$$

The average value of f_{even} over its period is equal to zero.

73

The coefficients A_n are given by

$$A_n = \frac{4}{2\pi} \int_0^\pi f_{\text{even}}(t) \cos(nt) \, dt$$

$$= \frac{2}{\pi} \left(\int_0^{\pi/2} \cos(nt) \, dt - \int_{\pi/2}^\pi \cos(nt) \, dt \right)$$

$$= \frac{2}{n\pi} \left([\sin(nt)]_0^{\pi/2} - [\sin(nt)]_{\pi/2}^\pi \right) = \frac{4}{n\pi} \sin\left(\frac{n\pi}{2}\right).$$

When n is an even integer, $\sin(n\pi/2) = 0$. When n is an odd integer, we can put $n = 2m - 1$ for $m = 1, 2, 3, \ldots$ and use equation (24) to get

$$\sin\left(\frac{n\pi}{2}\right) = \sin\left(\frac{(2m-1)\pi}{2}\right) = (-1)^{m+1}.$$

Hence

$$F_{\text{even}}(t) = \frac{4}{\pi} \sum_{m=1}^\infty \frac{(-1)^{m+1}}{2m-1} \cos((2m-1)t).$$

(c) The odd periodic extension is defined by

$$f_{\text{odd}}(t) = \begin{cases} 1 & \text{for } 0 \leq t \leq \frac{\pi}{2}, \\ -1 & \text{for } \frac{\pi}{2} < t \leq \pi, \\ -1 & \text{for } -\frac{\pi}{2} \leq t < 0, \\ 1 & \text{for } -\pi < t < -\frac{\pi}{2}, \end{cases}$$

$$f_{\text{odd}}(t + 2\pi) = f_{\text{odd}}(t),$$

Do not worry too much about the precise placement of the open circles; you would not be penalised in assessments or the exam for getting this wrong.

and is drawn below.

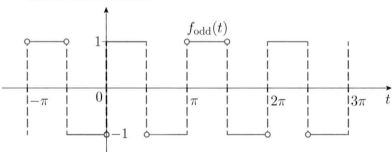

Because of the way the discontinuities of this function are defined, it has fundamental period $\tau = 2\pi$.

(d) The graph of the odd extension is very similar to the following graph, except for the points of discontinuity.

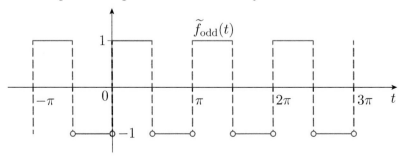

This function has fundamental period π and is defined by

$$\tilde{f}_{\text{odd}}(t) = \begin{cases} -1 & \text{for } -\frac{\pi}{2} < t < 0, \\ 1 & \text{for } 0 \leq t \leq \frac{\pi}{2}, \end{cases}$$

$$\tilde{f}_{\text{odd}}(t + \pi) = \tilde{f}_{\text{odd}}(t).$$

The Fourier series for this function was given in equation (27):

$$\tilde{F}_{\text{odd}}(t) = \frac{4}{\pi} \sum_{n=1}^{\infty} \frac{1}{2n-1} \sin\left(2(2n-1)t\right).$$

Since Fourier series cannot distinguish between functions that differ at isolated points, this is also the required Fourier series for the odd extension $f_{\text{odd}}(t)$.

Solution to Exercise 19

(a) $f(t)$ is discontinuous at $t = 1$. Just below $t = 1$, $f(t) = 1$, and just above $t = 1$, $f(t) = 0$. Hence at $t = 1$ the Fourier series converges to

$$F(1) = \tfrac{1}{2}.$$

(b) We can compare this with the Fourier series derived in Example 8:

$$F(t) = \frac{1}{4} + \sum_{n=1}^{\infty} \frac{1}{(n\pi)^2} \left((-1)^n - 1\right) \cos(n\pi t) - \sum_{n=1}^{\infty} \frac{(-1)^n}{n\pi} \sin(n\pi t).$$

But at $t = 1$, $\sin(n\pi t) = 0$ and $\cos(n\pi t) = (-1)^n$ for any integer n. So

$$F(1) = \frac{1}{2} = \frac{1}{4} + \sum_{n=1}^{\infty} \frac{1}{(n\pi)^2} \left((-1)^n - 1\right)(-1)^n.$$

Since $(-1)^{2n} = 1$, this rearranges to

$$\frac{1}{4} = \sum_{n=1}^{\infty} \frac{1}{(n\pi)^2} \left(1 - (-1)^n\right),$$

so

$$\frac{\pi^2}{4} = \sum_{n=1}^{\infty} \frac{1}{n^2} \left(1 - (-1)^n\right)$$

$$= \frac{2}{1^2} + \frac{2}{3^2} + \frac{2}{5^2} + \cdots$$

$$= \sum_{n=1}^{\infty} \frac{2}{(2n-1)^2}.$$

Hence

$$\frac{\pi^2}{8} = \sum_{n=1}^{\infty} \frac{1}{(2n-1)^2}.$$

Solution to Exercise 20

The function $f(x)$ is sketched below.

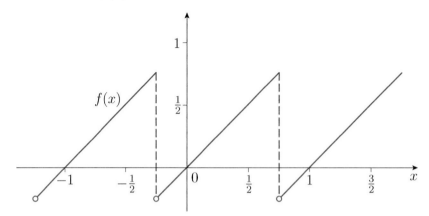

This function has fundamental period $\tau = 1$ and is neither odd nor even, so its Fourier series takes the form

$$f(x) = A_0 + \sum_{n=1}^{\infty} A_n \cos(2n\pi x) + \sum_{n} B_n \sin(2n\pi x).$$

If we were to take the fundamental interval of this function to be $-1/2 \le x \le 1/2$, it would be in two pieces and we would have to perform two integrals for each Fourier coefficient. Instead, let us use equations (41)–(43) with $t_0 = -\frac{1}{4}$ and $\tau = 1$. Then

$$A_0 = \frac{1}{\tau} \int_{t_0}^{t_0 + \tau} f(x)\, dx$$

$$= \frac{1}{1} \int_{-1/4}^{3/4} x\, dx$$

$$= \tfrac{1}{2} \left[x^2 \right]_{-1/4}^{3/4} = \tfrac{1}{2} \left(\tfrac{9}{16} - \tfrac{1}{16} \right) = \tfrac{1}{4}.$$

Similarly,

$$A_n = \frac{2}{\tau} \int_{t_0}^{t_0 + \tau} f(x) \cos\left(\frac{2n\pi x}{\tau} \right) dx$$

$$= 2 \int_{-1/4}^{3/4} x \cos(2n\pi x)\, dx.$$

Using the standard integral in equation (33), we get

$$A_n = \frac{2}{(2n\pi)^2} \left[\cos(2n\pi x) + 2n\pi x \sin(2n\pi x) \right]_{-1/4}^{3/4}$$

$$= \frac{2}{(2n\pi)^2} \left(\cos\left(\tfrac{3}{2} n\pi \right) + \tfrac{3}{2} n\pi \sin\left(\tfrac{3}{2} n\pi \right) \right.$$

$$\left. - \cos\left(-\tfrac{1}{2} n\pi \right) + \tfrac{1}{2} n\pi \sin\left(-\tfrac{1}{2} n\pi \right) \right).$$

When n is any integer, we have

$$\cos\left(-\tfrac{1}{2}n\pi\right) = \cos\left(-\tfrac{1}{2}n\pi + 2n\pi\right) = \cos\left(\tfrac{3}{2}n\pi\right)$$

and

$$\sin\left(-\tfrac{1}{2}n\pi\right) = \sin\left(-\tfrac{1}{2}n\pi + 2n\pi\right) = \sin\left(\tfrac{3}{2}n\pi\right).$$

So

$$A_n = \frac{1}{n\pi}\sin\left(\tfrac{3}{2}n\pi\right) \quad (n = 1, 2, 3, \ldots).$$

Similarly,

$$B_n = \frac{2}{\tau}\int_{t_0}^{t_0+\tau} f(x)\sin\left(\frac{2n\pi x}{\tau}\right) dx$$

$$= 2\int_{-1/4}^{3/4} x\sin(2n\pi x)\, dx.$$

Using the standard integral in equation (32), we get

$$B_n = \frac{2}{(2n\pi)^2}\left[\sin(2n\pi x) - 2n\pi x\cos(2n\pi x)\right]_{-1/4}^{3/4}$$

$$= \frac{2}{(2n\pi)^2}\left(\sin\left(\tfrac{3}{2}n\pi\right) - \tfrac{3}{2}n\pi\cos\left(\tfrac{3}{2}n\pi\right)\right.$$

$$\left. - \sin\left(-\tfrac{1}{2}n\pi\right) - \tfrac{1}{2}n\pi\cos\left(-\tfrac{1}{2}n\pi\right)\right).$$

We use $\cos\left(-\tfrac{1}{2}n\pi\right) = \cos\left(\tfrac{3}{2}n\pi\right)$ and $\sin\left(-\tfrac{1}{2}n\pi\right) = \sin\left(\tfrac{3}{2}n\pi\right)$ again to give

$$B_n = -\frac{1}{n\pi}\cos\left(\tfrac{3}{2}n\pi\right) \quad (n = 1, 2, 3, \ldots).$$

Hence the Fourier series is given by

$$F(x) = \frac{1}{4} + \sum_{n=1}^{\infty}\frac{1}{n\pi}\left(\sin\left(\tfrac{3}{2}n\pi\right)\cos\left(2n\pi x\right) - \cos\left(\tfrac{3}{2}n\pi\right)\sin\left(2n\pi x\right)\right).$$

Solution to Exercise 21

The function $c(t)$ is continuous, as can be seen from its graph, and $s'(t)$ is *minus* its derivative. The Fourier series for $s'(t)$ is denoted by $S(t)$ and is equal to *minus* the derivative of $C(t)$. Hence

$$S(t) = -\frac{4}{\pi}\sum_{n=1}^{\infty}\frac{(-1)^{n+1}}{4n^2 - 1}\frac{d}{dt}\left(\cos(2nt)\right)$$

$$= -\frac{4}{\pi}\sum_{n=1}^{\infty}\frac{(-1)^{n+1}}{4n^2 - 1}\left(-2n\sin(2nt)\right)$$

$$= \frac{4}{\pi}\sum_{n=1}^{\infty}(-1)^{n+1}\frac{2n}{4n^2 - 1}\sin(2nt).$$

Solution to Exercise 22

(a) $f(t)$ has fundamental period $\tau = 2$. Hence from equations (48) and (49), the exponential Fourier series is given by

$$F(t) = \sum_{n=-\infty}^{\infty} C_n e^{in\pi t},$$

with Fourier coefficients

$$
\begin{aligned}
C_n &= \frac{1}{2} \int_{-1}^{1} f(t) e^{-in\pi t} \, dt \\
&= \frac{1}{2} \int_{-1}^{1} e^{(\alpha - in\pi)t} \, dt \\
&= \frac{1}{2(\alpha - in\pi)} \left[e^{(\alpha - in\pi)t} \right]_{-1}^{1} \\
&= \frac{1}{2(\alpha - in\pi)} \left(e^{(\alpha - in\pi)} - e^{-(\alpha - in\pi)} \right).
\end{aligned}
$$

We have

$$e^{(\alpha - in\pi)} = e^{\alpha} e^{-in\pi} = e^{\alpha} \left(\cos(n\pi) - i \sin(n\pi) \right) = (-1)^n e^{\alpha},$$

and similarly,

$$e^{-(\alpha - in\pi)} = (-1)^n e^{-\alpha}.$$

Hence

$$C_n = \frac{(-1)^n}{2(\alpha - in\pi)} \left(e^{\alpha} - e^{-\alpha} \right).$$

Multiplying by $1 = (\alpha + in\pi)/(\alpha + in\pi)$, we get

$$C_n = \frac{(-1)^n (e^{\alpha} - e^{-\alpha})}{2(\alpha^2 + n^2\pi^2)} (\alpha + in\pi).$$

The exponential Fourier series for $f(t)$ is therefore

$$F(t) = \sum_{n=-\infty}^{\infty} \frac{(-1)^n (e^{\alpha} - e^{-\alpha})}{2(\alpha^2 + n^2\pi^2)} (\alpha + in\pi) e^{in\pi t}.$$

(b) Using equations (51) and the expression for C_n calculated in part (a), we get

$$
\begin{aligned}
A_0 &= C_0 = \frac{e^{\alpha} - e^{-\alpha}}{2\alpha}, \\
A_n &= 2 \operatorname{Re}(C_n) = \frac{(-1)^n (e^{\alpha} - e^{-\alpha})\alpha}{\alpha^2 + n^2\pi^2}, \\
B_n &= -2 \operatorname{Im}(C_n) = -\frac{(-1)^n (e^{\alpha} - e^{-\alpha})n\pi}{\alpha^2 + n^2\pi^2}.
\end{aligned}
$$

The trigonometric Fourier series for $f(t)$ is therefore given by

$$F(t) = (e^{\alpha} - e^{-\alpha}) \left[\frac{1}{2\alpha} + \sum_{n=1}^{\infty} \frac{(-1)^n}{\alpha^2 + n^2\pi^2} \left(\alpha \cos(n\pi t) - n\pi \sin(n\pi t) \right) \right].$$

Acknowledgements

Grateful acknowledgement is made to the following sources:

Figure 25: http://en.wikipedia.org/wiki/File:1st_commercial_Moog_synthesizer_(1964,_commissioned_by_the_Alwin_Nikolai_Dance_Theater_of_NY)_@_Stearns_Collection_(Stearns_2035),_University_of_Michigan.jpg. This file is licensed under the Creative Commons Attribution-NoDerivatives Licence http://creativecommons.org/licenses/by-nd/3.0.

Figure 42: Ukrainian Ministry of Emergencies.

Every effort has been made to contact copyright holders. If any have been inadvertently overlooked, the publishers will be pleased to make the necessary arrangements at the first opportunity.

Partial differential equations

Introduction

A **partial differential equation** is an equation relating a dependent variable and two or more independent variables through *partial derivatives* of the dependent variable. An example is

Partial derivatives were introduced in Unit 7.

$$\frac{\partial^2 u}{\partial x^2} + \frac{\partial^2 u}{\partial y^2} = e^{-(x^2+y^2)},$$

in which the dependent variable u is a function $u(x, y)$ of two independent variables, x and y.

Differential equations have played a very important role in the module so far. But until now, all the differential equations that you have solved have had just one independent variable, and contained *ordinary* derivatives with respect to that independent variable. Such equations are often called *ordinary differential equations* when it is necessary to distinguish them from partial differential equations. For many of the systems that we want to model, ordinary differential equations are inadequate because the states of the system can be specified only in terms of two – or even more – independent variables. When we are trying to describe the way in which such a system changes, we are inevitably led to consider partial differential equations.

Ordinary differential equations are the subject of Units 2, 3, 6 and 13.

Partial differential equations and fields

Much of the third book of this module was concerned with scalar and vector fields. You will be familiar with the idea that a scalar field can describe how a quantity such as temperature varies throughout space, and that this field is described by a function – for example, $\theta(x, y, z, t)$ might be the temperature at position (x, y, z) and time t. But we always regarded the fields as 'given' quantities: we specified the functions describing the fields, without discussing how these functions can be obtained.

In this unit, temperature is denoted by the symbol θ.

In fact, the laws of nature that determine scalar and vector fields are often formulated as partial differential equations. This makes the study of partial differential equations a key skill for anyone who wants to understand physical sciences at a quantitative level.

Having studied Units 1 and 2, you will appreciate that solving differential equations can be difficult, and that analytic solutions are not always available. It should be no surprise that partial differential equations are typically harder to solve. However, it turns out that many of the most important partial differential equations can be solved by the *method of separation of variables*, which is covered in this unit.

This unit concentrates on two examples of partial differential equations, namely the *wave equation* and the *diffusion equation*. Both of these equations describe how a scalar quantity (u, say) varies in space and time.

We concentrate on the simplest situation, the *one-dimensional* case, where there is only one coordinate, x, for the space dependence, and time is represented by t.

Wave equation and diffusion equation

The one-dimensional form of the **wave equation** is

$$\frac{1}{c^2} \frac{\partial^2 u}{\partial t^2} = \frac{\partial^2 u}{\partial x^2}, \tag{1}$$

where c is a positive constant called the **wave speed**.

The one-dimensional **diffusion equation** is

$$\frac{\partial u}{\partial t} = D \frac{\partial^2 u}{\partial x^2}, \tag{2}$$

where D is a positive constant called the **diffusion coefficient**.

The diffusion equation is also known as the **heat equation**. The contexts in which these equations arise will be described later in the unit.

Classification of partial differential equations

There are systematic ways of classifying partial differential equations, based on the classification of ordinary differential equations. You do not need to remember the definitions, but you should be aware of the terminology because you may meet it in more advanced courses.

- The *order* of a partial differential equation is the order of the highest derivative that occurs in it.

- A partial differential equation is *linear* if all terms that contain the dependent variable are proportional to the dependent variable, or one of its partial derivatives, but not both.

- A linear partial differential equation is *homogeneous* if there are no terms that are solely functions of the independent variables.

In this unit we deal only with *second-order linear homogeneous partial differential equations*. From these definitions you can see that both the wave equation (1) and the diffusion equation (2) are examples. By contrast, the partial differential equation

$$\frac{\partial u}{\partial t} + u \frac{\partial u}{\partial x} - \frac{\partial^2 u}{\partial x^2} = \sin(x + t)$$

is non-linear because of the term that is a product of u and $\partial u / \partial x$, and inhomogeneous because the term $\sin(x + t)$ does not contain u. Equations of this type are beyond the scope of this unit.

Study guide

Section 1 introduces the wave equation and considers how it is used to describe the vibrations of a plucked guitar string. The wave equation is then solved using the method of separation of variables. This very important technique has two main stages. First, we find a set of simple solutions that satisfy the partial differential equation and its boundary conditions. Then we find a linear combination of these simple solutions that satisfies the partial differential equation, its boundary conditions and the given initial conditions. The task of finding the appropriate linear combination in this case makes use of the Fourier methods covered in Unit 11.

Section 2 introduces the diffusion equation, which can be used to model the slow spread of materials, such as the slow spread of a pollutant as it contaminates groundwater. Most of this section is concerned with arguments that justify the form of the diffusion equation. You will not be asked to reproduce these arguments in assignments or in the exam. However, because of the importance of partial differential equations in the physical sciences, it is valuable to see one example of a partial differential equation being derived. The section ends by illustrating the solution of the diffusion equation, again using the method of separation of variables

As well as describing the spread of materials, the diffusion equation also describes the spread of heat. In this context, the diffusion equation is known as the heat equation. The heat equation and some of its solutions are considered in Section 3.

All the solutions considered in Sections 1 to 3 are for cases where the equations describe systems with boundaries. The wave equation and diffusion equation also apply to systems without boundaries, and in these cases useful solutions are available that are not easily obtained by the method of separation of variables. We discuss some useful alternative forms of solution of the wave and diffusion equations in Section 4. However, this section is optional reading.

1 The method of separation of variables

The most important idea that you will learn from this unit is the method of separation of variables for solving linear homogeneous partial differential equations. The wave equation can describe the motion of a plucked string, and we use this as our first example of a partial differential equation that is solved by the method of separation of variables.

1.1 Motion of a plucked guitar string

When asked to imagine a wave, you might think of an ocean wave rolling onto a beach (Figure 1(a)). This type of wave is called a **travelling wave**. But the wave equation can also describe a disturbance that varies in space, and oscillates at each point, but does not move through space. The motion of a guitar string is a good example (Figure 1(b)).

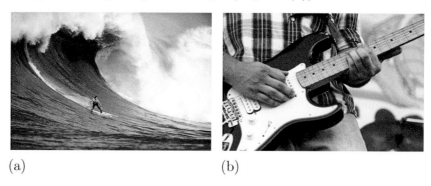

(a)　　　　　　　　　　　　　　　　(b)

Figure 1　Two waves: (a) a travelling wave in the ocean; (b) a standing wave on a guitar string

Figure 2 shows a possible motion for such a string. Each coloured curve indicates the shape of the string at a particular instant in time. The dark blue curve corresponds to the earliest time; the green curve to a slightly later time, and so on. The string vibrates 'on the spot', but no wave flows to the left or right, and there are some points (known as **nodes**) where the string remains permanently at rest. Motion such as this is called a **standing wave**.

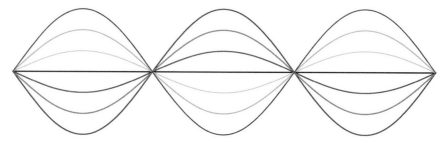

Figure 2　Shapes of a plucked guitar string at a succession of equally-spaced times: the time sequence corresponds to dark blue, green, cyan, black, magenta, orange, red, orange, magenta, black, cyan, green, dark blue, and so on

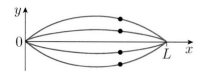

Figure 3　A point on a vibrating string moves up and down

Let us consider the motion of a plucked guitar string in more detail. In its equilibrium state, the string is taut and is anchored at two fixed points separated by a distance L. We take the string to lie along the x-axis, with one end at $x = 0$ and the other at $x = L$. The motion of the string is confined to a plane, which may be taken to be the xy-plane. The motion of each point of the string is assumed to be up and down (or *transverse*) – that is, parallel to the y-axis, with no motion along the x-axis (Figure 3). The transverse displacement of any point on the string is denoted u. The value of u depends on the position x of the point along the string, and also on time t. So we have two independent variables, x and t, and one dependent variable, u. We say that u is a function of x and t, and write $u = u(x, t)$.

At a fixed time $t = t_1$, the function $u(x, t_1)$ is a function of x alone; this describes the shape of the string at the given time t_1. For a given point on the string, labelled by $x = x_1$, the function $u(x_1, t)$ is a function of t alone; this describes the motion of the given point on the string as time progresses. Figure 4 illustrates both these aspects. Figure 4(a) is a typical graph of $u(x, t_1)$ against x, giving a snapshot of the shape of the string, while Figure 4(b) is a typical graph of $u(x_1, t)$ against t, showing the displacement of a single point on the string as a function of time.

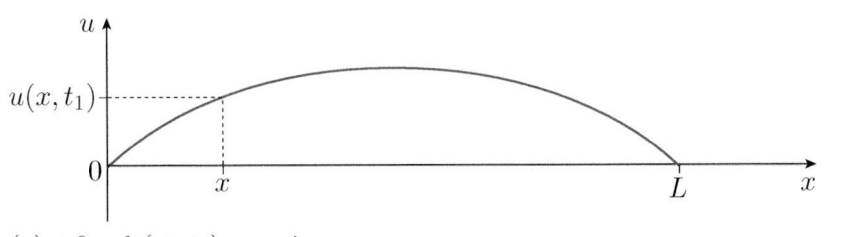

(a) t fixed (at t_1), varying x

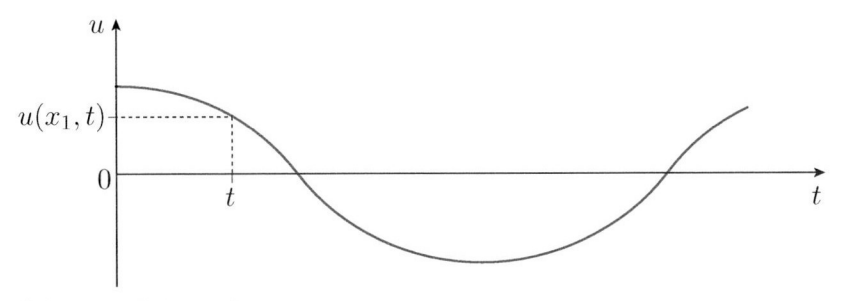

(b) x fixed (at x_1), varying t

Figure 4   Graphs of: (a) $u(x, t_1)$ against x, showing the shape of the string at time t_1; (b) $u(x_1, t)$ against t, showing the displacement of a single point on the string as a function of time

In order to describe the motion of the string, we need to find the function $u(x, t)$. Since u depends on both x and t, an equation that models the motion of the string is expected to involve partial derivatives of u with respect to both x and t. The appropriate differential equation for small vibrations of a flexible taut string is the **wave equation**

$$\frac{\partial^2 u}{\partial x^2} = \frac{1}{c^2} \frac{\partial^2 u}{\partial t^2}, \tag{3}$$

where c is a constant whose value depends on various physical characteristics of the string. This constant is called the **wave speed**, although the reason for this name will become apparent only at the end of this unit. The quantity $\partial^2 u/\partial t^2$ on the right-hand side of equation (3) is the acceleration of a tiny segment of the string. A lengthy analysis shows that the net force acting on this segment is proportional to $\partial^2 u/\partial x^2$. Equation (3) therefore embodies Newton's second law: force is proportional to acceleration. The derivation of the wave equation is not part of this unit.

In fact, c depends on the linear density and tension of the string.

It is easy to check whether or not a function is a solution of a partial differential equation by simply substituting the given function into the given equation, and seeing whether the equation is satisfied. The only difference from the case of an ordinary differential equation is that you have to calculate all the relevant partial derivatives. For example, let us check that

$$u(x, t) = \sin(kx)\cos(kct)$$

is a solution of the wave equation (3) for any constant k. We have

$$\frac{\partial u}{\partial x} = k\cos(kx)\cos(kct), \quad \frac{\partial u}{\partial t} = -kc\sin(kx)\sin(kct),$$

$$\frac{\partial^2 u}{\partial x^2} = -k^2\sin(kx)\cos(kct), \quad \frac{\partial^2 u}{\partial t^2} = -k^2c^2\sin(kx)\cos(kct).$$

So when $u(x, t) = \sin(kx)\cos(kct)$,

$$\frac{\partial^2 u}{\partial x^2} = \frac{1}{c^2}\frac{\partial^2 u}{\partial t^2},$$

and this function is indeed a solution of the wave equation.

Exercise 1

Determine whether $u(x, t) = A\sin(kx)\sin(kct)$, where A and k are real constants, is a solution of the wave equation.

Exercise 2

If the displacement of the string is $u(x, t) = A\sin(kx)\sin(kct)$, find expressions for the displacement and velocity of the string at position x and time $t = 0$. (*Hint*: The velocity at time t is the partial derivative of the displacement with respect to time t.)

Boundary conditions and initial conditions

Just giving a partial differential equation is never enough to specify a problem completely: some additional information in the form of boundary conditions and/or initial conditions is always required. The boundary conditions and initial conditions appropriate to obtaining a particular solution depend on the context. For example, for the wave equation as a model of the vibrations of a guitar string, we need *two* boundary conditions and *two* initial conditions.

Initial conditions and boundary conditions were discussed in Unit 3.

If the string is anchored at $x = 0$ and $x = L$, and we are interested in the motion following the string's release at $t = 0$, then the boundary conditions are

$$u(0, t) = u(L, t) = 0, \quad t \geq 0, \tag{4}$$

corresponding to the string being fixed at its ends.

The initial conditions model the action of releasing the string and setting it in motion. In particular, plucking consists of holding the string in a certain shape, at rest, and then releasing it. If the initial shape of the string is given by a function $f(x)$, then the initial conditions for a plucked string may be specified in the form

$$u(x,0) = f(x), \quad 0 \le x \le L, \tag{5}$$

and

$$\frac{\partial u}{\partial t}(x,0) = 0, \quad 0 \le x \le L. \tag{6}$$

The first initial condition describes the initial shape of the string, while the second corresponds to it being at rest initially. Note that for a partial differential equation, the initial condition is described by a *function* $f(x)$, whereas in the case of an ordinary differential equation an initial condition is described by a number. The initial conditions are often specified piecewise, as in the following example and exercise.

___

Example 1

A taut string of equilibrium length L is plucked at its midpoint, which is given an initial displacement d, as shown in Figure 5. The string is then released from rest. Write down the initial conditions for the wave equation describing transverse vibrations of this string.

Solution

The displacement shown in Figure 5 has two linear sections. The left-hand section has slope $d/(L/2) = 2d/L$ and has the value $u = 0$ at $x = 0$. It is described by the function $u(x) = (2d/L)x$. The right-hand section has slope $-2d/L$ and has the value $u = 0$ at $x = L$. It is described by a linear function of the form

$$u(x) = -\frac{2d}{L}x + C,$$

where C is a constant. Setting $u(L) = 0$ gives $C = 2d$, so the right-hand section is described by the function

$$u(x) = 2d - \frac{2d}{L}x = \frac{2d}{L}(L - x).$$

Hence the initial displacement is given by the piecewise function

$$u(x,0) = \begin{cases} \dfrac{2d}{L}x & \text{for } 0 \le x \le \tfrac{1}{2}L, \\ \dfrac{2d}{L}(L - x) & \text{for } \tfrac{1}{2}L < x \le L. \end{cases}$$

Because the string is released from rest, the transverse component of the initial velocity is given by

$$\frac{\partial u}{\partial t}(x,0) = 0, \quad 0 \le x \le L.$$

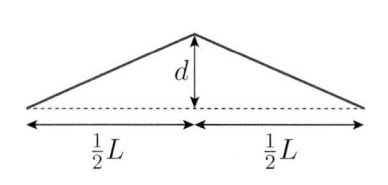

Figure 5   String plucked at its midpoint

Both parts of this expression give $u(x,0) = d$ at $x = L/2$. This is a useful check.

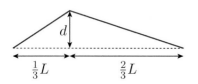

Figure 6   String plucked at a distance $L/3$ from $x = 0$

Exercise 3

A taut string of equilibrium length L is plucked at a point one-third of the way along its length, which is given an initial displacement d, as shown in Figure 6. What are the initial conditions for the wave equation describing transverse vibrations of this string?

We have seen that any function of the form $u(x,t) = \sin(kx)\cos(kct)$ is a solution of the wave equation, for any constant k. In particular, for $k = \pi/L$,

$$u(x,t) = \sin\left(\frac{\pi x}{L}\right)\cos\left(\frac{\pi ct}{L}\right) \tag{7}$$

is a solution of the wave equation for transverse vibrations of a taut string, where L is the equilibrium length of the string. This solution also satisfies the boundary conditions (4) and the initial condition $\partial u(x,0)/\partial t = 0$. It describes a special case where the initial displacement of the string is a sinusoidal function, that is, the function $f(x)$ in (5) is $f(x) = \sin(\pi x/L)$.

Exercise 4

Show that the solution given by equation (7) satisfies the boundary conditions

$$u(0,t) = u(L,t) = 0, \quad t \geq 0,$$

and the initial condition

$$\frac{\partial u}{\partial t}(x,0) = 0, \quad 0 \leq x \leq L.$$

Boundary conditions, initial conditions and uniqueness

In general, it may not be clear which boundary and initial conditions are required to go with a given partial differential equation. When solving practical problems, the boundary and initial conditions should contain enough information to determine a unique solution of the partial differential equation. There are mathematical conditions for determining when there is a unique solution. In practice, however, these are rarely used. Usually an understanding of the physics or engineering context is a reliable guide to what sort of initial and boundary conditions are required.

1.2 Separation of variables for the wave equation

The method described here is not the same as the separation of variables method in Unit 2, which applies to first-order ordinary differential equations.

We have already said that the most important idea that you will learn from this unit is the method of *separation of variables*. We now apply this method to the wave equation for vibrations of a taut flexible string.

The method has a number of stages. First, we find some special solutions of the wave equation that satisfy the given boundary conditions. Then we show that linear combinations of these special solutions also satisfy the wave equation. The final stage of the calculation selects the particular linear combination that is needed to ensure that the initial conditions are met. In this subsection, we concentrate on the first stage – finding a set of special solutions of the wave equation from which everything else will be constructed. We require the solutions to satisfy the boundary conditions, but we will not bother with any particular initial conditions at this stage.

The partial differential equation that we wish to solve is the wave equation for vibrations of a taut string:

$$\frac{\partial^2 u}{\partial x^2} = \frac{1}{c^2}\frac{\partial^2 u}{\partial t^2}, \tag{8}$$

Sections 2 and 3 will apply the same method to the diffusion equation (also called the heat equation).

subject to the boundary conditions

$$u(0,t) = u(L,t) = 0, \quad t \geq 0. \tag{9}$$

The first step in the method of separation of variables is to look for solutions of (8) and (9) in the form

$$u(x,t) = X(x)\,T(t), \tag{10}$$

where $X(x)$ is a function of x alone, and $T(t)$ is a function of t alone, so that the variables x and t occur in two separate functions. Note that we are *not* claiming that all the solutions of equation (8) are of this form. We are merely restricting attention to a simple type of solution, in which $u(x,t)$ happens to be the product of a function of x and a function of t. Such solutions are called **product solutions**.

We now prepare to substitute equation (10) into the wave equation. The partial derivative $\partial/\partial x$, with respect to x, acts only on the function $X(x)$, and $\partial/\partial t$ acts only on $T(t)$. Because $X(x)$ and $T(t)$ are both functions of a single variable, their derivatives are written with upright, rather than curly, dees. We therefore have

$$\frac{\partial u}{\partial x} = \frac{dX}{dx}\,T, \quad \frac{\partial u}{\partial t} = X\,\frac{dT}{dt}.$$

Differentiating again gives

$$\frac{\partial^2 u}{\partial x^2} = \frac{d^2 X}{dx^2}\,T, \quad \frac{\partial^2 u}{\partial t^2} = X\,\frac{d^2 T}{dt^2}.$$

Substituting these second-order partial derivatives into the wave equation then leads to

$$T\,\frac{d^2 X}{dx^2} = \frac{1}{c^2}X\,\frac{d^2 T}{dt^2}. \tag{11}$$

The secrets of this equation can be unlocked by dividing both sides by the product $X(x)\,T(t)$. This gives

We assume that $X(x)$ and $T(t)$ are non-zero (except possibly at isolated points).

$$\frac{1}{X}\frac{d^2 X}{dx^2} = \frac{1}{c^2}\frac{1}{T}\frac{d^2 T}{dt^2}.$$

Now, this equation has a very interesting property. Because the function $T(t)$ does not appear on the left-hand side, the expression to the left of the equals sign is a function of x only, and does not depend on t. Similarly, the right-hand side is a function of t only, and does not depend on x. But since these expressions are equal, neither expression can depend on either x or t. That means that both sides of the equation are equal to the *same* constant, which we call μ. We can therefore write

$$\frac{1}{X}\frac{d^2X}{dx^2} = \mu = \frac{1}{c^2}\frac{1}{T}\frac{d^2T}{dt^2}.$$

So equation (11) has yielded two ordinary differential equations:

$$\frac{1}{X}\frac{d^2X}{dx^2} = \mu \quad \text{and} \quad \frac{1}{c^2}\frac{1}{T}\frac{d^2T}{dt^2} = \mu.$$

Multiplying the first equation by $X(x)$ and the second by $T(t)$ gives

$$\frac{d^2X}{dx^2} = \mu X \tag{12}$$

and

$$\frac{d^2T}{dt^2} = c^2\mu T. \tag{13}$$

These ordinary differential equations for $X(x)$ and $T(t)$ must be satisfied in order for the product function $X(x)\,T(t)$ to be a solution of the wave equation (8). Conversely, the wave equation is satisfied by $X(x)\,T(t)$ if $X(x)$ satisfies equation (12) and $T(t)$ satisfies equation (13). The constant μ is called the **separation constant**. We have no information about this constant at this stage, but we can say that the same constant appears in both equation (12) and equation (13).

The ordinary differential equations (12) and (13) are linear and homogeneous, and they can both be solved using the methods of Unit 3. The nature of the solutions depends on the value of the separation constant μ, and we will consider three cases in turn, depending on whether μ is positive, negative or equal to zero. In each case we will determine the form of the solutions of equations (12) and (13), and consider whether these solutions can satisfy the given boundary conditions.

Separation constant positive

If $\mu > 0$, we can write $\mu = k^2$, where k is a real positive constant. Then equation (12) can be solved by substituting in the trial solution $X(x) = \exp(\lambda x)$. This leads to the auxiliary equation $\lambda^2 = \mu = k^2$, so $\lambda = \pm k$ and the general solution is

$$X(x) = A\exp(kx) + B\exp(-kx), \tag{14}$$

where A and B are arbitrary constants.

We could easily determine the solution for $T(t)$ using the same approach. We will not do this because the form of $T(t)$ is irrelevant for our purposes. We need to know only that the product function takes the form $X(x)\,T(t)$, where $X(x)$ is given by equation (14).

Having determined the form of the solution, we now consider whether the boundary conditions can be satisfied. The displacement $u(x,t) = X(x)\,T(t)$ must be zero at both ends of the string ($x = 0$ and $x = L$) for all positive values of t. This implies that the function $X(x)$ must satisfy the boundary conditions

$$X(0) = X(L) = 0. \tag{15}$$

We consider the conditions $X(0) = 0$ and $X(L) = 0$ in turn. For the function $X(x)$ in equation (14), the condition $X(0) = 0$ gives

$$A + B = 0,$$

and the condition $X(L) = 0$ gives

$$A\exp(kL) + B\exp(-kL) = 0.$$

Combining these equations gives

$$A\big(\exp(kL) - \exp(-kL)\big) = 0.$$

Since both k and L are positive, $kL > 0$, and the only way of satisfying this equation is to take $A = 0$. This gives $u(x,t) = 0$, which does solve the partial differential equation, but in a very dull way. It corresponds to a string that remains permanently in its equilibrium state, not vibrating at all. Such a solution is often referred to as a **trivial solution**, and is not the solution we are seeking.

For $kL > 0$, $\exp(kL) > 1$ and $\exp(-kL) < 1$.

Separation constant negative

If $\mu < 0$, we can write $\mu = -k^2$, where k is a real positive constant. Then equations (12) and (13) become

$$\frac{d^2 X}{dx^2} = -k^2 X, \tag{16}$$

$$\frac{d^2 T}{dt^2} = -k^2 c^2 T. \tag{17}$$

Again, we concentrate on the first of these equations. This can be recognised as the 'equation of simple harmonic motion' discussed in Unit 3, and it has the general solution

$$X(x) = C\cos(kx) + D\sin(kx), \tag{18}$$

where C and D are arbitrary constants. Let us see whether this function can satisfy the given boundary conditions (15). Applying the condition $X(0) = 0$ to the function in equation (18) gives $C = 0$, so the solution becomes

$$X(x) = D\sin(kx).$$

The condition $X(L) = 0$ then requires that either $D = 0$ or $\sin(kL) = 0$. The first possibility corresponds to the trivial solution $u(x,t) = 0$ mentioned earlier. The second possibility is more interesting. It is satisfied if, and only if, k takes one of the special set of values

$$k = \frac{n\pi}{L}, \quad \text{where } n \text{ is an integer,}$$

and this gives a set of solutions

$$X(x) = D \sin \left(\frac{n\pi x}{L} \right).$$

In fact, the values of n can be restricted further. The value $n = 0$ can be omitted because it gives the trivial solution $u(x, t) = 0$. Also, all negative values of n can be omitted because changing the sign of n is equivalent to changing the sign of D, which is an arbitrary constant anyway. We can therefore say that the most general solution of equation (16), consistent with the boundary conditions, is

$$X(x) = D \sin \left(\frac{n\pi x}{L} \right), \quad \text{where } n = 1, 2, 3, \ldots.$$

We will return to consider the corresponding solution for $T(t)$ shortly.

Separation constant equal to zero

If $\mu = 0$, the equation for $X(x)$ is

$$\frac{d^2 X}{dx^2} = 0.$$

The solution of this equation is

$$X(x) = Fx + G,$$

where F and G are arbitrary constants. The boundary condition $X(0) = 0$ gives $G = 0$, so the solution becomes $X(x) = Fx$. The boundary condition $X(L) = 0$ then gives $F = 0$. So $F = G = 0$, and the only solution consistent with the boundary conditions is the trivial solution $u(x, t) = 0$.

Review

Let us review what has been done. We looked for special solutions of the wave equation that are *product functions* of the form $X(x)\,T(t)$. We then saw that the functions $X(x)$ and $T(t)$ must obey the ordinary differential equations (12) and (13), which both involve the same separation constant μ.

We then considered whether the solutions of equation (12) can satisfy the boundary conditions (15). Assuming that μ is a positive constant, or zero, gave functions that do not obey the boundary conditions, or are trivial and of no interest. However, trying a negative value of the separation constant (writing $\mu = -k^2$, where k is a positive constant) gave a set of non-trivial solutions that do obey the boundary conditions. Whenever you try a solution by separation of variables, you need to check what happens for both signs of the separation constant (and you usually need to consider $\mu = 0$ separately as well); you cannot anticipate which choices will give useful solutions.

In order for the wave equation, with its associated boundary conditions, to have a non-trivial product solution $X(x)\,T(t)$, the separation constant μ must be negative. The allowed negative values of μ are not arbitrary.

Writing $\mu = -k^2$, where k is a real positive constant, we have seen that the allowed values of k are

$$k_n = \frac{n\pi}{L} \quad \text{for } n = 1, 2, 3, \ldots,$$

so the allowed values of the separation constant μ are

$$\mu_n = -k_n^2 = -\frac{n^2\pi^2}{L^2}. \tag{19}$$

Corresponding to each of these values, there is a solution for $X(x)$:

$$X_n(x) = D\sin\left(\frac{n\pi x}{L}\right). \tag{20}$$

We now consider the functions $T(t)$. The *same* separation constant occurs in the differential equations for $X(x)$ and $T(t)$, so if we are looking for the function $T(t)$ that accompanies the solution $X_n(x)$ in equation (20), we must use the value $\mu_n = -k_n^2$ in the differential equation for $T(t)$. Hence equation (17) takes the form

$$\frac{d^2 T_n}{dt^2} = -k_n^2 c^2 T_n.$$

This has general solution

$$\begin{aligned} T_n(t) &= \alpha\cos(k_n ct) + \beta\sin(k_n ct) \\ &= \alpha\cos\left(\frac{n\pi ct}{L}\right) + \beta\sin\left(\frac{n\pi ct}{L}\right), \end{aligned} \tag{21}$$

where α and β are arbitrary constants.

To obtain the possible product functions $u_n(x,t) = X_n(x)\,T_n(t)$, it only remains to multiply together the expressions in equations (20) and (21). We combine the constants by writing $A_n = \alpha D$ and $B_n = \beta D$. The resulting solution is then

$$u_n(x,t) = \sin\left(\frac{n\pi x}{L}\right)\left[A_n\cos\left(\frac{n\pi ct}{L}\right) + B_n\sin\left(\frac{n\pi ct}{L}\right)\right], \tag{22}$$

where A_n and B_n are arbitrary constants and $n = 1, 2, 3, \ldots$.

Equation (22) gives a whole family of solutions, each member of which satisfies the wave equation (8) and its boundary conditions (9). The arbitrary constants A_n and B_n need not be the same for different members of this family, so it is appropriate that they are labelled by the subscript n.

The function in equation (7) is a member of this family with $n = 1$, $A_1 = 1$ and $B_1 = 0$.

The initial displacement of the string for the product solution $u_n(x,t)$ is found by substituting $t = 0$ in equation (22). This gives

$$u_n(x,0) = A_n\sin\left(\frac{n\pi x}{L}\right). \tag{23}$$

The initial displacements for the first three solutions in family (22) are shown in Figure 7 (taking $A_n = 1$). These are the initial shapes of the string. Of course, these shapes are rather special, and do not correspond to the actions of any guitar player!

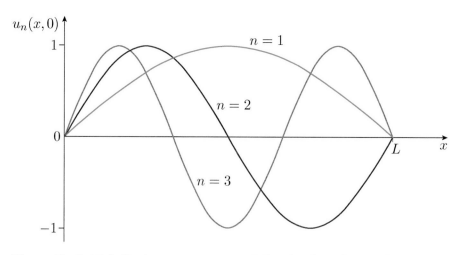

Figure 7   Initial displacements at $t = 0$ for the first three solutions in the family (22), taking $A_1 = A_2 = A_3 = 1$

Once the string is released, its motion obeys equation (22). The term in square brackets scales the shape described by $\sin(n\pi x/L)$ by a factor that oscillates sinusoidally in time. The motion is that of a *standing wave* – a wave that oscillates without travelling through space. For example, if $\sin(n\pi x/L) = 0$ at a particular point, then the disturbance will always be equal to zero at that point; this corresponds to the fact that the nodes of the standing wave remain fixed in space. Each solution in the family (22) has a definite angular frequency $\omega_n = n\pi c/L$. As n increases, ω_n increases, corresponding to a higher frequency of oscillation of the string.

Eigenvalues and eigenfunctions

In looking for solutions of the wave equation in the form $X(x)\,T(t)$, we were led to consider the ordinary differential equation

$$\frac{d^2 X}{dx^2} = \mu X, \tag{Eq. 12}$$

with boundary conditions $X(0) = X(L) = 0$. It is a remarkable fact that this equation has acceptable solutions (satisfying the boundary conditions) only for certain values of μ, namely

$$\mu_n = -\frac{n^2 \pi^2}{L^2}, \quad n = 1, 2, 3, \ldots.$$

Corresponding to each of these allowed values, there is a solution

$$X_n(x) = \sin\left(\frac{n\pi x}{L}\right), \quad n = 1, 2, 3, \ldots.$$

The special values μ_n that allow a solution are called **eigenvalues**, and the corresponding solutions $X_n(x)$ are called **eigenfunctions**.

Also, the functions $T_n(t)$ in equation (21) are eigenfunctions of differential equation (13).

When each solution $X_n(x)$ is joined to its partner $T_n(t)$, we get a solution to the wave equation with a sinusoidal time dependence characterised by a definite angular frequency $\omega_n = n\pi c/L$.

Matrices, normal modes and quantum mechanics

There are strong analogies with concepts met earlier in the module, and important applications to science and engineering.

- Recall that a matrix equation of the form

  $$\mathbf{A}\mathbf{x} = \lambda\mathbf{x},$$

  where $\mathbf{A}$ is a given square matrix, $\mathbf{x}$ is a column matrix, and λ is a number, is called an *eigenvalue equation*. The values of λ that allow solutions to be found for $\mathbf{x}$ are called *eigenvalues*, and the corresponding solutions $\mathbf{x}$ are called *eigenvectors*. Equation (12) is analogous to this, but instead of a matrix $\mathbf{A}$ acting on a vector $\mathbf{x}$, we have a differential operator d^2/dx^2 (supplemented by boundary conditions) acting on a function $X(x)$.

- Unit 6 discussed the oscillations of systems of particles, such as the atoms in a carbon dioxide molecule. You saw that there are some characteristic patterns of displacement that oscillate with definite angular frequencies. These patterns are called *normal modes*. They exist only at a discrete set of angular frequencies, which are determined by finding the eigenvalues of a matrix. The standing waves on a string are so reminiscent of this that they too are referred to as **normal modes**.

- In quantum mechanics, there is a partial differential equation called the *Schrödinger equation*. This is not the same as the wave equation for a string, but there are similarities. The Schrödinger equation can be solved for a hydrogen atom, using the method of separation of variables, much as we have done here. Again, there are eigenvalues and eigenfunctions: these are interpreted, respectively, as the allowed energies and the corresponding states of the atom. Because the eigenvalues form a discrete set, the atom has a discrete set of allowed energies. This is known as the *quantisation of energy*.

Exercise 5

Apply the method of separation of variables to the partial differential equation

$$\frac{\partial^2 u}{\partial t^2} = \frac{\partial^4 u}{\partial x^4},$$

which occurs in the theory of bending elastic rods. Write $u(x,t) = X(x)\,T(t)$, and establish ordinary differential equations for the functions $X(x)$ and $T(t)$. Do not attempt to solve these equations.

Exercise 6

Apply the method of separation of variables to the partial differential equation

$$\frac{\partial u}{\partial t} = \frac{\partial}{\partial x}(xu) + \frac{\partial^2 u}{\partial x^2},$$

which occurs in the theory of diffusion of solid particles in a fluid. Write $u(x, t) = X(x)\,T(t)$, and establish ordinary differential equations for the functions $X(x)$ and $T(t)$. Do not attempt to solve these equations.

1.3 Superposition and the general solution

So far, we have found a family of solutions of the wave equation (8) that satisfy the boundary conditions (9). These solutions, specified in equation (22), are all of the product form $X(x)\,T(t)$. You might ask why we decided to look for solutions like this. The reason is not very profound – it is just that these solutions are found relatively easily (provided that the method of separation of variables works at all).

However, we cannot pretend that every solution is a product solution. For example, equation (23) and Figure 7 show that the product solutions are produced by very special initial conditions at $t = 0$. When a guitar string is plucked at its midpoint, as in Figure 5, the initial conditions are quite different, and the subsequent motion of the string cannot be described by a product solution.

Fortunately, there is a way ahead. The wave equation is linear, and so are all the partial differential equations in this unit, which means that the principle of superposition applies. In the specific context of linear second-order partial differential equations, the **principle of superposition** states that if $u_1(x, t)$ and $u_2(x, t)$ are solutions of the equation, then any function of the form

$$u(x, t) = a_1\,u_1(x, t) + a_2\,u_2(x, t), \tag{24}$$

where a_1 and a_2 are constants, is also a solution of the equation.

The following exercise asks you to verify that this principle applies to the wave equation, and to show how it applies in the presence of the usual boundary conditions.

Exercise 7

Suppose that the functions $u_1(x, t)$ and $u_2(x, t)$ satisfy the wave equation

$$\frac{\partial^2 u}{\partial x^2} = \frac{1}{c^2}\frac{\partial^2 u}{\partial t^2},$$

together with the boundary conditions for fixed ends

$$u(0, t) = u(L, t) = 0.$$

Show that the linear combination $u = a_1 u_1 + a_2 u_2$, where a_1 and a_2 are any constants, is a solution of the same partial differential equation and satisfies the same boundary conditions.

The principle of superposition takes two solutions and generates a third. Repeating this process, we can add further solutions and expand the linear combination without limit, generating many more solutions. Moreover, if all the individual solutions satisfy the boundary conditions $u(0, t) = 0$ and $u(L, t) = 0$, then so does the linear combination formed from them.

Starting from the product solutions in equation (22), it follows that *any* linear combination of the form

$$u(x, t) = \sum_{n=1}^{\infty} \sin\left(\frac{n\pi x}{L}\right) \left[A_n \cos\left(\frac{n\pi ct}{L}\right) + B_n \sin\left(\frac{n\pi ct}{L}\right)\right], \qquad (25)$$

where A_n and B_n are constants, is a solution of the wave equation that satisfies the boundary conditions for fixed ends, $u(0, t) = 0$ and $u(L, t) = 0$.

The sum in equation (25) may stop after a finite number of terms; this happens if all the A_n and B_n are equal to zero beyond a certain value of n. However, it is also possible that the sum continues without ever ending. The value of such an infinite sum is defined as the limiting value of the sum of the first N terms, as N tends to infinity. However, this technicality is really beyond the scope of this unit. We assume that sums of this type are 'well-behaved' so that there is no difficulty, for example, in differentiating $u(x, t)$ by differentiating each term in the infinite series.

The principle of superposition greatly extends the range of known solutions. In fact, it delivers something even more powerful. It turns out that for a string that is anchored at $x = 0$ and $x = L$, *every* solution can be written in the form (25). In other words, equation (25) is the **general solution** of the wave equation subject to these conditions.

General solution for motion of a string

The general solution of the wave equation on the interval from 0 to L with boundary conditions $u(0, t) = u(L, t) = 0$ is

$$u(x, t) = \sum_{n=1}^{\infty} \sin\left(\frac{n\pi x}{L}\right) \left[A_n \cos\left(\frac{n\pi ct}{L}\right) + B_n \sin\left(\frac{n\pi ct}{L}\right)\right], \quad (26)$$

where A_n and B_n are arbitrary constants.

This is a wonderful gift. We started with a restricted family of solutions – the product solutions. These are just a small subset of all the possible solutions, but it turns out that *any* solution can be expressed as a linear combination of them. We do not prove this fact, but we can say that it is a common feature of many linear partial differential equations.

For different partial differential equations, the functions that emerge from the method of separation of variables are not always sines and cosines, but they often provide a set of functions that is broad enough for any solution to be expressed as a linear combination of them. Such a family of functions is sometimes said to form a **complete set** for the problem at hand.

1.4   Initial conditions and Fourier series

The constants $A_1, A_2, A_3, \ldots$ and $B_1, B_2, B_3, \ldots$ in the general solution are determined by the initial conditions.

An important case is that of a plucked string, released from rest at $t = 0$, with an initial displacement specified by a function $f(x)$. These initial conditions are described by the equations

$$\frac{\partial u}{\partial t}(x, 0) = 0, \quad u(x, 0) = f(x), \quad 0 \le x \le L. \tag{27}$$

Consider the first condition, which describes release from rest. Differentiating both sides of equation (26) with respect to t, and assuming that the derivative of the right-hand side is obtained by differentiating each term in the sum, we get

$$\frac{\partial u}{\partial t} = \sum_{n=1}^{\infty} \sin\left(\frac{n\pi x}{L}\right)\left(\frac{n\pi c}{L}\right)\left[-A_n \sin\left(\frac{n\pi ct}{L}\right) + B_n \cos\left(\frac{n\pi ct}{L}\right)\right].$$

Setting $\partial u/\partial t = 0$ at $t = 0$ then gives

$$0 = \sum_{n=1}^{\infty} \left(\frac{n\pi c}{L}\right) B_n \sin\left(\frac{n\pi x}{L}\right). \tag{28}$$

One way of satisfying this equation is to take $B_n = 0$ for all n. In fact, the right-hand side of equation (28) is a Fourier series with Fourier coefficients $n\pi c B_n/L$. These Fourier coefficients are uniquely defined by the zero function on the left-hand side, and are all equal to zero, so the *only* way of satisfying equation (28) is to take $B_n = 0$ for all n. The general solution given in equation (26) then reduces to the following expression.

> The general solution for a plucked string released from rest is
>
> $$u(x, t) = \sum_{n=1}^{\infty} A_n \sin\left(\frac{n\pi x}{L}\right) \cos\left(\frac{n\pi ct}{L}\right). \tag{29}$$

We must now choose the constants A_n so that the other initial condition is satisfied, namely $u(x, 0) = f(x)$, where $f(x)$ describes the displacement of the string at time $t = 0$.

Putting $t = 0$ in equation (29), and using $u(x, 0) = f(x)$, we get

$$f(x) = \sum_{n=1}^{\infty} A_n \sin\left(\frac{n\pi x}{L}\right) \quad (0 \le x \le L). \tag{30}$$

The sum on the right-hand side is a Fourier series for the function $f(x)$ that involves sine terms only. At first sight this may seem rather strange because $f(x)$ is not a periodic function, but is defined only over the finite interval $0 \leq x \leq L$. However, you saw in Unit 11 that a function defined over a finite interval can be extended outside this interval to give a periodic function.

Because equation (30) involves sine terms only, we need the *odd periodic extension* here. Note that this choice is determined by the form of equation (30). There is no essential connection between the names used for the coefficients in this equation and the traditional names A_0, A_n and B_n used in the Fourier series of Unit 11.

To take a definite case, suppose that the string is released from rest by being plucked at its midpoint, which has an initial displacement d. You saw in Example 1 that this initial displacement is described by the piecewise function

$$f(x) = \begin{cases} \dfrac{2d}{L}x & \text{for } 0 \leq x \leq \tfrac{1}{2}L, \\ \dfrac{2d}{L}(L - x) & \text{for } \tfrac{1}{2}L < x \leq L, \end{cases} \tag{31}$$

and a diagram of this initial displacement is reproduced in Figure 8.

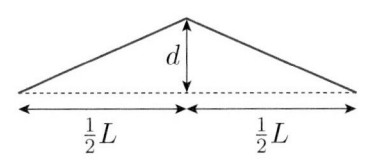

Figure 8   String plucked at its midpoint

We can extend $f(x)$ to give the periodic function $f_{\text{odd}}(x)$ shown in Figure 9, which is given by the formula

$$f_{\text{odd}}(x) = \begin{cases} f(x) & \text{for } 0 \leq x \leq L, \\ -f(x) & \text{for } -L < x < 0, \end{cases}$$

$$f_{\text{odd}}(x + 2L) = f_{\text{odd}}(x).$$

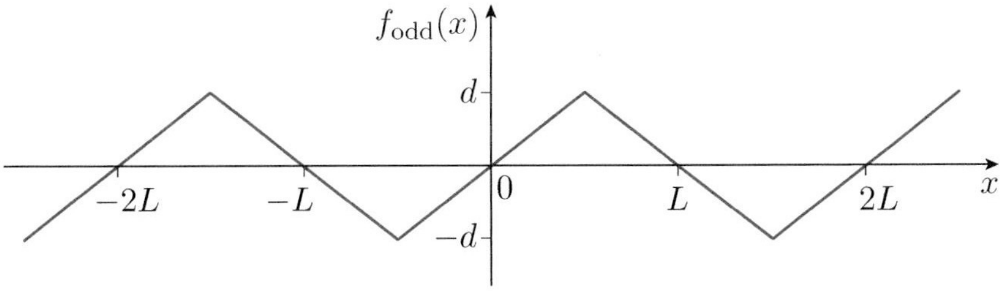

Figure 9   The odd periodic extension of the function in Figure 8

This is the odd periodic extension of $f(x)$, and it has fundamental period $2L$. Because the functions $f(x)$ and $f_{\text{odd}}(x)$ are identical in the region of interest $0 \leq x \leq L$, the constants A_n required in equation (30) are identical to the Fourier coefficients of $f_{\text{odd}}(x)$. Since $f_{\text{odd}}(x)$ is an odd function with period $2L$, we have

$$A_n = \frac{4}{2L} \int_0^L f_{\text{odd}}(x) \sin\left(\frac{n\pi x}{L}\right) dx.$$

See Unit 11, equation (37) with suitably adjusted notation.

Finally, the functions $f(x)$ and $f_{\text{odd}}(x)$ are identical throughout the interval $0 \leq x \leq L$, so we have the following result.

$$A_n = \frac{2}{L} \int_0^L f(x) \sin\left(\frac{n\pi x}{L}\right) dx, \quad n = 1, 2, 3, \ldots. \tag{32}$$

To illustrate the use of a periodic extension, we have looked at the function illustrated in Figures 8 and 9, but it is clear that the same argument would work for any initial displacement. Hence equation (32) gives a general formula for the coefficients A_n in equations (29) and (30) – we just have to insert the function $f(x)$ that describes the initial displacement of the plucked string, as it is released from rest.

For the initial displacement in equation (31) and Figure 8, the Fourier coefficients are

$$A_n = \frac{4d}{L^2}\left[\int_0^{L/2} x \sin\left(\frac{n\pi x}{L}\right) dx + \int_{L/2}^L (L-x) \sin\left(\frac{n\pi x}{L}\right) dx\right].$$

As is often the way, the Fourier integrals are messy to evaluate. There is nothing really difficult, but patience and care are essential. Fortunately, we have already calculated these integrals in Example 11 of Unit 11, so we can just quote the result. In this case, the Fourier coefficients are given by

$$A_n = \frac{8d}{n^2\pi^2} \sin\left(\frac{n\pi}{2}\right),$$

so the values of the first few coefficients are

$$A_1 = \frac{8d}{\pi^2}, \quad A_2 = 0, \quad A_3 = -\frac{8d}{9\pi^2}, \quad A_4 = 0, \quad A_5 = \frac{8d}{25\pi^2}.$$

Substituting these coefficients into equation (29), we conclude that the displacement of the plucked string at any time $t > 0$ is

$$u(x,t) = \frac{8d}{\pi^2}\left[\sin\left(\frac{\pi x}{L}\right)\cos\left(\frac{\pi ct}{L}\right) - \frac{1}{9}\sin\left(\frac{3\pi x}{L}\right)\cos\left(\frac{3\pi ct}{L}\right)\right.$$
$$\left. + \frac{1}{25}\sin\left(\frac{5\pi x}{L}\right)\cos\left(\frac{5\pi ct}{L}\right) - \cdots\right]. \tag{33}$$

The exact solution is given by an infinite sum of terms, but a very good approximation is obtained by adding the first 30 terms on a computer. When this is done, the shape of the string is predicted to vary as shown in Figure 10. You may find this prediction surprising, especially the kinks that exist throughout the motion of the string. But if one films the motion of a real string that is released in the way assumed, the film captures a succession of images that match Figure 10 almost exactly!

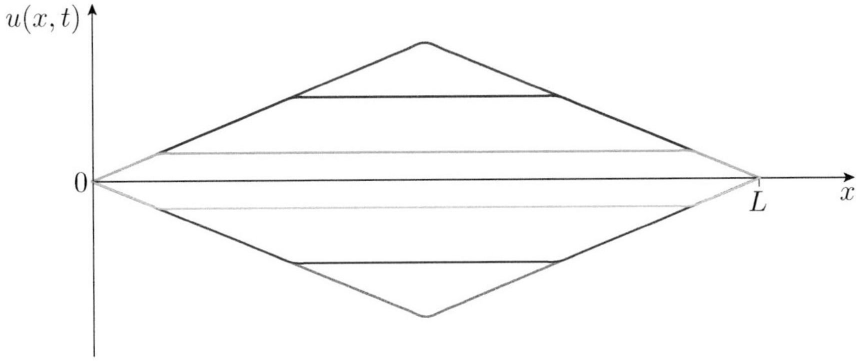

Figure 10   The motion predicted by equation (33), with the time sequence red, dark blue, green, cyan, magenta, orange, magenta, etc.; this shows the displacements at a sequence of times

Fourier's masterpiece

Fourier series were invented to aid the solution of partial differential equations by separation of variables.

Joseph Fourier (1768–1830) is best remembered for the contributions in his work *The Analytic Theory of Heat*, published in 1822, which combined the results of two decades of investigation. This work developed most of the ideas contained in Unit 11 as well as this unit. Fourier derived the heat equation (2) and solved it using the method of separation of variables. He represented the initial condition as a series in the form (30), now known as a Fourier series, and discovered the technique to determine the coefficients A_n.

Alternative initial conditions

The general solution in equation (26) can be adapted to deal with the case where the initial conditions are

$$u(x,0) = 0, \quad \frac{\partial u}{\partial t}(x,0) = v(x), \quad 0 \leq x \leq L, \tag{34}$$

that is, where the initial displacement of the string is zero, but the initial velocity is given by a function $v(x)$. This corresponds more closely to a piano string that is struck by one of the piano's hammers than to a guitar string that is plucked and released from rest.

Because the coefficients A_n in equation (26) are Fourier coefficients of the initial displacement, which is equal to zero for all x, we must have $A_n = 0$ for all $n = 1, 2, \ldots$. The general solution for the motion of the string can then be written in the form

$$u(x,t) = \sum_{n=1}^{\infty} B_n \sin\left(\frac{n\pi x}{L}\right) \sin\left(\frac{n\pi ct}{L}\right). \tag{35}$$

The coefficients B_n can be determined by an approach similar to that used for the initially stationary string, as the following exercise shows.

Exercise 8

Consider a string, clamped at $x = 0$ and at $x = L$, with a displacement $u(x,t)$ that satisfies the wave equation, with boundary conditions $u(0,t) = u(L,t) = 0$ for $t \geq 0$.

At $t = 0$, the displacement is zero, so $u(x,0) = 0$. However, the string is set in motion so that its initial velocity at x is $v(x)$, where $v(x)$ is a specified function. The odd periodic extension of $v(x)$ has Fourier coefficients C_n, so for $0 \leq x \leq L$ the initial velocity of the string is given by

$$v(x) = \sum_{n=1}^{\infty} C_n \sin\left(\frac{n\pi x}{L}\right).$$

Use equation (35) to express the coefficients B_n in terms of the Fourier coefficients C_n.

The methods used in this section can be applied to a variety of linear homogeneous partial differential equations, not just the wave equation. The general method is summarised in the following procedure, which can be used for all the partial differential methods in this unit.

Procedure 1   The method of separation of variables

Given a linear homogeneous partial differential equation with dependent variable u and independent variables x and t, subject to given boundary and initial conditions, a solution can often be found by the following steps.

1. Write the unknown function $u(x,t)$ as a product of functions of one variable:

    $$u(x,t) = X(x)\,T(t).$$

    Find the required partial derivatives of u in terms of the ordinary derivatives of the functions X and T.

2. Substitute the partial derivatives found in Step 1 into the partial differential equation. Rearrange the equation so that each side consists of a function of a single independent variable. Equate each side of the rearranged equation to the same separation constant μ, and hence obtain ordinary differential equations for X and T.

3. Use the given boundary conditions for u to find boundary conditions for X.

4. Solve the differential equation for X, and apply the boundary conditions. Consider different choices for the separation constant μ. (Typically, the solutions $X(x)$ take a different form depending on whether the separation constant is positive, negative or zero.) The boundary conditions generally produce a discrete set of solutions $X_n(x)$ and a corresponding discrete set of values μ_n for the separation constant.

5. For each allowed μ_n, determine the corresponding solution $T_n(t)$ of the differential equation for $T(t)$.

6. Combine $X_n(x)$ and $T_n(t)$ to obtain a family of product solutions

    $$u_n(x,t) = X_n(x)\,T_n(t), \quad n = 1,2,3,\dots.$$

    Express the general solution as an infinite linear combination of these product solutions containing a set of coefficients. For example,

    $$u(x,t) = \sum_{n=1}^{\infty} a_n\,u_n(x,t).$$

7. Use the initial conditions and results about Fourier series to determine (when possible) the set of coefficients.

Exercise 9

Use Steps 1–6 of Procedure 1 to find the general solution of the partial differential equation

$$\frac{\partial^2 u}{\partial x^2} + \frac{\partial^2 u}{\partial t^2} = 0,$$

subject to boundary conditions

$$u(0,t) = u(1,t) = 0, \quad t \geq 0.$$

This equation is known as the two-dimensional *Laplace equation.*

---

2 The diffusion equation

The **diffusion equation** takes the form

$$\frac{\partial c}{\partial t} = D\,\frac{\partial^2 c}{\partial x^2}, \tag{36}$$

where D is a positive constant called the **diffusion coefficient**, and $c = c(x,t)$ is a function of x and t. In solving this equation, the aim is to find a function $c(x,t)$ that satisfies the equation, subject to given boundary and initial conditions. The diffusion equation is one of the most widely studied partial differential equations, and it arises in many different contexts.

The section begins by discussing the physical concepts that lie behind the diffusion equation before going on to derive it. *This material will not be assessed or examined.* Nevertheless, the process of deriving a partial differential equation from physical assumptions is a vital skill for scientists and applied mathematicians, and you should study Subsections 2.1–2.4 to see an example of this process in action.

Subsection 2.5 uses the method of separation of variables to solve the diffusion equation for a particular example; this skill is assessable.

2.1 Diffusion

On a microscopic scale, matter consists of molecules, with each chemical substance having its own type of molecule. Very often, samples of matter are mixtures of different types of molecule. For example, air contains a mixture of nitrogen and oxygen molecules, with small quantities of many other molecules.

The molecules are always in motion, and in gases or liquids these motions are random and unpredictable. The molecules are very small, typically about 10^{-9} m across, and at room temperature they move very quickly (at speeds of about $300 \, \mathrm{m \, s^{-1}}$). They travel only very short distances in between collisions: in a gas they move about 10^{-7} m before colliding and changing direction. Figure 11 is a schematic illustration of the motion of a carbon dioxide molecule in air.

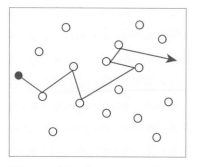

Figure 11   A carbon dioxide molecule (coloured) moves erratically as it collides with other molecules in air

This random motion of molecules gives rise to an important mechanism for mixing substances: it results in substances spreading out in space, as illustrated in Figure 12. This process, called **diffusion**, mixes substances by means of the microscopic random motion of molecules, without the need for any macroscopic motion (such as the stirring motion that helps to dissolve sugar in coffee).

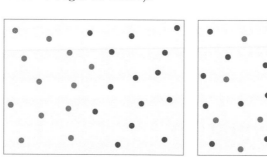

$$t = 0 \qquad\qquad t > 0$$

Figure 12   The random motion of molecules leads to mixing of substances

The process of diffusion is vitally important for biological processes. For example, your body creates carbon dioxide as a waste product, and this must be removed from your tissues very efficiently. Your blood vessels and lungs play an important role in carrying carbon dioxide out of your body, but it is diffusion that enables carbon dioxide molecules to move out of your cells and into the blood vessels.

2.2 Concentration and flux density

In principle, diffusion can be described by tracking the motion of a vast number of molecules, but this is obviously impractical. For most purposes, we do not care about the motion of individual molecules, but we want to know how the molecules as a whole reposition themselves. In this subsection, we introduce two quantities – *concentration* and *flux density* – that help us to model the process of diffusion.

Diffusion generally refers to molecules of a definite type or species, mixed in with other molecules that are not of interest.

Molecular concentration

The **concentration** of molecules of a given type at position **r** is the number of those molecules per unit volume, found in a small region centred on **r**.

If the region has volume ΔV and contains ΔN molecules of the given type at time t, then the concentration is

$$c(\mathbf{r}, t) = \frac{\Delta N}{\Delta V}. \tag{37}$$

Figure 13 illustrates this definition for a two-dimensional case.

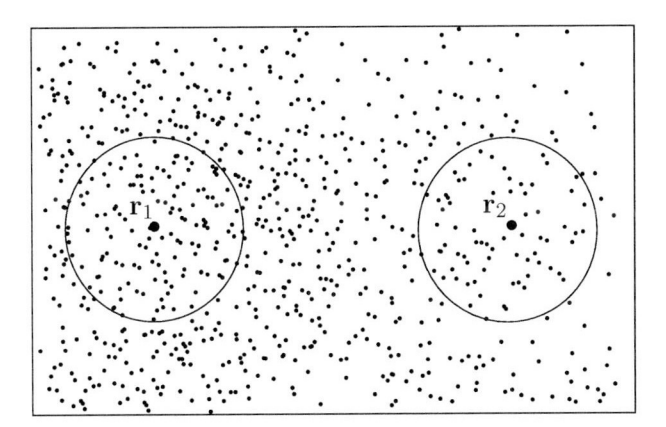

Figure 13   The distribution of molecules of a particular type in two dimensions (other molecules are not shown). The circles define imaginary regions centred on $\mathbf{r}_1$ and $\mathbf{r}_2$. Counting molecules of the given type in these regions shows that their concentration is higher at $\mathbf{r}_1$ than at $\mathbf{r}_2$.

To give a detailed description of the distribution of molecules, the volume ΔV should be small on an everyday scale. But it must not be too small, or it is unlikely to contain any molecules of the given type! In practice, a suitable compromise can generally be reached, giving a function $c(\mathbf{r}, t)$ that varies smoothly with **r** and t.

We also need to describe the motion of molecules. In the case of diffusion, the molecules are moving around at random, but we can talk about the net motion in a given direction.

Suppose that we wish to describe the net flow of molecules of the given type *in the x-direction* at a particular position $\mathbf{r}$. Then we imagine a small *imaginary* planar surface element that is centred on position $\mathbf{r}$. The surface element has area ΔA, and it is oriented so that it is perpendicular to the x-direction, with its unit normal vector pointing in the x-direction (see Figure 14).

In the small time interval between t and $t + \delta t$, we count the number of molecules of the given type that pass through this surface element in the sense of increasing x (i.e. from the back to the front of the surface in Figure 14). Let this number be δn^+. We also count the corresponding number of molecules passing through the surface in the opposite sense. Let this number be δn^-. We care only about the *net migration* across the surface in the x-direction, which is defined by

$$\delta n = \delta n^+ - \delta n^-.$$

We expect δn to be proportional to the time interval δt, and to the area ΔA. We therefore write

$$\delta n = J_x\, \Delta A\, \delta t, \tag{38}$$

where J_x is a quantity called the *flux density* in the x-direction. Making J_x the subject of this equation leads to the following definition.

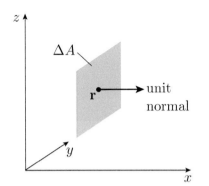

Figure 14 An imaginary surface element used to define flux density

---

Molecular flux density

For a given type of molecule, the **flux density** in the x-direction at position $\mathbf{r}$ and time t is defined as

$$J_x(\mathbf{r}, t) = \frac{1}{\Delta A}\frac{\delta n}{\delta t}, \tag{39}$$

where ΔA is the area of a surface element, centred on $\mathbf{r}$ and perpendicular to the x-axis, and $\delta n / \delta t$ is the rate of net migration across this surface in the direction of increasing x at time t.

The same sort of caveats surround this definition as for concentration: the area ΔA and the time interval δt should be taken to be small, but not too small! Again, this is no cause for concern, and the flux density defined by equation (39) can be assumed to vary smoothly in space and time.

A comment on notation

Note that δn in the above equations is the number of molecules migrating across a surface in time δt. It should not be confused with ΔN in equation (37), which is the number of molecules in a small volume.

In this section, we use Δ to indicate small quantities associated with a small volume or a small area, and δ to indicate small quantities associated with a small time interval.

2.3 The equation of continuity and Fick's law

Our aim is to derive the diffusion equation (36), which is a partial differential equation for the concentration c of molecules of a particular type. To achieve this, we use two different relationships between the concentration c and the flux density J_x. Then, by eliminating the flux density from these equations, we obtain the diffusion equation.

This subsection develops the two required relationships, beginning with the equation of continuity for diffusing molecules, which is very similar to the equation of continuity for a fluid discussed in Unit 10. Because equation (36) contains only one spatial variable, x, we consider a one-dimensional situation.

The equation of continuity

Consider the diffusion of molecules in a narrow glass tube containing a gas. To take a concrete example, suppose that the tube contains air with a small amount of carbon dioxide gas. The tube is aligned with the x-axis, and we focus on the small element of it that lies between x and $x + \Delta x$, where Δx is small. Taking the internal cross-sectional area of the tube to be ΔA, the volume of gas contained in the volume element is $\Delta V = \Delta A \, \Delta x$. If at time t the concentration of carbon dioxide molecules is $c(x, t)$, then the number of carbon dioxide molecules in the element is

$$\Delta N = c(x,t) \, \Delta V = c(x,t) \, \Delta A \, \Delta x. \tag{40}$$

We now make the key assumption that carbon dioxide molecules are neither created nor destroyed in the tube. This implies that no chemical reactions take place in the tube that create carbon dioxide molecules from other substances or that split carbon dioxide molecules apart. Assuming that the walls of the glass tube are impermeable to gases, it follows that any change in ΔN must be caused by molecules that flow into or out of the element by crossing one of the two plane surfaces of area ΔA at its ends. We consider the flows of carbon dioxide molecules through these surfaces in the time interval between t and $t + \delta t$ (see Figure 15).

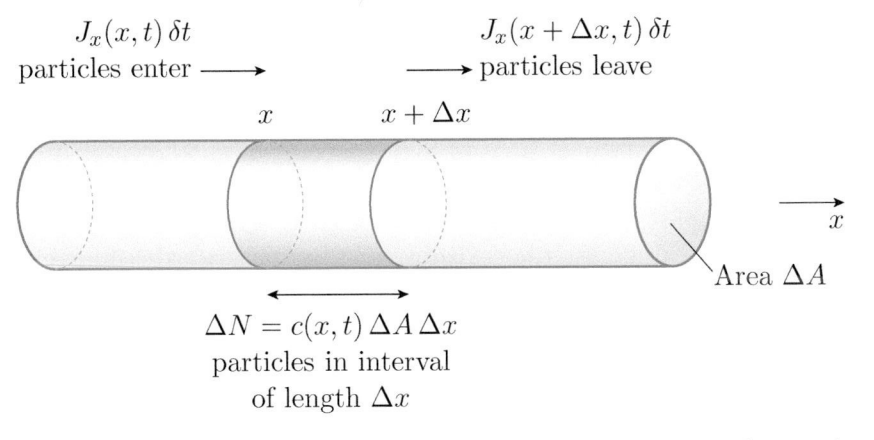

Figure 15   The equation of continuity is derived by considering the change in concentration that results from flow into and out of a volume element

From equation (38), the net number of carbon dioxide molecules that *enter* the volume element by passing through the left-hand surface at x is

$$\delta n(x) = J_x(x, t) \, \Delta A \, \delta t.$$

Similarly, the net number of carbon dioxide molecules that *leave* the volume element by passing through the right-hand surface at $x + \Delta x$ is

$$\delta n(x + \Delta x) = J_x(x + \Delta x, t) \, \Delta A \, \delta t$$
$$\simeq \left[J_x(x, t) + \frac{\partial J_x}{\partial x}(x, t) \, \Delta x \right] \Delta A \, \delta t,$$

where we have used the first-order Taylor polynomial approximation for $J_x(x + \Delta x, t)$ in the last step.

Taking the difference between $\delta n(x)$ and $\delta n(x + \Delta x)$ gives the net *change* in the number of carbon dioxide molecule in the volume element:

$$\delta(\Delta N) = \delta n(x) - \delta n(x + \Delta x) = -\frac{\partial J_x}{\partial x}(x, t) \, \Delta x \, \Delta A \, \delta t.$$

From equation (40), this can also be expressed in terms of a change in concentration in the volume element:

$$\delta(\Delta N) = \delta c(x, t) \, \Delta A \, \Delta x.$$

Comparing these last two equations, we see that

$$\delta c(x, t) = -\frac{\partial J_x}{\partial x}(x, t) \, \delta t.$$

Finally, we divide by δt and take the limit as $\delta t \to 0$ at constant x, so that $\delta c / \delta t$ becomes the partial derivative $\partial c / \partial t$. We obtain the following result.

The equation of continuity for diffusion

$$\frac{\partial c}{\partial t} + \frac{\partial J_x}{\partial x} = 0. \tag{41}$$

This is the first of the equations that links concentration to flux density.

Fick's law

The second equation linking concentration to flux density is called *Fick's law*. We know from observing the process of diffusion that molecules of a given type tend to move from regions of high concentration to regions of low concentration (see, for example, Figure 12). This suggests that the flux density of diffusing particles might be related to the *gradient* of their concentration. In one dimension, a plausible relation between the flux density J_x and the concentration c is as follows.

Fick's law of diffusion

Fick's law of diffusion states that

$$J_x = -D \frac{\partial c}{\partial x}, \tag{42}$$

where D is a positive constant called the **diffusion coefficient**. The minus sign indicates that the net flow is from regions of high concentration to regions of low concentration.

When Fick's law was first proposed in 1855 it was an inspired piece of guesswork. While Fick's law can now be derived from a microscopic theory of diffusion, the methods are far beyond the scope of this module. Together with the equation of continuity, Fick's law leads directly to the diffusion equation, as you will see in the next subsection.

2.4   The diffusion equation

Equations (41) and (42) are two partial differential equations that relate the concentration c to the flux density J_x. If we substitute (42) into (41), we obtain an equation that contains c alone:

$$\frac{\partial c}{\partial t} = -\frac{\partial J_x}{\partial x} = -\frac{\partial}{\partial x}\left(-D\frac{\partial c}{\partial x}\right)$$

so

$$\frac{\partial c}{\partial t} = D\frac{\partial^2 c}{\partial x^2},$$

which is the diffusion equation in one dimension, x. This is the form of the diffusion equation that is used in this unit. However, *for interest only*, the following box indicates how a diffusion equation arises in three dimensions.

The diffusion equation in three dimensions

In order to extend the diffusion equation to three dimensions, we must first define a *flux density vector*. You have seen how J_x is defined in the x-direction. By orienting surface elements perpendicular to the y- and z-axes, we can also define the flux density J_y in the y-direction and the flux density J_z in the z-direction. It can be shown that these three quantities are the components of a vector

$$\mathbf{J} = J_x\,\mathbf{i} + J_y\,\mathbf{j} + J_z\,\mathbf{k},$$

which is called the **flux density vector**. This is a vector field, and in three dimensions the **equation of continuity** takes the form

$$\frac{\partial c}{\partial t} + \boldsymbol{\nabla}\cdot\mathbf{J} = 0. \tag{43}$$

Moreover, in three dimensions **Fick's law** takes the form

$$\mathbf{J} = -D\,\boldsymbol{\nabla}c, \tag{44}$$

where $\boldsymbol{\nabla}c$ is the gradient of the concentration, and D is the diffusion coefficient.

Combining equations (43) and (44), and using the methods of
Unit 10, it can be shown that

$$\frac{\partial c}{\partial t} = D \left[\frac{\partial^2 c}{\partial x^2} + \frac{\partial^2 c}{\partial y^2} + \frac{\partial^2 c}{\partial z^2} \right],$$

and this is the **three-dimensional diffusion equation**. It is often
expressed in terms of the more compact notation

$$\frac{\partial c}{\partial t} = D\, \nabla^2 c,$$

where

$$\nabla^2 = \frac{\partial^2}{\partial x^2} + \frac{\partial^2}{\partial y^2} + \frac{\partial^2}{\partial z^2}$$

is called the **Laplacian operator**.

An interesting facet of the diffusion equation (whether in one dimension or
more) is that it is a *deterministic* equation that contains no random
numbers, but which nevertheless describes the *random* motion of many
molecules. Of course, an important element of diffusion is that the
molecules in a gas or liquid make many small unpredictable steps. Many
other situations involve a large number of random changes, and the
diffusion equation has been adapted to describe a vast range of
phenomena. One important application relates to finance.

The Black–Scholes equation

The price of a traded commodity or share rises and falls in an
unpredictable manner, similar to a coordinate of a molecule in a gas.
Thus a diffusion equation might be used to predict how the future
value of a portfolio of shares is expected to vary. A particular form of
diffusion equation, known as the *Black–Scholes equation*, is widely
used by financial institutions to determine the value of contracts that
involve commitments to buy or sell on a date in the future.

Trading 'options' represents a vast amount of economic activity, and
the value of the diffusion-based model for valuing these contracts was
recognised by the award of a Nobel prize in economics in 1997.

2.5 Solving the diffusion equation

This subsection returns to the major theme of this unit – the solution of
partial differential equations by the method of separation of variables. It
presents a problem involving the diffusion equation, broken down into a
number of steps. Study it carefully because it differs in several details from
the guitar string problem discussed in Section 1.

Example 2

In this question, you are asked to use the method of separation of variables to solve the diffusion equation in the form

$$\frac{\partial^2 c}{\partial x^2} = \frac{1}{D}\frac{\partial c}{\partial t} \quad (0 < x < 1,\ t > 0)$$

for the function $c(x,t)$, where $D > 0$ is a constant. The equation is subject to the boundary conditions

$$\frac{\partial c}{\partial x}(0, t) = \frac{\partial c}{\partial x}(L, t) = 0 \quad (t > 0)$$

and the initial condition

$$c(x, 0) = f(x) \quad (0 \le x \le L).$$

The solution can be found by completing the following steps.

(a) Use the method of separation of variables, with $c(x,t) = X(x)\,T(t)$, and show that the function $X(x)$ satisfies the differential equation

$$X'' - \mu X = 0 \tag{45}$$

for some constant μ. What boundary conditions must X also satisfy?

(b) Show that if $\mu > 0$, then there are no non-trivial solutions of equation (45).

(c) Show that if $\mu = 0$, then there is a non-trivial solution of equation (45). Determine a form of this solution that satisfies the boundary conditions.

(d) Find the non-trivial solutions of equation (45) satisfying the boundary conditions when $\mu < 0$, stating clearly what values μ is allowed to take.

(e) Find and solve the differential equation that T must satisfy.

(f) Use your answers to write down a family of product solutions $c(x, t) = X(x)\,T(t)$ that satisfy the boundary conditions. You may assume that the general solution of the partial differential equation may be expressed as an arbitrary linear combination of members of this family. Write down an expression for the general solution.

(g) Briefly describe how you would use the initial condition $c(x, 0) = f(x)$ to determine the particular solution of the partial differential equation.

Solution

(a) Writing $c(x,t) = X(x)\,T(t)$ and substituting into the diffusion equation gives

$$X''(x)\,T(t) = \frac{1}{D}\,X(x)\,T'(t),$$

and dividing through by $X(x)\,T(t)$ gives

$$\frac{X''(x)}{X(x)} = \frac{1}{D}\frac{T'(t)}{T(t)}.$$

Only one initial condition is needed because the diffusion equation is first-order in time. By contrast, the wave equation is second-order in time and needs two initial conditions.

For brevity, we use primes to denote derivatives: $X' = dX/dx$ and $T' = dT/dt$, and so on.

Because the left-hand side is a function only of x, and the right-hand side is a function only of t, both sides must be equal to the same separation constant μ, so

$$\frac{X''(x)}{X(x)} = \mu = \frac{1}{D}\frac{T'(t)}{T(t)}.$$

Thus we obtain two ordinary differential equations:

$$X'' = \mu X, \quad T' = \mu D T.$$

Noting that $\partial c/\partial x = X'(x)\,T(t)$, the boundary conditions imply that

$$X'(0) = X'(L) = 0.$$

(b) If $\mu = k^2 > 0$, where k is a positive constant, then the differential equation for $X(x)$ has the auxiliary equation $\lambda^2 = k^2$, so $\lambda = \pm k$ and the solutions are of the form

$$X(x) = A\exp(kx) + B\exp(-kx),$$

where A and B are arbitrary constants.

Differentiating $X(x)$ gives

$$X'(x) = kA\exp(kx) - kB\exp(-kx),$$

so the boundary conditions $X'(0) = 0$ and $X'(L) = 0$ become, respectively,

$$kA - kB = 0 \quad \text{and} \quad kA\exp(kL) - kB\exp(-kL) = 0.$$

The first condition implies that $A = B$. Substituting this into the second condition, and remembering that $k \neq 0$, we get either $A = 0$ or $\exp(kL) = \exp(-kL)$. The first possibility is not considered further, because it leads to the trivial solution $c(x, t) = 0$. The second possibility gives

$$\exp(2kL) = 1,$$

which cannot be satisfied for $k > 0$ and $L > 0$. We conclude that there is no non-trivial solution for $\mu > 0$.

(c) If $\mu = 0$, then solutions are of the form

$$X(x) = A + Bx,$$

Throughout this solution, we reuse the letters A and B for different arbitrary constants.

where A and B are arbitrary constants. The derivative of this solution is $X'(x) = B$. This time, both the boundary conditions imply that $B = 0$, but they do not constrain A. Therefore if $\mu = 0$, there is a non-trivial solution of the partial differential equation, say $X(x) = A_0$, where A_0 is an arbitrary constant.

(d) If $\mu = -k^2$, where k is a positive constant, then the general solution of the equation for $X(x)$ is of the form

$$X(x) = A\cos(kx) + B\sin(kx),$$

where A and B are arbitrary constants. The derivative of this solution is

$$X'(x) = -Ak\sin(kx) + Bk\cos(kx).$$

The boundary condition $X'(0) = 0$ gives $Bk = 0$, so we must have $B = 0$, allowing us to write

$$X'(x) = -Ak \sin(kx).$$

The boundary condition $X'(L) = 0$ then gives either $Ak = 0$ or $\sin(kL) = 0$. Because $k \neq 0$, the first possibility gives $A = 0$. This leads to the trivial solution $c(x,t) = 0$, and is neglected. The remaining possibility gives $k = n\pi/L$, where n is any integer. The allowed values of $\mu = -k^2$ are therefore

$$\mu = -\frac{n^2\pi^2}{L^2}.$$

The value $n = 0$ can be excluded because it gives $\mu = 0$, and we are currently assuming $\mu < 0$. The corresponding solutions for $X(x)$ are

$$X(x) = A_n \cos\left(\frac{n\pi x}{L}\right).$$

In both this equation and the equation for μ, the values for n can be restricted to the positive integers $n = 1, 2, 3, \ldots$, because $-n$ gives exactly the same solutions and values as $+n$.

(e) Since $\mu = -n^2\pi^2/L^2$, the differential equation satisfied by $T(t)$ is

$$T'(t) = -\frac{n^2\pi^2 D}{L^2} T(t),$$

with $n = 1, 2, 3, \ldots$. The general solution is of the form

$$T_n(t) = \alpha_n \exp\left(-\frac{n^2\pi^2 Dt}{L^2}\right) \quad (n = 1, 2, 3, \ldots),$$

where α_n is an arbitrary constant.

(f) Assimilating the two arbitrary constants into one (i.e. replacing $A_n\alpha_n$ with C_n), the family of product solutions is

$$c_n(x,t) = C_n \cos\left(\frac{n\pi x}{L}\right) \exp\left(-\frac{n^2\pi^2 Dt}{L^2}\right) \quad (n = 1, 2, 3, \ldots),$$

supplemented by the constant solution

$$c_0(x,t) = C_0.$$

The general solution is therefore of the form

$$c(x,t) = C_0 + \sum_{n=1}^{\infty} C_n \cos\left(\frac{n\pi x}{L}\right) \exp\left(-\frac{n^2\pi^2 Dt}{L^2}\right).$$

(g) Setting $t = 0$ in the general solution, the initial condition $c(x,0) = f(x)$ gives

$$c(x,0) = C_0 + \sum_{n=1}^{\infty} C_n \cos\left(\frac{n\pi x}{L}\right) = f(x).$$

The coefficients C_0 and C_n can therefore be recognised as the coefficients that appear in the cosine Fourier series for $f(x)$ over the interval $0 \leq x \leq L$. We can therefore find these coefficients by using the *even* periodic extension of $f(x)$.

Note carefully why the *even* periodic extension of $f(x)$ is needed here.

Assuming that this has fundamental period $2L$, and using equations (39) and (40) from Unit 11, we get

$$C_0 = \frac{2}{2L} \int_0^L f(x) \, dx, \quad C_n = \frac{4}{2L} \int_0^L f(x) \cos\left(\frac{n\pi x}{L}\right) dx.$$

3 Modelling heat flow

3.1 The heat equation

It turns out that the diffusion equation (36) also describes the conduction of heat. In a one-dimensional situation, if $\theta(x, t)$ is the temperature at position x and time t, then it is often valid to assume that

$$\frac{\partial \theta}{\partial t} = D \frac{\partial^2 \theta}{\partial x^2}. \tag{46}$$

This is identical to the diffusion equation but, in this context, the equation is called the **heat equation**, and the constant D is called the **thermal diffusivity**. We do not derive the heat equation here, but the link with diffusion is intriguing, so we make a few remarks about it.

Some authors use a different symbol, such as α, for the thermal diffusivity.

If you apply heat to a metal object, such as a saucepan, by holding it over a flame, then its temperature increases at the point where the heat is supplied. If you remove the pan from the flame, then the heat spreads out so that hot parts become cooler but other parts of the pan become warmer. Although heat is not a substance (it is a form of energy), it does behave in many respects like a fluid, diffusing from hot regions to cooler ones.

The quantities of concentration and flux density, which you met in the context of molecular diffusion, have analogues in the context of heat flow. Temperature can be modelled as being proportional to the heat energy density, which is analogous to concentration, and there is a heat flux density that is analogous to the flux density for molecules. Moreover, it is reasonable to assume that the heat energy density obeys an equation of continuity, and by analogy with Fick's law of diffusion, the heat flux density obeys the equation

$$\text{heat flux density} \propto -\text{temperature gradient}, \tag{47}$$

which is called **Fourier's law**. When all these things are put together, it is possible to justify equation (46), following much the same route as used for the diffusion equation in Section 2.

At a broader level, the analogy is that the conduction of heat occurs via many random steps that involve the transport of heat energy, while molecular diffusion occurs via many random steps that involve the transport of matter.

3.2 Heat flow in rods

We consider a straight thin metal rod of length L with a uniform cross-section. The position of a point on the rod is measured by the distance x from one end. The temperature at this point is θ, which is a function of position x and time t. Two different problems are introduced in this subsection, and then solved in the subsections that follow.

A thermally insulated rod

The simplest case occurs when the only direction of heat flow is along the rod. In this case the temperature satisfies the one-dimensional heat equation

$$\frac{\partial \theta}{\partial t} = D\,\frac{\partial^2 \theta}{\partial x^2}. \tag{Eq. 46}$$

Usually, a heated metal rod loses heat to its surroundings, so that heat flows out of its sides as well as along its length. This flow of heat to the surroundings can be stopped (or at least greatly reduced) by covering the rod with a thermal insulating layer (an example is the layer of foam plastic that is used to cover water pipes in houses). For this reason we will refer to the case where the temperature satisfies equation (46) as the **insulated rod**.

The boundary conditions depend on what happens at the ends of the rod. There are two important cases.

- If the ends of the rod are insulated, then no heat can enter or leave them. Fourier's law (47) then implies that the temperature gradient $\partial \theta / \partial x$ is equal to zero at both ends of the rod. This applies at all times of interest, so in mathematical notation, the boundary conditions are

$$\frac{\partial \theta}{\partial x}(0,t) = 0, \quad \frac{\partial \theta}{\partial x}(L,t) = 0, \quad t > 0. \tag{48}$$

- If the ends of the rod are in contact with a body that is at a fixed temperature θ_0, then the boundary conditions are

$$\theta(0,t) = \theta_0, \quad \theta(L,t) = \theta_0, \quad t > 0. \tag{49}$$

  In this case, heat may flow from the centre of the rod and out through its ends, even though these are maintained at a fixed temperature. Hence, by Fourier's law, the temperature gradient $\partial \theta / \partial x$ need not be equal to zero at the ends of the rod.

In addition to the boundary conditions, we need an initial condition. Typically, this is given by a function $f(x)$ that describes the initial distribution of temperature along the rod at time $t = 0$. This initial condition is written as

$$\theta(x,0) = f(x), \quad 0 \le x \le L. \tag{50}$$

Exercise 10

Show that the function

$$\theta(x, t) = \sin\left(\frac{\pi x}{L}\right) \exp\left(-\frac{\pi^2 D t}{L^2}\right)$$

satisfies the heat equation (46) and boundary conditions (49) if $\theta_0 = 0$.

A convecting rod

The second case that we will discuss is that of a rod that is not thermally insulated, but is surrounded by air. In this case, heat is not only conducted along the rod, but also lost from its sides. Loss of heat from the sides of the rod occurs through a process called **convection**. In this process, as the air around the rod is heated, it expands and rises, so air currents are set up. The process of convection differs from the process of conduction that leads to the heat equation (just as the process of stirring a liquid differs from diffusion). It is therefore not surprising that heat loss due to convection is not described by the heat equation.

Convection is a complex process, but if a hot body at a uniform temperature θ is surrounded by cooler air at temperature θ_{air}, the rate of drop of temperature of the body can be modelled as being proportional to the temperature difference $\theta - \theta_{air}$. We therefore write

This relationship was introduced by Newton and is sometimes called **Newton's law of cooling**.

$$\left[\frac{d\theta}{dt}\right]_{convection} = -\gamma(\theta - \theta_{air}), \tag{51}$$

where γ is a positive constant that depends on the body's size, shape and composition. The initial minus sign on the right-hand side shows that the temperature of the body is decreasing.

In equation (51), the body is assumed to have a single temperature at each moment in time. In general, the temperature of a convecting rod depends on both position x and time t. We can take account of both conduction along the rod and convection away from the sides of the rod by adding a term $-\gamma(\theta - \theta_{air})$ to the right-hand side of the diffusion equation (46), where $\theta = \theta(x, t)$ is now a function of position as well as time, and θ_{air} is a constant. We therefore take the partial differential equation for a convecting rod to be

$$\frac{\partial\theta}{\partial t} = D\frac{\partial^2\theta}{\partial x^2} - \gamma(\theta - \theta_{air}). \tag{52}$$

The boundary and initial conditions are as for an insulated rod.

Exercise 11

Write down the initial condition describing the temperature distribution if the central third of a rod with ends at $x = 0$ and $x = L$ is initially heated to a temperature θ_1 while the remainder of the rod is at the temperature θ_0.

We now solve the two types of problem in turn: first the insulated rod in Subsection 3.3, and then the convecting rod in Subsection 3.4.

3.3 The insulated rod problem solved

This subsection uses Procedure 1 (the method of separation of variables) to solve the heat equation for the insulated rod problem introduced in Subsection 3.2.

In our model, the temperatures at the ends of the rod are zero ($\theta(0,t) = \theta(L,t) = 0$ in appropriate units), and we suppose that the initial temperature of the rod at $t = 0$ is given by a function $f(x)$ that is very similar to the initial displacement function for the taut string problem considered in Section 1 (equation (31)). This initial temperature distribution is sketched in Figure 16.

In mathematical terms, the model is

$$\frac{\partial^2 \theta}{\partial x^2} = \frac{1}{D} \frac{\partial \theta}{\partial t}, \tag{53}$$

subject to boundary conditions

$$\theta(0,t) = \theta(L,t) = 0, \quad t \geq 0, \tag{54}$$

and initial condition

$$\theta(x,0) = f(x) = \begin{cases} \dfrac{2\theta_1}{L} x & \text{for } 0 < x \leq \tfrac{1}{2}L, \\ \dfrac{2\theta_1}{L}(L - x) & \text{for } \tfrac{1}{2}L < x < L. \end{cases} \tag{55}$$

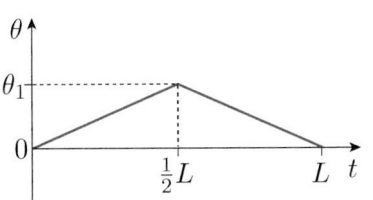

Figure 16 Initial temperature distribution for the insulated rod problem

You will see that the solution of this problem is simplified by having $\theta = 0$ at the ends of the rod. This might seem strange because there are many different temperature scales, and a temperature of zero degrees Fahrenheit, for example, has no great physical significance. In fact, the choice of boundary conditions in equation (54) is made purely for mathematical convenience. You will see later how our solution can be adapted to cover any fixed temperatures at the ends of the rod.

- **Step 1 Prepare a product solution**

  We prepare to separate the variables by writing

  $$\theta(x,t) = X(x)\,T(t), \tag{56}$$

  and finding the relevant partial derivatives:

  $$\frac{\partial^2 \theta}{\partial x^2} = X''T, \tag{57}$$

  $$\frac{\partial \theta}{\partial t} = XT'. \tag{58}$$

- **Step 2 Separate the variables**

  To get separate ordinary differential equations for $X(x)$ and $T(t)$, we substitute the formulas for the partial derivatives into the partial differential equation, and rearrange.

Substituting equations (57) and (58) into equation (53) gives

$$X''T = \frac{1}{D}XT'.$$

Dividing by XT then gives

$$\frac{X''}{X} = \frac{1}{D}\frac{T'}{T}. \tag{59}$$

The left-hand side is a function of the variable x alone, and the right-hand side is a function of the variable t alone, so both are equal to the same separation constant μ. Thus the single equation (59) gives us the pair of equations

$$X'' - \mu X = 0, \tag{60}$$

$$T' - D\mu T = 0. \tag{61}$$

- **Step 3   Prepare the boundary conditions**

To find the boundary conditions for $X(x)$, we write $\theta(x,t) = X(x)\,T(t)$, substitute in $x = 0$ and $x = L$, and then use the given boundary conditions for $\theta(x,t)$. This gives $X(0)\,T(t) = X(L)\,T(t) = 0$ for $t \geq 0$, and hence

$$X(0) = X(L) = 0. \tag{62}$$

- **Step 4   Find the functions $X_n(x)$**

The differential equation (60) for X, and its boundary conditions (62), are the same as in Subsection 1.2, so we need not repeat the arguments. You have seen that a non-trivial solution occurs only if the constant μ is negative. Hence, as before, we replace μ by $-k^2$.

As before, k must take one of the values $k_n = n\pi/L$, where n is an integer. As explained in Section 1, n can be restricted further to the positive integers, $n = 1, 2, 3, \ldots$. The allowed values of the separation constant are $\mu_n = -k_n^2 = -n^2\pi^2/L^2$, and each of these values corresponds to a solution

$$X_n(x) = B_n \sin(k_n x) = B_n \sin\left(\frac{n\pi x}{L}\right), \quad n = 1, 2, 3, \ldots, \tag{63}$$

where B_n is an arbitrary constant.

- **Step 5   Find the functions $T_n(x)$**

The function $T(t)$ satisfies the differential equation $T' = D\mu\,T$, where μ is restricted to the values $\mu_n = -k_n^2$. We therefore need to solve the first-order differential equation

$$T_n'(t) = -Dk_n^2 T,$$

which has general solution

$$T_n(t) = \alpha_n \exp(-Dk_n^2 t) = \alpha_n \exp\left(-\frac{n^2\pi^2 Dt}{L^2}\right), \tag{64}$$

where α_n is an arbitrary constant and $n = 1, 2, 3, \ldots$.

- **Step 6   Construct the general solution**

  By combining $X_n(t)$ and $T_n(t)$, we obtain a family of product solutions $X_n(x)\,T_n(t)$ that satisfy the heat equation (53) and its associated boundary conditions (54). This family is

  $$\theta_n(x,t) = C_n \sin\left(\frac{n\pi x}{L}\right) \exp\left(-\frac{n^2\pi^2 Dt}{L^2}\right), \quad n = 1, 2, 3, \ldots, \quad (65)$$

  where $C_n = B_n \alpha_n$ is obtained by combining the arbitrary constants B_n and α_n. The *general solution* is an infinite linear combination of members from this family:

  $$\theta(x,t) = \sum_{n=1}^{\infty} C_n \sin\left(\frac{n\pi x}{L}\right) \exp\left(-\frac{n^2\pi^2 Dt}{L^2}\right). \quad (66)$$

- **Step 7   Apply the initial condition**

  Setting $t = 0$ in equation (66) gives

  $$\theta(x,0) = \sum_{n=1}^{\infty} C_n \sin\left(\frac{n\pi x}{L}\right).$$

  The function $f(x)$ used in initial condition (55) is essentially the same as that used in Section 1, hence we arrive at the same values for the coefficients C_n. The required particular solution is therefore

  $$\theta(x,t) = \frac{8\theta_1}{\pi^2}\left[\sin\left(\frac{\pi x}{L}\right)\exp\left(-\frac{\pi^2 Dt}{L^2}\right)\right.$$
  $$-\frac{1}{9}\sin\left(\frac{3\pi x}{L}\right)\exp\left(-\frac{9\pi^2 Dt}{L^2}\right)$$
  $$\left.+\frac{1}{25}\sin\left(\frac{5\pi x}{L}\right)\exp\left(-\frac{25\pi^2 Dt}{L^2}\right) - \cdots\right]. \quad (67)$$

As promised earlier, let us now see how to adjust this solution to cover the case where the ends of the rod are maintained at a constant non-zero temperature $\theta_0 \neq 0$, i.e. where the boundary conditions are

$$\theta(0,t) = \theta(L,t) = \theta_0, \quad t \geq 0. \quad (68)$$

The trick is to notice that the constant function $\theta(x,t) = \theta_0$ satisfies the heat equation (53). This is because all of its partial derivatives are equal to zero, so substituting into the heat equation gives $0 = 0$. If we ignore the boundary conditions for the moment, then the principle of superposition tells us that any linear combination of solutions of the heat equation is also a solution. So we can add the constant solution θ_0 to the solution obtained in equation (66) to get another solution of the heat equation:

$$\theta(x,t) = \theta_0 + \sum_{n=1}^{\infty} C_n \sin\left(\frac{n\pi x}{L}\right) \exp\left(-\frac{n^2\pi^2 Dt}{L^2}\right). \quad (69)$$

If we substitute $x = 0$ or $x = L$ into this expression, we already know that all the terms in the summation will give zero (because they satisfy the boundary conditions $\theta(0,t) = \theta(L,t) = 0$).

It follows that $\theta(x,t)$ in equation (69) satisfies the new boundary conditions in equation (68). In fact, it is the *general solution* of the heat equation subject to these boundary conditions.

Exercise 12

Consider the heat equation

$$\frac{\partial^2 \theta}{\partial x^2} = \frac{1}{D}\frac{\partial \theta}{\partial t},$$

subject to the boundary conditions

$$\theta(0,t) = \theta(L,t) = \theta_0, \quad t \geq 0,$$

where $\theta_0 \neq 0$. Explain how you would obtain the particular solution that satisfies the initial condition

$$\theta(x,0) = f(x), \quad 0 \leq x \leq L,$$

where $f(x)$ is a given function that is equal to θ_0 at $x = 0$ and $x = L$.

Exercise 13

Consider the heat equation

$$\frac{\partial^2 \theta}{\partial x^2} = \frac{1}{D}\frac{\partial \theta}{\partial t},$$

These boundary conditions model the situation where the ends of the rod are kept at two different fixed temperatures.

subject to boundary conditions

$$\theta(0,t) = \theta_0, \quad \theta(L,t) = \theta_L, \quad t \geq 0,$$

where θ_0 and θ_L are non-zero constants, and initial condition

$$\theta(x,0) = f(x), \quad 0 < x < L,$$

for some function $f(x)$.

(a) Show that the function

$$\theta(x,t) = \frac{L-x}{L}\theta_0 + \frac{x}{L}\theta_L$$

satisfies the differential equation and the boundary conditions.

(b) Write down the general solution of the partial differential equation subject to the boundary conditions.

(c) Explain how you would go on to obtain a solution that also satisfies the initial condition.

3.4 The convecting rod problem solved

In this subsection, we again use Procedure 1 (the method of separation of variables). This time, we solve the heat equation for the convecting rod problem, sharing the solution between text and exercises.

We suppose that the ambient temperature of the air, and the temperature at the ends of the rod, are equal to zero (in appropriate units). The initial condition is the same as for the insulated rod. In mathematical terms, the problem is

$$\frac{\partial \theta}{\partial t} = D \frac{\partial^2 \theta}{\partial x^2} - \gamma \theta, \tag{70}$$

where $D > 0$, subject to the boundary conditions

$$\theta(0, t) = \theta(L, t) = 0, \quad t \geq 0, \tag{71}$$

and the initial condition

$$\theta(x, 0) = \begin{cases} \dfrac{2\theta_1}{L} x & \text{for } 0 < x \leq \frac{1}{2}L, \\ \dfrac{2\theta_1}{L}(L - x) & \text{for } \frac{1}{2}L < x \leq L. \end{cases} \tag{72}$$

Exercise 14

Carry out Steps 1 and 2 of Procedure 1 for the convecting rod problem, as follows.

(a) Prepare a product solution for substitution into equation (70).

(b) Separate the variables.

The ordinary differential equations derived in Exercise 14 are

$$X'' - \mu X = 0,$$
$$T' = (D\mu - \gamma)T.$$

Steps 3 and 4 in Procedure 1 tell us to prepare the boundary conditions for $X(x)$ and to solve the differential equation for $X(x)$ subject to them. Applying the given boundary conditions to the product function $\theta(x, t) = X(x) T(t)$ gives $X(0) T(t) = X(L) T(t) = 0$, so the boundary conditions for $X(x)$ are

$$X(0) = 0 \quad \text{and} \quad X(L) = 0.$$

These are the same boundary conditions as those used for an insulated rod (in Subsection 3.2) and for a string (in Section 1). The same arguments apply, so we do not repeat them here – although you would need to when answering an assignment question!

In brief, the conclusions are as follows. In order to get non-trivial solutions that satisfy the boundary conditions, μ must be negative. Writing $\mu = -k^2$, the boundary conditions require that k takes one of the values $k_n = n\pi/L$, where n is an integer. The corresponding solutions for $X(x)$ are

$$X_n(x) = B_n \sin\left(\frac{n\pi x}{L}\right), \quad n = 1, 2, 3, \ldots,$$

where B_n is an arbitrary constant. The values of n have been restricted to the positive integers because $n = 0$ gives the trivial solution and $-n$ gives the same solution as $+n$.

Exercise 15

Step 5 in Procedure 1 asks us to solve the differential equation for $T(t)$, to find the functions $T_n(t)$ that accompany $X_n(x)$ in the product solutions. Carry out this step using the differential equation for T obtained above.

In Step 6 of Procedure 1 we combine the solutions for $X_n(x)$ and $T_n(t)$, to obtain a family of product solutions of equation (70) subject to boundary conditions (71):

$$\theta_n(x,t) = C_n \sin\left(\frac{n\pi x}{L}\right) \exp\left[-\left(D\frac{n^2\pi^2}{L^2} + \gamma\right)t\right]$$

$$= C_n \sin\left(\frac{n\pi x}{L}\right) \exp\left[-D\frac{n^2\pi^2 t}{L^2}\right] e^{-\gamma t}, \quad n = 1, 2, 3, \ldots,$$

where we have combined the arbitrary constants B_n and α_n to give $C_n = B_n \alpha_n$. The general solution of the partial differential equation, satisfying the associated boundary conditions, is then given by the infinite sum

$$\theta(x,t) = e^{-\gamma t} \sum_{n=1}^{\infty} C_n \sin\left(\frac{n\pi x}{L}\right) \exp\left[-D\frac{n^2\pi^2 t}{L^2}\right].$$

The factor $e^{-\gamma t}$ has been brought outside the summation because it is independent of n.

Finally, Step 7 of Procedure 1 asks us to apply the given initial condition. Setting $t = 0$ in the expression for the general solution gives

$$\theta(x,0) = \sum_{n=1}^{\infty} C_n \sin\left(\frac{n\pi x}{L}\right),$$

and we can equate this to the given initial temperature distribution $f(x)$, given in equation (72). The computation of the Fourier coefficients is exactly the same as in the previous cases (see, for example, equation (67)).We conclude that the required particular solution is

$$\theta(x,t) = \frac{8\theta_1}{\pi^2} e^{-\gamma t} \left[\sin\left(\frac{\pi x}{L}\right) \exp\left(-\frac{\pi^2 Dt}{L^2}\right) \right.$$

$$- \frac{1}{9} \sin\left(\frac{3\pi x}{L}\right) \exp\left(-\frac{9\pi^2 Dt}{L^2}\right)$$

$$\left. + \frac{1}{25} \sin\left(\frac{5\pi x}{L}\right) \exp\left(-\frac{25\pi^2 Dt}{L^2}\right) - \cdots \right]. \quad (73)$$

This is the same as the solution for the insulated rod except for the $e^{-\gamma t}$ factor, which ensures that the convecting rod cools more quickly towards the ambient zero temperature than the insulated rod.

4   Taking a broader view

This final section will not be assessed in continuous assessment or in the exam, but you should read it, especially if you plan to study further modules in the physical sciences or applied mathematics.

This section differs in style from the rest of the unit because it takes a light-touch approach, emphasising concepts rather than problem solving. After a brief review of some areas of science that use partial differential equations, we consider solutions of the wave equation and the diffusion equation that apply when the region of interest has no boundaries, or has boundaries that are so far away that they do not influence the solutions. Under these circumstances, there are alternative methods of solution, not based on the method of separation of variables.

4.1   The importance of partial differential equations

Partial differential equations have a vast range of applications. This is partly because many fundamental laws of physics are expressed directly in terms of them. So when physical theories are applied to other subjects, such as climate science, astrophysics or physiology, partial differential equations are often used.

Partial differential equations in action

- The laws of electromagnetism are expressed as a system of equations called *Maxwell's equations*. These lead to a three-dimensional version of the wave equation that describes light and similar waves. Electrostatic phenomena are also described using a partial differential equation called *Poisson's equation*.

- Atoms and molecules are best described using quantum mechanics. The description often involves using a partial differential equation called the *Schrödinger equation* that is closely related to both the wave equation and the diffusion equation.

- A vast range of phenomena involve the effects of numerous small random motions, and are described by variants of the diffusion equation, including the *Black–Scholes equation* for price fluctuations.

- The motion of fluids is described by non-linear partial differential equations called the *Navier–Stokes equations*. These equations are used in oceanography and weather science.

> • The most successful theory of gravity, called *general relativity*, is expressed as a system of non-linear partial differential equations. These equations are used to model the expansion of the Universe and the collapse of black holes.

A basic classification of partial differential equations distinguishes between linear and non-linear equations. The fundamental partial differential equations of electromagnetism and quantum mechanics are linear, and so is the diffusion equation. But the Navier–Stokes equations of fluid mechanics are non-linear, and so are the equations of general relativity.

This distinction is important because non-linear partial differential equations are usually very hard to solve using mathematical analysis alone. The solutions may be too complex to allow description by manageable mathematical formulas, and investigations using computer programs may be the only practical approach. An example is given in Figure 17, which shows a solution of the Navier–Stokes equations for the flow of a gas above a hot surface.

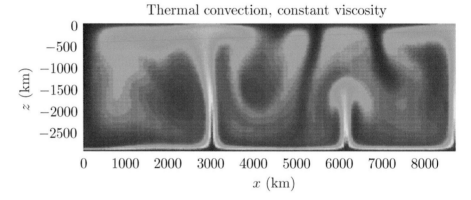

Figure 17 A computer-generated colour-coded image of the temperature of air above a hot surface, with 'plumes' of hot air rising at apparently random positions

4.2 Travelling wave solutions of the wave equation

When discussing waves on a string earlier, we kept the ends of the string clamped. This introduced boundary conditions that restricted the family of product solutions obtained by the method of separation of variables.

However, there are many situations where boundary conditions are irrelevant. When a stone is dropped into the middle of a large lake, the ripples that spread out do not depend strongly on the details of the lake's shoreline (Figure 18). It therefore makes sense to consider solutions of the wave equation that apply in the absence of boundary conditions. In the context of a string, we simply ignore the ends of the string and treat it as if it were infinitely long. This may seem rather artificial for a string, but it is often a good way of thinking about the propagation of light, sound and many other types of wave.

Figure 18 Wave ripples produced by dropping a stone into a lake

In the absence of boundary conditions, a proposed solution need only satisfy the wave equation. One function that does so is

$$u(x,t) = A \sin[k(x - ct)], \tag{74}$$

where A and k are constants, and c is the wave speed that appears in the wave equation. You can check this by calculating the relevant partial derivatives and substituting into the wave equation.

Exercise 16

Check that the function in equation (74) satisfies the wave equation

$$\frac{\partial^2 u}{\partial x^2} - \frac{1}{c^2} \frac{\partial^2 u}{\partial t^2} = 0.$$

Exercise 16 showed that the function $A \sin[k(x - ct)]$ is a solution of the wave equation for any values of k and A. This function varies sinusoidally, and gives a train of wave crests and troughs that move through space as time progresses (Figure 19). The distance between two successive wave crests is the **wavelength** of this sinusoidal wave. The wavelength λ is related to the constant k in equation (74) by $k\lambda = 2\pi$, so $\lambda = 2\pi/k$.

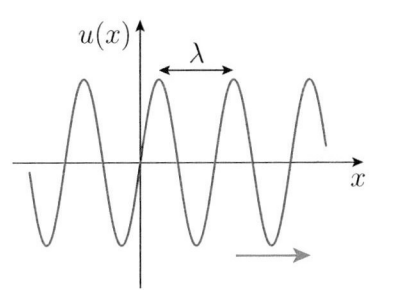

Figure 19   A sinusoidal wave solution travelling in the positive x-direction

Suppose that at time t, a particular crest is at position x. At a slightly later time $t + \Delta t$, the same crest has moved to position $x + \Delta x$. The function $A \sin[k(x - ct)]$ must take the same value at both these instants, so

$$A \sin[k(x + \Delta x - c(t + \Delta t))] = A \sin[k(x - ct)].$$

We need to satisfy this equation in a way that ensures that $\Delta x \to 0$ as $\Delta t \to 0$. This is achieved by taking

$$\Delta x = c \, \Delta t.$$

The constant c is positive, so $\Delta x > 0$ when $\Delta t > 0$, and we see that the wave crest (and every other part of the wave) moves in the positive x-direction at the constant speed $\Delta x / \Delta t = c$. This is why the constant c in the wave equation is called the *wave speed*. A disturbance that travels in this way is called a **travelling wave** solution of the wave equation.

Instead of $u(x,t) = A \sin[k(x - ct)]$, we could consider $u(x,t) = A \sin[k(x + ct)]$: the same steps show that this is another travelling wave solution of the wave equation. In this case, the wave moves in the negative x-direction with speed c. We could also replace $A \sin[k(x - ct)]$ by $A \cos[k(x \pm ct)]$ and find that these too are solutions.

In fact, the crucial feature for a travelling wave solution of the wave equation is that x and t should appear in one of the combinations $x - ct$ or $x + ct$. If we take any reasonable function, and work out the partial derivatives, we find that $f(x - ct)$ and $f(x + ct)$ are solutions of the wave equation, provided that the function f can be differentiated twice.

To check that this is true, note that if $u(x, t) = f(x - ct)$, then

$$\frac{\partial u}{\partial x} = f'(x - ct), \quad \frac{\partial u}{\partial t} = -cf'(x - ct),$$

$$\frac{\partial^2 u}{\partial x^2} = f''(x - ct), \quad \frac{\partial^2 u}{\partial t^2} = c^2 f''(x - ct).$$

Hence

$$\frac{\partial^2 u}{\partial x^2} - \frac{1}{c^2}\frac{\partial^2 u}{\partial t^2} = f''(x - ct) - \frac{1}{c^2}c^2 f''(x - ct) = 0,$$

showing that $f(x - ct)$ satisfies the wave equation. A similar argument applies to $f(x + ct)$.

In general, if f and g are two functions that can be differentiated twice, then the following function is a solution of the wave equation:

$$u(x, t) = f(x - ct) + g(x + ct). \tag{75}$$

This is known as **d'Alembert's solution** of the wave equation. It is the general solution of the wave equation without boundary conditions. It consists of two travelling waves, moving in opposite directions, but one or other of these waves may be missing in particular cases. There is an immense amount of freedom built into this general solution, which can be restricted by considering particular initial conditions.

A solution like $f(x - ct)$ describes a pulse of disturbance that travels at constant speed, unchanged in shape, as in Figure 20. The fact that the pulse travels unchanged in shape is a consequence of our assumption that the wave speed c is a constant. There are other types of wave for which this is not true, and whose pulses broaden out as they travel. These are described by partial differential equations that are more complicated than the wave equation of this unit. Some examples are given in the box below.

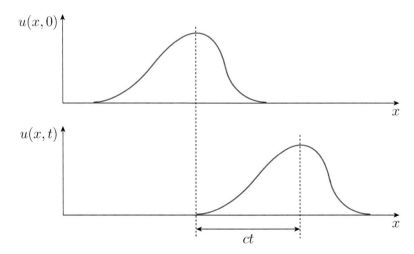

Figure 20   A pulse travels at constant speed, unchanged in shape

Waves are everywhere

A wave is a disturbance of some kind that either forms standing waves or propagates through space as time progresses. The partial differential equations satisfied by waves are called *wave equations*, although they may differ from equation (3).

- **Electromagnetic waves** are disturbances of electric and magnetic fields. In empty space, they satisfy a three-dimensional version of equation (3). This equation has sinusoidal solutions with definite wavelengths, and the wavelength determines the name given to the wave. Radio waves have very long wavelengths; as the wavelength decreases, we progress through infrared radiation, microwaves, visible light, ultraviolet radiation, X-rays and gamma rays. In a vacuum, all these waves have the same wave speed, $c = 3.0 \times 10^8 \, \text{m s}^{-1}$, which is called the speed of light.

- **Sound waves** are disturbances of the pressure in a gas or liquid. They also obey a three-dimensional version of equation (3). In air, sound waves have a speed that is roughly $330 \, \text{m s}^{-1}$.

- **Water waves** on the surface of the sea are very familiar. Their wave speed is not a constant, but depends on the wavelength.

- **Quantum-mechanical waves** arise in the most fundamental theory of nature, *quantum mechanics*. The relevant wave equation is called the *Schrödinger equation*, which differs from equation (3) because it involves complex numbers and only the first-order partial derivative with respect to time.

4.3   Point-source solutions of the diffusion equation

Finally, let us briefly consider the phenomenon of diffusion in a region that is large enough for its boundaries to be irrelevant. If you inject a drop of dye into the centre of a large tank of still water, the dye molecules gradually spread out from their starting point: this is the essence of the phenomenon of diffusion.

We can imagine an idealised one-dimensional situation in which all the molecules start out at $x = 0$ at $t = 0$. Because all the molecules start from a single point, this initial condition is referred to as a **point source**. Figure 21 shows the spread of concentrations that arise from this source at a series of later times. Of course, the spreading out is accompanied by a reduction in concentration at the injection point, $x = 0$.

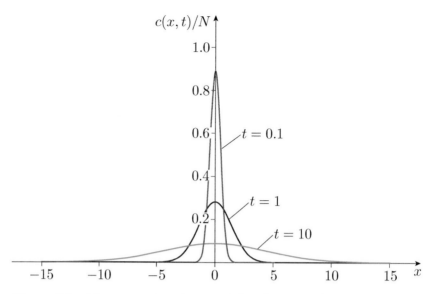

Figure 21   The concentration resulting from a point source at $x = 0$ injected at time $t = 0$. (The diffusion coefficient D has been taken as 1.)

The function that describes this spreading out of concentration turns out to be

$$c(x, t) = \frac{N}{\sqrt{4\pi D t}} \exp\left(-\frac{x^2}{4Dt}\right) \quad (t > 0), \tag{76}$$

where N is a constant. Although there are powerful techniques for deriving this function, they are not discussed here. However, you can verify for yourself that this function does satisfy the diffusion equation.

Exercise 17

Show that the function $c(x, t)$ in equation (76) satisfies

$$\frac{\partial c}{\partial x} = -\frac{x}{2Dt} c \quad \text{and} \quad \frac{\partial c}{\partial t} = \left(\frac{x^2}{4Dt^2} - \frac{1}{2t}\right) c.$$

Then carry out a further partial differentiation to show that $c(x, t)$ satisfies the diffusion equation.

Because it describes the diffusion of a point source at $x = 0$, released at $t = 0$, the function in equation (76) is called a **point-source solution** of the diffusion equation.

If the particles had been released from a different point, say $x = s$, at $t = 0$, then the corresponding point-source solution would be of the form

$$c(x, t) = \frac{N_1}{\sqrt{4\pi D t}} \exp\left[-\frac{(x - s)^2}{4Dt}\right],$$

where N_1 is another constant.

It turns out (although again we do not give the details) that the general solution of the diffusion equation without boundaries can be expressed as

$$c(x, t) = \frac{1}{\sqrt{4\pi Dt}} \int_{\infty}^{\infty} \exp\left[-\frac{(x-s)^2}{4Dt} \right] c_0(s) \, du,$$

where $c(x, t)$ satisfies the initial condition $c(x, 0) = c_0(x)$. Thinking of this integral as a sort of 'continuous sum', you can see that it can be interpreted as a linear superposition of point-source solutions. This is not too surprising, since we know that the diffusion equation is linear and satisfies the principle of superposition.

Learning outcomes

After studying this unit, you should be able to do the following.

- Understand how the wave and diffusion/heat partial differential equations are used to model certain systems.

- Use the method of separation of variables to find families of product solutions for the wave equation, diffusion equation and similar linear homogeneous second-order partial differential equations, subject to simple boundary conditions.

- Construct the general solution of a partial differential equation from a family of product solutions.

- Find the values of the coefficients in the general solution of a partial differential equation by using given initial conditions to determine the coefficients of a Fourier series.

Solutions to exercises

Solution to Exercise 1

The partial derivatives are

$$\frac{\partial u}{\partial x} = Ak\cos(kx)\sin(kct), \quad \frac{\partial u}{\partial t} = Akc\sin(kx)\cos(kct),$$

$$\frac{\partial^2 u}{\partial x^2} = -Ak^2\sin(kx)\sin(kct), \quad \frac{\partial^2 u}{\partial t^2} = -Ak^2 c^2\sin(kx)\sin(kct),$$

so

$$\frac{\partial^2 u}{\partial x^2} = \frac{1}{c^2}\frac{\partial^2 u}{\partial t^2}.$$

The function does satisfy the wave equation.

Solution to Exercise 2

The displacement at $t = 0$ is

$$u(x, 0) = A\sin(kx)\sin(0) = 0.$$

The velocity at position x and time t is

$$\frac{\partial u}{\partial t} = Akc\sin(kx)\cos(kct),$$

so the velocity at position x and time $t = 0$ is

$$\frac{\partial u}{\partial t}(x, 0) = Akc\sin(kx).$$

Solution to Exercise 3

The initial displacement has two linear sections.

The left-hand section has slope $d/(L/3) = 3d/L$ and has the value $u = 0$ at $x = 0$. It is described by the function $u(x) = (3d/L)x$.

The right-hand section has slope $-d/(2L/3) = -3d/2L$ and has the value $u = 0$ at $x = L$. It is described by a linear function of the form

$$u(x) = -\frac{3d}{2L}x + C,$$

where C is a constant. Setting $u(L) = 0$ gives $C = 3d/2$, so the right-hand section is described by the function

$$u(x) = \frac{3d}{2} - \frac{3d}{2L}x = \frac{3d}{2L}(L - x).$$

The initial condition for the shape of the string is therefore

$$u(x, 0) = \begin{cases} \dfrac{3d}{L}x & \text{for } 0 \le x \le \tfrac{1}{3}L, \\ \dfrac{3d}{2L}(L - x) & \text{for } \tfrac{1}{3}L < x \le L. \end{cases}$$

You can check that both parts of this expression give $u(x, 0) = d$ at $x = L/3$.

The condition for the initial shape of the string is supplemented by the condition that a plucked string is released from rest:

$$\frac{\partial u}{\partial t}(x,0) = 0, \quad 0 \leq x \leq L.$$

Solution to Exercise 4

The function under consideration is

$$u(x,t) = \sin\left(\frac{\pi x}{L}\right) \cos\left(\frac{\pi c t}{L}\right).$$

The boundary conditions are satisfied since

$$u(0,t) = \sin 0 \cos\left(\frac{\pi c t}{L}\right) = 0, \quad u(L,t) = \sin \pi \cos\left(\frac{\pi c t}{L}\right) = 0.$$

The initial condition is satisfied since

$$\frac{\partial u}{\partial t}(x,t) = -\frac{\pi c}{L} \sin\left(\frac{\pi x}{L}\right) \sin\left(\frac{\pi c t}{L}\right),$$

so at $t = 0$,

$$\frac{\partial u}{\partial t}(x,0) = -\frac{\pi c}{L} \sin\left(\frac{\pi x}{L}\right) \sin(0) = 0.$$

Solution to Exercise 5

Substituting $u(x,t) = X(x)\,T(t)$ into the partial differential equation gives

$$X\frac{d^2 T}{dt^2} = T\frac{d^4 X}{dx^4}.$$

Dividing by XT and equating both sides to the same separation constant μ, we get

$$\frac{1}{T}\frac{d^2 T}{dt^2} = \mu = \frac{1}{X}\frac{d^4 X}{dx^4},$$

and this leads to the ordinary differential equations

$$\frac{d^2 T}{dt^2} = \mu\,T, \quad \frac{d^4 X}{dx^4} = \mu X.$$

Solution to Exercise 6

Substituting $u(x,t) = X(x)\,T(t)$ into the partial differential equation gives

$$X\frac{dT}{dt} = T\left[\frac{d}{dx}(xX) + \frac{d^2 X}{dx^2}\right].$$

Dividing by XT and equating both sides to the same separation constant μ, we get

$$\frac{1}{T}\frac{dT}{dt} = \mu = \frac{1}{X}\left[\frac{d}{dx}(xX) + \frac{d^2 X}{dx^2}\right],$$

and this leads to the ordinary differential equations

$$\frac{dT}{dt} = \mu\,T, \quad \frac{d}{dx}(xX) + \frac{d^2 X}{dx^2} = \mu X.$$

Solution to Exercise 7

When $u(x,t) = a_1\, u_1(x,t) + a_2\, u_2(x,t)$,

$$\frac{\partial^2 u}{\partial x^2} = \frac{\partial^2}{\partial x^2}(a_1 u_1 + a_2 u_2)$$

$$= a_1\,\frac{\partial^2 u_1}{\partial x^2} + a_2\,\frac{\partial^2 u_2}{\partial x^2}$$

$$= a_1\,\frac{1}{c^2}\,\frac{\partial^2 u_1}{\partial t^2} + a_2\,\frac{1}{c^2}\,\frac{\partial^2 u_2}{\partial t^2}$$

$$= \frac{1}{c^2}\,\frac{\partial^2}{\partial t^2}(a_1 u_1 + a_2 u_2) = \frac{1}{c^2}\,\frac{\partial^2 u}{\partial t^2},$$

so the linear combination satisfies the wave equation.

The given boundary conditions lead to

$$u(0,t) = a_1\, u_1(0,t) + a_2\, u_2(0,t) = 0,$$
$$u(L,t) = a_1\, u_1(L,t) + a_2\, u_2(L,t) = 0,$$

Hence the linear combination $u = a_1 u_1 + a_2 u_2$ satisfies the wave equation *and* the given boundary conditions.

Solution to Exercise 8

From equation (35), the velocity at $t = 0$ is

$$v(x) = \frac{\partial u}{\partial t}(x,0) = \sum_{n=1}^{\infty}\left(\frac{n\pi c}{L}\right) B_n \sin\left(\frac{n\pi x}{L}\right)\cos(0).$$

If the Fourier coefficients of $v(x)$ are C_n, then

$$B_n = \frac{L}{n\pi c}\, C_n, \quad n = 1, 2, 3, \ldots.$$

Solution to Exercise 9

Step 1   Setting $u(x,t) = X(x)\,T(t)$, the required partial derivatives are

For brevity, primes are used to denote derivatives.

$$\frac{\partial^2 u}{\partial x^2} = X''T, \quad \frac{\partial^2 u}{\partial t^2} = XT''.$$

Step 2   Substituting into the partial differential equation and dividing by XT gives

$$\frac{X''}{X} + \frac{T''}{T} = 0,$$

from which it follows that

$$\frac{X''}{X} = -\frac{T''}{T}.$$

Both sides of the equation must be equal to the same constant μ, giving

$$\frac{X''}{X} = \mu \quad \text{and} \quad -\frac{T''}{T} = \mu,$$

or equivalently,

$$X'' - \mu X = 0 \quad \text{and} \quad T'' + \mu T = 0.$$

Step 3   The boundary conditions become $X(0) = X(1) = 0$.

Step 4   Arguing as in Subsection 1.2, only negative μ gives a non-trivial solution for X. Hence we can write $\mu = -k^2$, and the differential equation for X becomes

$$X'' + k^2 X = 0.$$

This equation has the general solution

$$X(x) = C\cos(kx) + D\sin(kx),$$

where C and D are arbitrary constants. In order to satisfy the boundary condition at $x = 0$, we must have $C = 0$. Then, to satisfy the boundary condition at $x = 1$, we must have $k = n\pi$ for some integer n. So there is a family of solutions

$$X_n(x) = D_n \sin(n\pi x), \quad n = 1, 2, 3, \ldots,$$

where we have dropped the value $n = 0$ because it gives the trivial solution $X(x) = 0$, and we have dropped negative values of n because $-n$ gives the same solution as $+n$ (since D_n is an arbitrary constant).

Step 5   With $\mu = -k^2$, the differential equation for T becomes

$$T'' - k^2 T = 0.$$

This equation has the general solution

$$T(t) = Ae^{kt} + Be^{-kt}.$$

Using the allowed values for k, the allowed solutions are

$$T_n(t) = A_n e^{n\pi t} + B_n e^{-n\pi t}, \quad n = 1, 2, 3, \ldots.$$

Step 6   Replacing $D_n A_n$ and $D_n B_n$ by α_n and β_n, respectively, the required family of product solutions is

$$u_n(x, t) = \sin(n\pi x)\left(\alpha_n e^{n\pi t} + \beta_n e^{-n\pi t}\right), \quad n = 1, 2, 3, \ldots,$$

where α_n and β_n are arbitrary constants. The general solution is therefore

$$u(x, t) = \sum_{n=1}^{\infty} \sin(n\pi x)\left(\alpha_n e^{n\pi t} + \beta_n e^{-n\pi t}\right).$$

Solution to Exercise 10

We have

$$\frac{\partial \theta}{\partial x} = \frac{\pi}{L}\cos\left(\frac{\pi x}{L}\right)\exp\left(-\frac{\pi^2 D t}{L^2}\right),$$

so

$$\frac{\partial^2 \theta}{\partial x^2} = -\frac{\pi^2}{L^2}\sin\left(\frac{\pi x}{L}\right)\exp\left(-\frac{\pi^2 D t}{L^2}\right) = -\frac{\pi^2}{L^2}\theta(x, t).$$

Also,

$$\frac{\partial \theta}{\partial t} = -\frac{\pi^2 D}{L^2}\sin\left(\frac{\pi x}{L}\right)\exp\left(-\frac{\pi^2 D t}{L^2}\right) = -\frac{\pi^2 D}{L^2}\theta(x, t).$$

Hence

$$\frac{1}{D}\frac{\partial\theta}{\partial t} = -\frac{\pi^2}{L^2}\,\theta(x,t) = \frac{\partial^2\theta}{\partial x^2},$$

showing that equation (46) is satisfied.

At the ends of the rod,

$$\theta(0,t) = \exp\left(-\frac{\pi^2 Dt}{L^2}\right)\sin 0 = 0,\quad \theta(L,t) = \exp\left(-\frac{\pi^2 Dt}{L^2}\right)\sin\pi = 0,$$

so the boundary conditions are satisfied if $\theta_0 = 0$.

Solution to Exercise 11

The initial condition is

$$\theta(x,0) = \begin{cases} \theta_0 & \text{for } 0 \le x < \tfrac{1}{3}L, \\ \theta_1 & \text{for } \tfrac{1}{3}L \le x \le \tfrac{2}{3}L, \\ \theta_0 & \text{for } \tfrac{2}{3}L < x \le L. \end{cases}$$

Solution to Exercise 12

The general solution satisfying the given boundary conditions is

$$\theta(x,t) = \theta_0 + \sum_{n=1}^{\infty} C_n \sin\left(\frac{n\pi x}{L}\right)\exp\left(-\frac{n^2\pi^2 Dt}{L^2}\right).$$

Setting $t = 0$, we obtain

$$\theta(x,0) = \theta_0 + \sum_{n=1}^{\infty} C_n \sin\left(\frac{n\pi x}{L}\right).$$

So to satisfy the initial condition $\theta(x,0) = f(x)$, we need to obtain the C_n from the Fourier sine series coefficients of the function $f(x) - \theta_0$. Substituting these coefficients into equation (69) then gives the required solution.

Solution to Exercise 13

(a) For

$$\theta(x,t) = \frac{L-x}{L}\,\theta_0 + \frac{x}{L}\,\theta_L,$$

we have

$$\frac{\partial^2\theta}{\partial x^2} = 0 \quad\text{and}\quad \frac{\partial\theta}{\partial t} = 0,$$

so the heat equation reduces to $0 = 0$ and is satisfied.

At $x = 0$, we have

$$\theta(0,t) = \frac{L-0}{L}\,\theta_0 + 0 = \theta_0,$$

and at $x = L$, we have

$$\theta(L,t) = \frac{L-L}{L}\,\theta_0 + \frac{L}{L}\,\theta_L = \theta_L,$$

so the boundary conditions are satisfied.

(b) The general solution takes the form

$$\theta(x,t) = \frac{L-x}{L}\,\theta_0 + \frac{x}{L}\,\theta_L$$
$$+ \sum_{n=1}^{\infty} C_n \sin\left(\frac{n\pi x}{L}\right) \exp\left(-\frac{n^2\pi^2 Dt}{L^2}\right), \qquad (*)$$

where the C_n are arbitrary constants, and the sum on the right satisfies the same differential equation, but with boundary conditions corresponding to zero temperature at both ends of the rod. By the principle of superposition, the general solution $(*)$ satisfies the partial differential equation. It also satisfies the given boundary conditions. This is because substituting in $x = 0$ gives θ_0 from the terms outside the sum and zero from the sum. Similarly, substituting in $x = L$ gives θ_L from the terms outside the sum and zero from the sum.

(c) To find a solution that satisfies the initial condition, we set $t = 0$ in equation $(*)$. This gives

$$\theta(x,0) = \frac{L-x}{L}\,\theta_0 + \frac{x}{L}\,\theta_L + \sum_{n=1}^{\infty} C_n \sin\left(\frac{n\pi x}{L}\right).$$

So to satisfy $\theta(x,0) = f(x)$, we need to obtain the C_n as the Fourier sine series coefficients of the function

$$g(x) = f(x) - (L-x)\theta_0/L - x\theta_L/L.$$

> The Fourier sine series coefficients are found using the odd periodic extension of $g(x)$.

Substituting these into equation $(*)$ gives the required result.

Solution to Exercise 14

(a) Set $\theta(x,t) = X(x)\,T(t)$. Then

$$\frac{\partial^2 \theta}{\partial x^2} = X''T \quad \text{and} \quad \frac{\partial \theta}{\partial t} = XT'.$$

(b) Equation (70) becomes

$$XT' = DX''T - \gamma XT,$$

and dividing by XT gives

$$\frac{T'}{T} = D\frac{X''}{X} - \gamma.$$

Thinking a step ahead, we soon need to solve a differential equation for $X(x)$. To make this equation as simple as possible, we make a rearrangement to get

$$\frac{X''}{X} = \frac{1}{D}\left(\frac{T'}{T} + \gamma\right).$$

The left-hand side is a function of x alone, and the right-hand side is function of t alone, so both must be equal to the same constant μ (the separation constant). We therefore get the ordinary differential equations

$$X'' - \mu X = 0, \quad T' = (D\mu - \gamma)T.$$

Solution to Exercise 15

The relevant differential equation is

$$T' = (D\mu - \gamma)T.$$

For a particular value of n, this takes the form

$$T' = -(Dk_n^2 + \gamma)T,$$

which has general solution

$$T_n(t) = \alpha_n \exp(-(Dk_n^2 + \gamma)t)$$
$$= \alpha_n \exp\left[-\left(D\frac{n^2\pi^2}{L^2} + \gamma\right)t\right], \quad n = 1, 2, 3, \dots,$$

where α_n is an arbitrary constant.

Solution to Exercise 16

The required partial derivatives are calculated using the chain rule:

$$\frac{\partial u}{\partial x} = kA\cos[k(x - ct)], \quad \frac{\partial u}{\partial t} = -kcA\cos[k(x - ct)],$$
$$\frac{\partial^2 u}{\partial x^2} = -k^2 A\sin[k(x - ct)], \quad \frac{\partial^2 u}{\partial t^2} = -k^2 c^2 A\sin[k(x - ct)].$$

Substituting these partial derivatives into the wave equation gives

$$\frac{\partial^2 u}{\partial x^2} - \frac{1}{c^2}\frac{\partial^2 u}{\partial t^2} = -k^2 A\sin[k(x - ct)] + \frac{1}{c^2}\left(k^2 c^2 A\sin[k(x - ct)]\right) = 0,$$

as required. So we see that $A\sin[k(x - ct)]$ is a solution of the wave equation, for any values of k and A.

Solution to Exercise 17

The chain rule of differentiation gives

$$\frac{\partial c}{\partial x} = \frac{N}{\sqrt{4\pi Dt}}\exp(-x^2/4Dt) \times \left(\frac{-2x}{4Dt}\right) = -\frac{x}{2Dt}c.$$

Also,

$$\frac{\partial c}{\partial t} = -\frac{1}{2}t^{-3/2}\frac{N}{\sqrt{4\pi D}}\exp(-x^2/4Dt) + \frac{N}{\sqrt{4\pi Dt}}\exp(-x^2/4Dt) \times \left(\frac{x^2}{4Dt^2}\right)$$
$$= -\frac{1}{2t}c + \frac{x^2}{4Dt^2}c = \left(\frac{x^2}{4Dt^2} - \frac{1}{2t}\right)c.$$

Partially differentiating $\partial c/\partial x$ with respect to x again, we get

$$\frac{\partial^2 c}{\partial x^2} = \frac{x^2}{4D^2t^2}c - \frac{1}{2Dt}c = \left(\frac{x^2}{4D^2t^2} - \frac{1}{2Dt}\right)c.$$

Taking all the derivatives in the diffusion equation onto the left-hand side, and substituting in the above results, then gives

$$\frac{\partial c}{\partial t} - D\frac{\partial^2 c}{\partial x^2} = \left(\frac{x^2}{4Dt^2} - \frac{1}{2t}\right)c - D\left(\frac{x^2}{4D^2t^2} - \frac{1}{2Dt}\right)c = 0,$$

as required.

Acknowledgements

Grateful acknowledgement is made to the following sources:

Figure 1(a): Shalom Jacobovitz. This file is licensed under the Creative Commons Attribution-Share Alike Licence http://creativecommons.org/licenses/by-sa/3.0.

Figure 18: Harald Hoyer. This file is licensed under the Creative Commons Attribution-Share Alike Licence http://creativecommons.org/licenses/by-sa/3.0.

Every effort has been made to contact copyright holders. If any have been inadvertently overlooked, the publishers will be pleased to make the necessary arrangements at the first opportunity.

Non-linear differential equations

Introduction

In this unit we have a final look at differential equations. We considered the solution of several types of first-order differential equation in Unit 2, including examples of non-linear equations. However, the other units devoted to differential equations considered only linear equations (in Unit 3 we looked at linear constant-coefficient second-order differential equations, in Unit 6 we studied simultaneous linear ordinary differential equations, and in Unit 12 we considered linear partial differential equations).

One reason for the emphasis on linear differential equations is that non-linear equations are difficult to solve. Usually they do not have a solution that can be expressed in terms of standard functions. But these equations arise in many interesting investigations in science, engineering and economics. It is therefore important to be able to understand their solutions. This unit describes approaches that give *approximate* or *qualitative* information about solutions, rather than trying to find the solution itself. This information may be in the form of a diagram or an approximate expression. In practice *numerical solutions* using a computer are also used, but they are outside the scope of this module.

In this unit we consider pairs of first-order non-linear differential equations involving two variables. All of the models that appear in this unit can be represented as pairs of differential equations of the form

$$\frac{dx}{dt} = u(x,y), \quad \frac{dy}{dt} = v(x,y), \tag{1}$$

where the functions u and v depend on x and y but not on t. Systems of this form, where t does not appear explicitly in the right-hand side, are said to be **autonomous** (and conversely, if the equations contained functions such as $u(x,y,t)$ and $v(x,y,t)$, they would be described as *non-autonomous*).

In this unit we use examples relating two interacting populations of animals, one a predator and the other its prey. An example is given by the *Lotka–Volterra* pair of equations

$$\dot{x} = kx\left(1 - \frac{y}{Y}\right), \quad \dot{y} = -hy\left(1 - \frac{x}{X}\right), \tag{2}$$

where h, k, X and Y are known positive constants, and $x = x(t)$ and $y = y(t)$ represent the two population sizes at time t. A derivation of the Lotka–Volterra equations will be given in Section 1.

These equations are non-linear because of the xy terms on the right-hand sides.

While describing populations of animals is a vibrant area of science, a more typical application of non-linear differential equations is to describe the motion of mechanical systems. Such systems can range in complexity from a stone launched by a slingshot to a system of planets and asteroids orbiting a star. This unit will discuss the motion of a rigid pendulum as a simple example of a mechanical system.

The equation of motion for the undamped motion of a rigid pendulum is the second-order differential equation

$$\ddot{x} + \omega^2 \sin x = 0, \tag{3}$$

This equation is non-linear because of the $\sin x$ term.

where ω is a constant and $x = x(t)$ is the angle in radians that the pendulum makes with the downward vertical at time t. As might be expected, this equation is in the form of Newton's second law, $m\ddot{x} = F(x)$ (where the force is $F(x) = -m\omega^2 \sin x$). But equation (3) does not appear to be in the same form as equations (1). To make the connection clear, consider the following system of equations:

$$\dot{x} = y, \quad \dot{y} = -\omega^2 \sin x. \tag{4}$$

Note that this pair of differential equations is in the form of equations (1), with $u(x, y) = y$ and $v(x, y) = -\omega^2 \sin x$. Also, observe that if you differentiate the first equation of (4) and substitute in the second, you recover equation (3). There is a general principle here: you can convert a single second-order differential equation into two coupled first-order equations of the form of equations (1). By means of this approach, the methods developed in this unit can also be applied to second-order differential equations.

Non-linear equations and chaos

Sometimes non-linear differential equations have solutions that are relatively easy to understand, even if you cannot find an exact mathematical expression. For example, a set of equations such as (1) may have solutions in which $x(t)$ and $y(t)$ approach an *equilibrium point* (also known as a *fixed point*), so that $x(t) \to X$ and $y(t) \to Y$ as $t \to \infty$, for two constants X and Y.

Non-linear equations may also produce complicated and apparently erratic behaviour that defies conventional mathematical descriptions. An example is shown in Figure 1. This is a plot of a solution of a system of three coupled first-order differential equations, called the *Lorenz equations*:

$$\dot{x} = \sigma(y - x), \quad \dot{y} = x(\rho - z) - y, \quad \dot{z} = xy - \beta z, \tag{5}$$

where the constants are $\sigma = 28$, $\rho = 10$ and $\beta = 8/3$ in this case.

This type of motion is called *chaotic*. The solution $(x(t), y(t), z(t))$ spends most of the time spiralling around two surfaces, but it occasionally jumps between these surfaces. Despite the fact that the equation of motion is known precisely, these jumps occur at times that are very hard to predict. The possibility that simple systems of differential equations could produce highly unpredictable motion was not widely appreciated until late in the twentieth century.

This discovery has had a profound influence on research in the sciences, and has stimulated the development of a new mathematical discipline called *dynamical systems theory*.

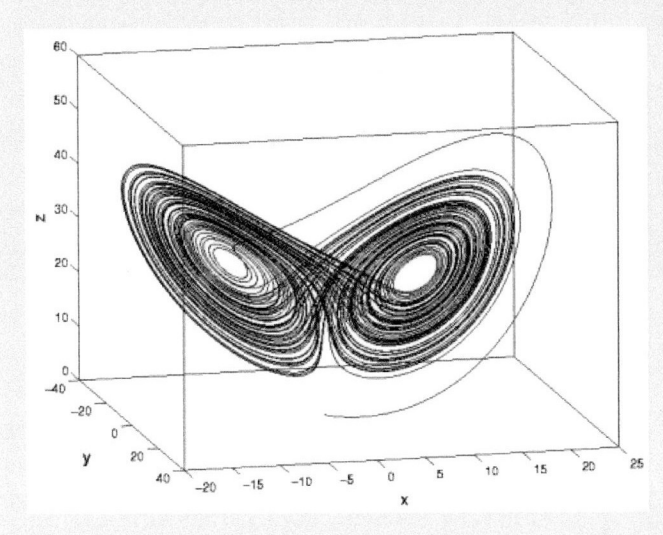

Figure 1 A solution of the Lorenz equations (5), obtained using a computer; as t increases, the solution $(x(t), y(t), z(t))$ follows a trajectory that cannot be described by standard mathematical functions

To see examples of chaos, you need to have more than two variables (as in equations (5)), or you need to consider non-autonomous equations. Although chaos does not occur in solutions of equations (1) for any choice of the functions u and v, the methods developed in this unit can also be applied to analyse chaotic motion.

For equations of form (1), we consider the paths defined by $(x(t), y(t))$ in the xy-plane. A very powerful approach starts out by seeking a constant solution (which describes an equilibrium state of the system). For example, the Lotka–Volterra equations (2) have a constant solution $x(t) = X$, $y(t) = Y$, which describes a situation where the two populations are in equilibrium. Near such a solution, you will see that some useful information can be obtained by replacing the original non-linear equations by linear approximations to the differential equations. The equilibrium states and the behaviour of the system when it is nearly in equilibrium play a major part in obtaining a qualitative overview of the behaviour of the model. This approach of determining *equilibrium points* or *fixed points* of a non-linear system, and then using *linearised equations* to study motion in the neighbourhood of equilibrium points, is the most powerful available tool for analysing systems of non-linear differential equations.

We use the notations x or $x(t)$, $\dot{x}$ or $\dot{x}(t)$, etc., interchangeably to suit the context.

Study guide

We begin in Section 1 with the Lotka–Volterra equations, which apply to a pair of interacting populations. In Section 2 we see how these equations can be *linearised* (that is, approximated by linear equations) near an equilibrium state. The resulting system of linear differential equations was discussed in Unit 6, but here, in Section 3, we use graphical representations of the solutions near an equilibrium state to get qualitative information about solutions of the original non-linear equations. Section 4 looks at models for the motion of a rigid pendulum: second-order differential equations are transformed to systems of first-order equations, and the techniques developed earlier in the unit are applied to find and interpret graphical solutions.

You need to be familiar with the techniques developed in Unit 5 for finding eigenvalues and eigenvectors, and in Unit 6 for the solution of systems of first-order linear differential equations.

1 Modelling populations of predators and prey

In this section we develop models for populations of a predator and its prey. A predator population depends for its survival on there being sufficient prey to provide it with food. Intuition suggests that when the number of predators is low, the prey population may increase quickly, and that this will eventually result in an increase in the predator population. On the other hand, a large number of predators may diminish the prey population until it is very small, and this will eventually lead to a collapse in the predator population. Our mathematical models will need to reflect this behaviour.

It is not possible to find exact solutions to all such models, so we will introduce you to a geometric approach, based on the notion that a point $(x, y) = (x(t), y(t))$ in a plane may be used to represent two populations $x = x(t)$ and $y = y(t)$ at time t. As t increases, the point $(x(t), y(t))$ traces out a path that represents the variation of both populations with time.

1.1 Exponential growth of a single population

Before we consider a system of two interacting populations, we first develop a simple continuous model of the growth of a single population, which is called the *exponential model*. This allows us to develop some basic concepts of population models in a simple context.

This model was originally discussed in Unit 2.

We model the population size x, which we usually simply refer to as the population x (omitting the word 'size'), as a function of time t. This function cannot take negative values (since there are no negative populations), but we allow it to take the value zero. We normally assume that t is measured in years. We deal with a continuous model, rather than a discrete one, so the derivative $\dot{x} = dx/dt$ represents the rate of increase of the population, which we often refer to as the **growth rate** (even though when $\dot{x} < 0$ it actually represents a decay rate).

In the exponential model, we make the assumption that the growth rate $\dot{x}$ is proportional to the current population x. (This means that if the growth rate is 20 per year when the population is 100, then the growth rate will be 40 per year when the population is 200, the growth rate will be 60 per year when the population is 300, and so on.) This assumption leads directly to the differential equation

$$\dot{x} = kx \quad (x \geq 0), \tag{6}$$

where k is a constant. If k is positive, then x is an increasing function of time, while if k is negative, then x is a decreasing function of time.

A population x can take only integer values, so we say that x is a discrete variable. Here, however, we approximate the population by a variable that can take any real value, referred to as a continuous variable.

Exercise 1

Under what circumstances is it reasonable to assume that the growth rate of a population is proportional to the current population? (This is an open-ended question that is primarily about modelling rather than mathematics.)

Equation (6) can be solved explicitly. Choosing a value for the population at time $t = 0$, for example $x(0) = x_0$, gives the solution

$$x(t) = x_0 e^{kt} \quad (x_0 \geq 0). \tag{7}$$

The nature of this solution depends on the sign of the constant k. If $k = 0$, the population remains constant in time. If $k > 0$, the population increases exponentially, and if $k < 0$, the population decreases exponentially. The two situations shown in Figure 2 are described, respectively, as *exponential growth* and *exponential decay* (although we could also say that the latter exhibits 'negative growth'). For this reason we refer to equation (6) as the **exponential differential equation**, or, when applied to a population, the **exponential model**.

The **proportionate growth rate** $\dot{x}/x$ represents the rate of increase of the population per unit of the current population, and may be considered as the difference between the birth and death rates *per head of population*. It may be positive (for a growing population in which the birth rate exceeds the death rate), negative (for a declining population in which the death rate exceeds the birth rate) or zero (for a static population in which the birth and death rates are equal). In the case of the exponential model (6), we have $\dot{x}/x = k$, so the proportionate growth rate is constant. (We previously assumed that $x \geq 0$. While talking about proportionate growth rate, we exclude the possibility that x takes the value zero.)

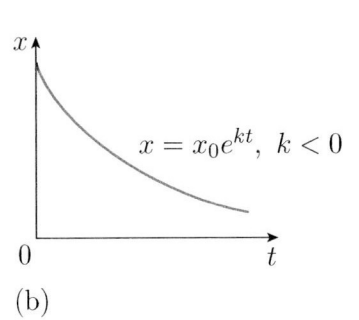

(a)

(b)

Figure 2   Behaviour of a population modelled by equation (7). For $k > 0$ there is exponential growth, and for $k < 0$ there is exponential decay.

Exercise 2

Can you suggest any reason why, in the case $k > 0$, the assumption that the proportionate growth rate $\dot{x}/x$ is a constant is unrealistic for real populations?

The exponential model is fairly accurate for many populations in a state of rapid increase, but it is reasonable only over a restricted domain of time. As a model of the behaviour of increasing populations over longer periods of time, the exponential model is clearly unsatisfactory because it predicts unbounded growth. In Unit 2 we mentioned one way of addressing this deficiency when we considered the *logistic equation*: this allows for the fact that the rate of population growth decreases as the population increases, due to competition for resources. However, in this unit we now adopt a more sophisticated approach by explicitly including variables representing the populations of two species, a population and its prey.

1.2   Motion in phase space

In the rest of this section we will be concerned with developing models for populations of rabbits (the prey) and foxes (the predators). Our purpose is to determine how these populations evolve with time. At a particular time t, we suppose that these populations are $x(t)$ and $y(t)$, respectively. Before discussing the differential equations that determine these functions, we introduce some geometrical language that will help us to discuss equations of motion written in the form (1).

At any given time, we represent this system by a point in the xy-plane. We call this two-dimensional space the **phase space** (or **phase plane**) for the system, and the point is called the **phase point**. We can think of x and y as the coordinates of the position vector $\mathbf{x}$ of the phase point. The evolution of the two populations can then be represented by a path, called a **phase path** (or **phase trajectory**), in the phase space, as shown in Figure 3. Here, the direction of the arrows indicates the direction in which the phase point $(x(t), y(t))$ moves along the phase path with increasing time. However, this type of representation does not show how quickly or slowly the point moves along the path.

x is the prey population; y is the predator population.

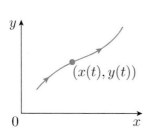

Figure 3   A phase path in phase space

The position of the phase point at time t is represented by the column vector

$$\mathbf{x}(t) = \begin{bmatrix} x(t) \\ y(t) \end{bmatrix},$$

and the corresponding velocity of the phase point is

$$\dot{\mathbf{x}}(t) = \begin{bmatrix} \dot{x}(t) \\ \dot{y}(t) \end{bmatrix}.$$

Using equations (1), this can be expressed as

$$\dot{\mathbf{x}}(t) = \begin{bmatrix} u(x, y) \\ v(x, y) \end{bmatrix}.$$

The functions $u(x,y)$ and $v(x,y)$ can be regarded as representing a *vector field*

In this context, the term vector field simply means a field with two components.

$$\mathbf{u}(x,y) = \begin{bmatrix} u(x,y) \\ v(x,y) \end{bmatrix},$$

and equations (1) can then be written in the vector form

$$\dot{\mathbf{x}} = \mathbf{u}(x,y). \tag{8}$$

This is an equation of motion for the phase point: the velocity of the phase point, $\dot{\mathbf{x}}$, is equal to $\mathbf{u}(\mathbf{x})$, that is, to the value of a vector field $\mathbf{u}$ evaluated at the position of the phase point $\mathbf{x} = (x,y)$. As the phase point moves along the phase path, the velocity $\dot{\mathbf{x}}$ of the phase point is always tangential to the phase path. We therefore reach the following conclusion.

The vector field $\mathbf{u}(x,y)$ is tangential to the phase path at (x,y).

This geometrical concept is a powerful method for getting insight into the behaviour of systems of differential equations that cannot be solved exactly.

Multiple meanings of phase

The word 'phase' crops up in many different areas of science with no obvious connections. In this unit we have defined *phase point*, *phase path* and *phase space*. In Unit 3 we wrote an equation for an oscillation in the form $x(t) = A\sin(\omega t + \phi)$, and referred to ϕ as the *phase constant* of the oscillation. In physics and chemistry you will also find discussions of *phase transitions*, which are abrupt changes of the properties of a substance in response to changes of temperature. Don't seek a deep connection: there isn't one.

The word *phase* is derived from a Greek word with a meaning similar to 'appearance', so it is natural that it was adopted independently by different branches of science. Its use in discussing oscillations arose from the fact that the phases of the moon are a periodic phenomenon.

1.3   A first predator–prey model: sketching phase paths

In our mathematical models of rabbit and fox populations we make the following assumptions.

More sophisticated models also take account of the fact that there is a time delay for the population to increase due to animals breeding, or for the population to decrease due to starvation.

- There is plenty of vegetation for the rabbits to eat.
- The rabbits are the only source of food for the foxes.
- An encounter between a fox and a rabbit contributes to the fox's larder, which leads directly to a decrease in the rabbit population and indirectly to an increase in the number of foxes.

We may, for convenience, measure the populations in hundreds or thousands, as appropriate, so that we are able to use quite small numbers in our models. The population of rabbits will be described by a function $x(t)$, and the population of foxes by $y(t)$.

We begin with a very simple model for the two populations; this generalises the exponential model of the previous subsection, which applies to a single population. Our simple model has the advantage that we can easily find an explicit solution, and this will help us to explore the geometric approach.

As a first model, we assume that the populations are evolving independently (perhaps on separate islands). Because there are *no interactions*, the populations may be modelled by the pair of equations

$$\dot{x} = kx, \quad \dot{y} = -hy \quad (x \geq 0, \ y \geq 0), \tag{9}$$

where k and h are positive constants. The conditions $x \geq 0$, $y \geq 0$ in parentheses apply here, as well as in similar situations throughout the unit, to the first equation $\dot{x} = kx$, as well as the second equation $\dot{y} = -hy$.

The first equation models a colony of rabbits not affected by the predation of foxes, growing exponentially according to a rule of the form

$$x(t) = x_0 e^{kt}, \tag{10}$$

When $t = 0$, $x = x_0$.

where x_0 is a positive constant representing the initial rabbit population at $t = 0$.

Exercise 3

Determine a formula for the population $y(t)$ of foxes. How would you interpret this solution for the population of foxes?

Equations (9) form a system of linear differential equations similar to those that you met in Unit 6. Let us now consider the solution of these equations from the geometrical viewpoint of motion in phase space, which we discussed above. Using vector notation, the pair of populations may be represented by the vector $\mathbf{x} = [x \quad y]^T$. The system of equations (9) then becomes the vector equation

$$\dot{\mathbf{x}} = \begin{bmatrix} \dot{x} \\ \dot{y} \end{bmatrix} = \mathbf{u}(x, y) = \begin{bmatrix} kx \\ -hy \end{bmatrix}. \tag{11}$$

Recall also that $\mathbf{u}(x, y)$ is tangential to the phase path describing a particular solution of $\dot{\mathbf{x}} = \mathbf{u}(x, y)$ at the point (x, y).

This suggests a geometric way of finding a particular solution of equation (11). On a diagram, we draw a selection of arrows representing the directions of the vector field $\mathbf{u}(x, y)$ at a selection of points (x, y). Since the magnitudes of $\mathbf{u}(x, y)$ may vary considerably and so make the diagram difficult to interpret, we often use arrows of a fixed length. Then, choosing a particular starting point (x_0, y_0), we follow the directions of the arrows to obtain a phase path corresponding to a particular solution.

An exception, which we discuss later, occurs when $\dot{x} = \dot{y} = 0$ at (x_0, y_0), so $\mathbf{u}(x_0, y_0) = \mathbf{0}$ and there is no tangent vector to follow.

To see how this works, consider equation (11) with $k = 1$ and $h = 1$. In this case the vector field $\mathbf{u}(x, y)$ is given by

$$\mathbf{u}(x, y) = \begin{bmatrix} x \\ -y \end{bmatrix}.$$

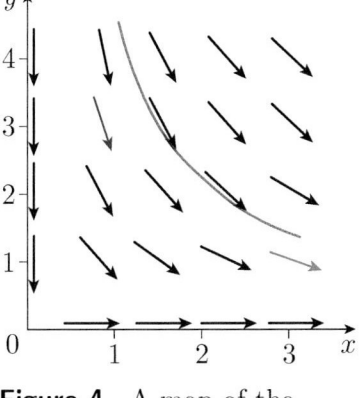

Figure 4 shows the directions of this vector field at a selection of points in the xy-phase space. For example, the red arrow centred at $x = 1$, $y = 3$ points in the direction of $[1 \quad -3]^T$, while the blue arrow centred at $x = 3$, $y = 1$ points in the direction of $[3 \quad -1]^T$. The phase path at any point (x, y) is tangential to $\mathbf{u}(x, y)$, so the continuous curve in Figure 4 is a reasonable estimate of a phase path representing a particular solution of equation (11) (with $k = h = 1$). This phase path is in broad agreement with the results of equation (10) and Exercise 3: it shows that a decrease in y (the fox population) is accompanied by an increase in x (the rabbit population).

Figure 4   A map of the vector field $\mathbf{u}(x, y)$ for equation (11) with $k = h = 1$ $(x \geq 0,\ y \geq 0)$

The methods that we have just used to analyse a simple population model can be applied more generally. To explore these methods, we now widen the discussion and look at similar systems that do not arise from populations. In this broader context, we allow x and y to take positive or negative values.

Example 1

(a) Using arrows of a fixed length, sketch a map of the vector field

$$\mathbf{u}(x, y) = \begin{bmatrix} 0.2x \\ 0.3y \end{bmatrix}$$

for $-4 \leq x \leq 4$ and $-4 \leq y \leq 4$. Sketch a few phase paths for various initial conditions.

(b) Write down the system of differential equations $\dot{\mathbf{x}} = \mathbf{u}(\mathbf{x})$ corresponding to this vector field. Find the general solutions of this system of equations, and hence obtain an equation for y in terms of x for each path in the xy-plane represented by this general solution.

(c) Use your answer to part (b) to sketch a sample of the paths in the xy-plane that represent typical particular solutions.

(d) Comment on the relationship between the vector field map in part (a) and the phase paths sketched in part (c).

Solution

(a) We use values of $\mathbf{u}(x, y)$ to construct Figure 5. For example, the red arrow at $x = 1$, $y = 1$ points in the direction of $[0.2 \quad 0.3]^T$, while the blue arrow at $x = -2$, $y = 3$ points in the direction of $[-0.4 \quad 0.9]^T$. In each case, the arrow at (x, y) represents a vector of a fixed length parallel to $\mathbf{u}(x, y)$, and therefore indicates the direction of a phase path through the point (x, y). A few phase paths have been (tentatively) sketched on this diagram.

It is time-consuming to draw vector field maps by hand, but computers can help. The subsequent sketching of phase paths is not a precisely defined process, and different people may get slightly different results.

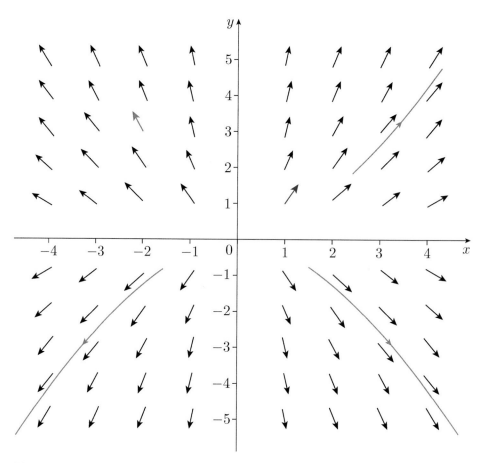

Figure 5   A map of the vector field and some phase paths

(b) We have

$$\mathbf{u}(x, y) = \begin{bmatrix} \dot{x} \\ \dot{y} \end{bmatrix} = \begin{bmatrix} 0.2x \\ 0.3y \end{bmatrix},$$

so the system of equations is

$$\dot{x} = 0.2x, \quad \dot{y} = 0.3y.$$

Each of these equations can be solved separately. The general solutions are

$$x(t) = x_0 e^{0.2t}, \quad y(t) = y_0 e^{0.3t}.$$

To obtain the equation for the paths in the form of a function $y(x)$, we must eliminate t from $x = x_0 e^{0.2t}$ and $y = y_0 e^{0.3t}$.

Cubing the first equation and squaring the second gives $x^3 = x_0^3 e^{0.6t}$ and $y^2 = y_0^2 e^{0.6t}$, so $x^3/x_0^3 = y^2/y_0^2$. Hence the equations of the paths are of the form

$$y = K|x|^{3/2},$$

for some constant K.

The modulus sign around x ensures that we do not try to obtain the square root of a negative number. The arbitrariness of K ensures that the equation represents all possible cases.

(c) As we have been able to find the equations of the paths in part (b), namely $y = K|x|^{3/2}$, we can use these to sketch the phase paths in the xy-plane. These are shown in Figure 6.

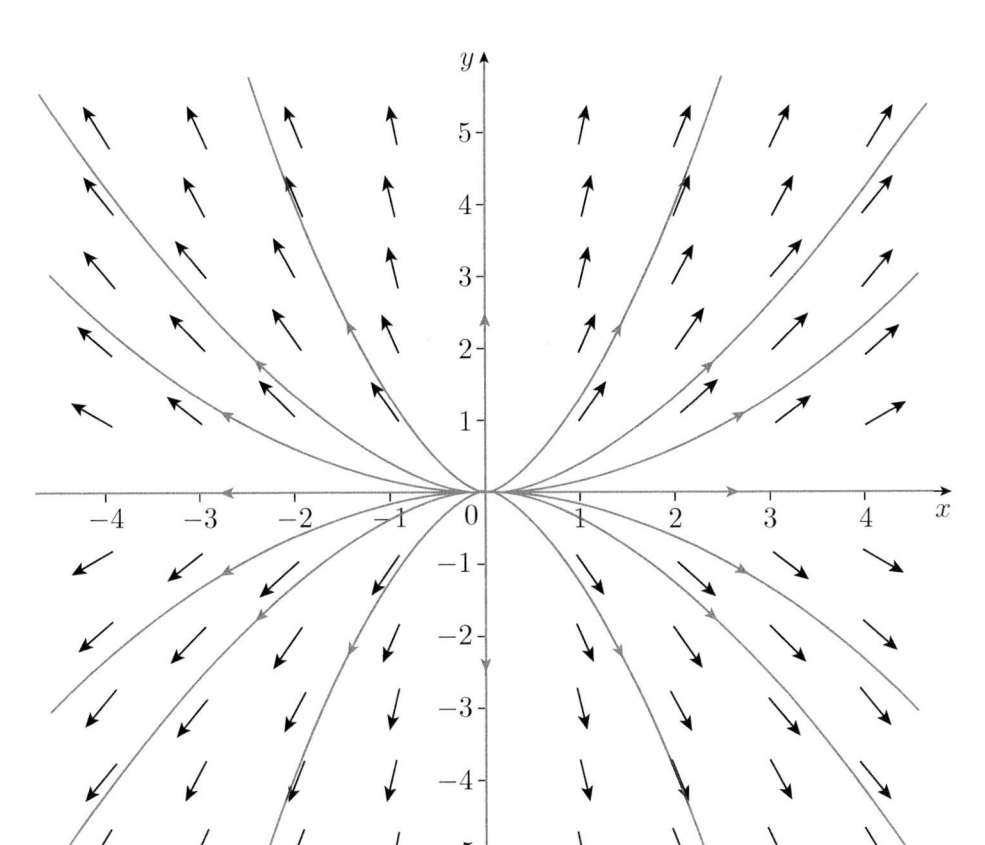

Figure 6 Phase paths superimposed over the vector field

The arrows on these paths indicate the direction of motion as time increases, and may be determined as follows.

The first of the differential equations is $\dot{x} = 0.2x$. So for positive x we have $\dot{x} > 0$, and x is an increasing function of time. Therefore in the right half-plane, the arrows on the paths point to the right. Similarly, for negative x we have $\dot{x} < 0$, and x is a decreasing function of time. Hence the arrows on the paths point to the left in the left half-plane. (Consideration of the second differential equation, $\dot{y} = 0.3y$, confirms the directions of the arrows on the paths.) The arrows on the paths along the positive and negative y-axes can be deduced from consideration of the differential equation $\dot{y} = 0.3y$. Note that the origin is also a path, corresponding to $K = 0$, but it has no time arrow associated with it.

(d) The vector field $\mathbf{u}(x, y)$ is tangential at (x, y) to the phase path passing through (x, y). The arrows in Figure 6 show the directions of the vector field at an array of points. We should therefore expect the direction of an arrow at (x, y) to be close to the direction of any phase path that passes close to (x, y). This expectation is borne out by the arrows and phase paths in Figure 6. The tentative paths sketched in Figure 5 are close to the exact paths in Figure 6.

Given a vector map of arrows at a closely-spaced set of points, it is possible to sketch the general form and directions of phase paths passing near these points. A diagram showing a selection of these phase paths in the phase plane is called a **phase diagram**. The significance of such a diagram is that each of the phase paths corresponds to a particular solution of the system of equations.

Before we leave Example 1, you may have noticed in Figure 6 that the paths radiate *outwards* from the origin in all directions. For this reason, we refer to the origin as a *source*.

A source can occur at a point other than the origin.

We now look at the phase paths for a similar system, for which

$$\mathbf{u}(x, y) = \begin{bmatrix} -0.2x \\ -0.3y \end{bmatrix}. \tag{12}$$

This system behaves in a similar fashion to the system in Example 1. The general solution is

$$x = x_0 e^{-0.2t}, \quad y = y_0 e^{-0.3t}.$$

Eliminating t gives

$$y = K|x|^{3/2},$$

as before. However, in this case, as t increases, the direction of motion along the phase paths is the opposite to that in Example 1. At any point (x, y), the vector field $[-0.2x \quad -0.3y]^T$ has the same magnitude but the opposite direction to the vector field $[0.2x \quad 0.3y]^T$. The phase diagram is therefore identical to Figure 6 except that the directions now point *towards* the origin. In a case like this, the origin is said to be a *sink*.

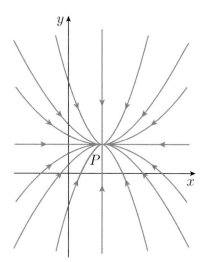

Figure 7 A sink at a point other than the origin

Sources and sinks need not always be at the origin. In general, if all the phase paths in the vicinity of any point P radiate outwards from P, then P is a **source**, and if all the phase paths in the vicinity of P converge inwards towards P, then P is a **sink** (see Figure 7).

Exercise 4

Write down the system of differential equations $\dot{\mathbf{x}} = \mathbf{u}(x, y)$ given by the vector field

$$\mathbf{u}(x, y) = \begin{bmatrix} x \\ -y \end{bmatrix}.$$

This is the equation for our first model for the predator–prey populations (equation (11)) with $k = 1$ and $h = 1$, but without the restrictions $x \geq 0$, $y \geq 0$.

Find the general solution of this system of equations. Hence find an equation for y in terms of x for the phase paths in the xy-plane represented by this solution. Sketch some of these paths. Do any of the paths include the origin?

The phase diagram for the vector field examined in Exercise 4 is shown in Figure 8. You can see that the vast majority of paths do not radiate into or out of the origin. On these paths, a point initially travels towards the origin, but eventually travels away from it again. The only paths that actually radiate inwards towards, or outwards from, the origin are those along the x- and y-axes. In this case we call the origin a **saddle** (because the phase paths resemble contour lines near a saddle point).

Note that the model described by equations (9) has phase paths in the form of a saddle, because the coefficients have different signs. The behaviour of the populations of rabbits and foxes illustrated in the quadrant $x \geq 0$, $y \geq 0$ of Figure 8 is what we would expect from our first model. The population x of rabbits increases without limit, as they are isolated from their predators. On the other hand, the population y of foxes decreases to zero, as they have no access to their sole source of food.

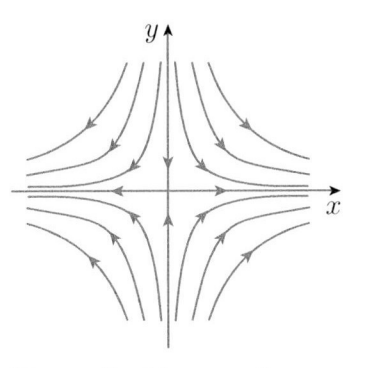

Figure 8   Phase paths near a saddle, discussed in Exercise 4

1.4 A second predator–prey model

In the previous subsection we looked at a simple model for rabbit and fox populations when there was no interaction between the two populations. This model may be reasonable when both species inhabit the same environment but with population sizes that are so small that the rabbits and foxes rarely meet. As we saw, for initial positive populations, this first model predicts that rabbits will increase without limit and foxes will die out. However, this is not what we expect for interacting populations, when encounters are inevitable.

In this subsection we look at a revised model, based on the assumption that the number of encounters between foxes and rabbits is proportional both to the population x of rabbits and to the population y of foxes. In addition to the assumptions listed at the beginning of Subsection 1.3, our revised model assumes that

- the number of encounters between foxes and rabbits is proportional to the product xy.

For a population x of rabbits in a fox-free environment, our first model for population change was given by the equation $\dot{x} = kx$, where k is a positive constant. This represents exponential growth. However, if there is a population y of predator foxes, we should expect the growth rate $\dot{x}$ of the rabbit population to be reduced. A simple assumption is that

- the growth rate $\dot{x}$ of the rabbit population decreases by a term that is proportional to the number of encounters between rabbits and foxes, i.e. by a term proportional to xy.

We revise our first model to include this extra term, so the differential equation that models the population x of rabbits is now

$$\dot{x} = kx - Axy,$$

for some positive constant A. As you will see later, it is convenient to write $A = k/Y$, for some positive constant Y, giving

$$\dot{x} = kx\left(1 - \frac{y}{Y}\right). \tag{13}$$

In a period of time δt, the change in the rabbit population is the number $kx\,\delta t$ of additional rabbits born (taking into account those dying from natural causes) minus the number $Axy\,\delta t$ of rabbits eaten.

Similarly, for a population y of foxes in a rabbit-free environment, our first model for the population change is given by the equation $\dot{y} = -hy$, where h is a positive constant. This represents exponential decay. However, if there is a population x of rabbits for the foxes to eat, we should expect the growth rate $\dot{y}$ of the fox population to increase. A simple assumption is that

- the growth rate $\dot{y}$ of the fox population increases by a term that is proportional to the number of encounters between foxes and rabbits, i.e. by a term proportional to xy.

Our revised model for the foxes is given by

$$\dot{y} = -hy + Bxy,$$

for some positive constant B. Again, it is convenient to write $B = h/X$, for some positive constant X, so that this equation becomes

$$\dot{y} = -hy\left(1 - \frac{x}{X}\right). \tag{14}$$

Together, the differential equations (13) and (14) model the pair of interacting populations.

Exercise 5

Use equations (13) and (14) to sketch the graph of the proportionate growth rate $\dot{x}/x$ of rabbits as a function of the population y of foxes, and the graph of the proportionate growth rate $\dot{y}/y$ of foxes as a function of the population x of rabbits. Interpret these graphs.

Equations (13) and (14) provided one of the first applications of mathematical models to biological ecosystems. They were proposed independently by the American biophysicist Alfred Lotka (in 1925) and by the Italian mathematician Vito Volterra (in 1926), and they are called the Lotka–Volterra equations.

The Lotka–Volterra equations

The evolution of two interacting populations x and y can be modelled by the **Lotka–Volterra equations**

$$\dot{x} = kx\left(1 - \frac{y}{Y}\right), \quad \dot{y} = -hy\left(1 - \frac{x}{X}\right) \quad (x \geq 0,\ y \geq 0), \tag{15}$$

where x is the population of the prey, y is the population of the predators, and k, h, X and Y are positive constants.

The Lotka–Volterra equations are non-linear because their right-hand sides contain a term proportional to xy.

As for equations (9), the conditions $x \geq 0$, $y \geq 0$ apply to both differential equations.

The Lotka–Volterra equations can also be written as

$$\dot{\mathbf{x}} = \mathbf{u}(x, y),$$

where $\dot{\mathbf{x}} = [\dot{x} \quad \dot{y}]^T$ and the vector field $\mathbf{u}(x, y)$ is given by

$$\mathbf{u}(x, y) = \begin{bmatrix} kx\left(1 - \dfrac{y}{Y}\right) \\ -hy\left(1 - \dfrac{x}{X}\right) \end{bmatrix}. \tag{16}$$

Exercise 6

Suppose that in equations (15), $k = 0.05$, $h = 0.1$, $X = 1000$ and $Y = 100$. Find the values of the corresponding vector field $\mathbf{u}(x, y)$ at the following points.

(a) $(0, 0)$ (b) $(0, 100)$ (c) $(500, 100)$ (d) $(1000, 0)$

(e) $(1000, 100)$ (f) $(1500, 100)$ (g) $(1000, 50)$ (h) $(1000, 150)$

Previously, we were able to find exact solutions for the pairs of differential equations that arose from our mathematical model, but for the Lotka–Volterra equations (15), no explicit solutions for $x(t)$ and $y(t)$ are available. We will therefore rely on geometrical arguments, based on vector field maps in the phase plane. For the parameters and (x, y) points given in Exercise 6, we can begin to construct a vector field map, as shown in Figure 9, where we have used arrows of fixed length.

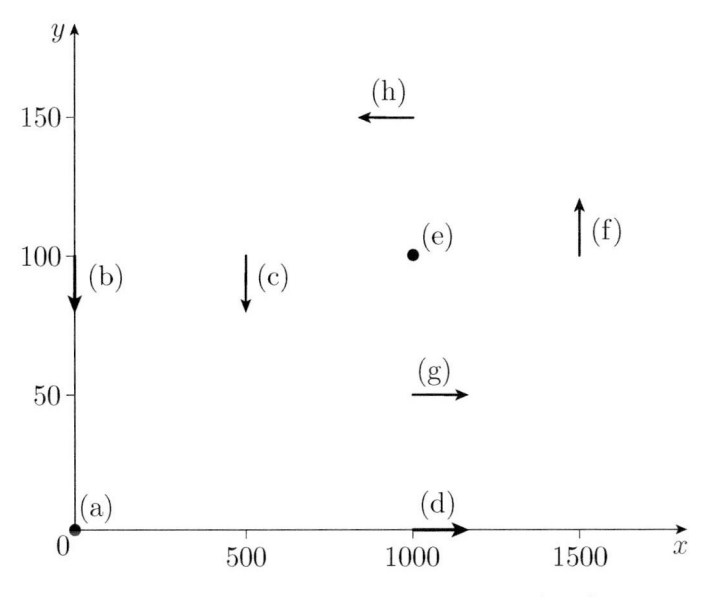

Figure 9   Directions of the vector field $\mathbf{u}(x, y)$ for the Lotka–Volterra equations as calculated in Exercise 6

Figure 10 continues this process by adding more arrows.

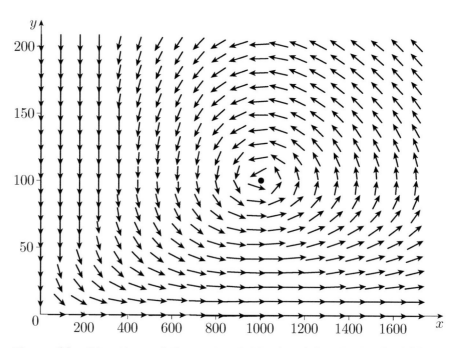

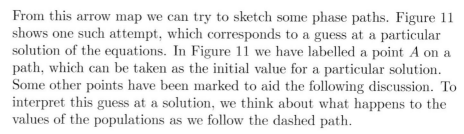

Figure 10   Directions of the vector field $\mathbf{u}(x,y)$ for the Lotka–Volterra equations at many points

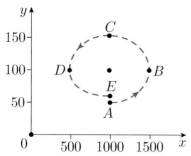

Figure 11   A phase path consistent with Figure 10 might spiral in to the fixed point

From this arrow map we can try to sketch some phase paths. Figure 11 shows one such attempt, which corresponds to a guess at a particular solution of the equations. In Figure 11 we have labelled a point A on a path, which can be taken as the initial value for a particular solution. Some other points have been marked to aid the following discussion. To interpret this guess at a solution, we think about what happens to the values of the populations as we follow the dashed path.

Initially, at the point A, there are 1000 rabbits and 50 foxes. As we follow the path, the rabbit population increases and so does the fox population, until at the point B we have reached a maximum rabbit population. As the fox population continues to rise, the rabbit population goes into decline. At C, the fox population has reached its maximum, while rabbits decline further. After this point, there are not enough rabbits available to sustain the number of foxes, and the fox population also goes into decline. At D, the declining fox population gives some relief to the rabbit population, which begins to pick up. Finally, at E, the decline of the fox population is halted as the rabbit population continues to increase.

While it is clear from the form of the vector field that we must return close to the point A, it is impossible to decide exactly what will happen from this geometrical picture. The path could 'spiral in', as illustrated in Figure 11, it could 'spiral out', or the phase path might close on itself exactly, in which case the cycle will repeat indefinitely. In fact, we will show later (in Subsection 3.5) that for the Lotka–Volterra equations, the paths close on themselves (so that the point E in Figure 11 is the same as point A). This implies that the populations for the Lotka–Volterra model are periodic functions of time.

Exercise 7

Consider the Lotka–Volterra system of differential equations defined in equations (15), with $k = 0.05$, $h = 0.1$, $X = 1000$ and $Y = 100$, and with $x \geq 0$, $y \geq 0$.

(a) For what values of x and y do the following hold?

   (i) $\dot{x} = 0$ (ii) $\dot{x} > 0$ (iii) $\dot{x} < 0$

(b) For what values of x and y do the following hold?

   (i) $\dot{y} = 0$ (ii) $\dot{y} > 0$ (iii) $\dot{y} < 0$

(c) Using your answers to parts (a) and (b), and Figures 9 and 10, sketch some more phase paths representing solutions of the system of differential equations. You may assume that for the Lotka–Volterra model, paths that return close to the starting point are closed.

Recall that the Lotka–Volterra equations are defined only in the quadrant $x \geq 0$, $y \geq 0$.

2 Equilibrium and stability

2.1 Equilibrium points

Systems of differential equations such as (1) usually have solutions where both $x(t)$ and $y(t)$ are constant, taking values denoted x_e and y_e, respectively. These solutions are known as *equilibrium* or *fixed point* solutions. A particular solution $(x(t), y(t))$ may or may not approach (x_e, y_e) as $t \to \infty$; this depends on the **stability** of the equilibrium point. But equilibrium point solutions are important because they are the most easily calculated property that gives quantitative information about a pair of non-linear differential equations.

Examples of equilibrium points are the point $(0, 0)$ in Figure 8 and the point $(1000, 100)$ in Exercises 6 and 7. The equilibrium point $(1000, 100)$ corresponds to the fact that a rabbit population of 1000 and a fox population of 100 can coexist in equilibrium, not changing with time.

As you will see later, the point $(1000, 100)$ is an isolated point through which no phase path passes.

More generally, if $x(t) = C$, $y(t) = D$ is a constant solution of a system of differential equations, it follows that $\dot{x}(t) = 0$, $\dot{y}(t) = 0$, and we can use this property to find all the equilibrium points of the system.

Definition

An **equilibrium point** (or **fixed point**) of a system of differential equations

   $$\dot{\mathbf{x}} = \mathbf{u}(x, y)$$

is a point (x_e, y_e) such that $x(t) = x_e$, $y(t) = y_e$ is a constant solution of the system of differential equations, i.e. (x_e, y_e) is a point at which $\dot{x}(t) = 0$ and $\dot{y}(t) = 0$.

> **Procedure 1   Finding equilibrium points**
>
> To find the equilibrium points of the system of differential equations
>
> $$\dot{\mathbf{x}} = \mathbf{u}(x, y),$$
>
> for some vector field $\mathbf{u}$, solve the equation
>
> $$\mathbf{u}(x, y) = \mathbf{0},$$
>
> for x and y. If the variables x and y represent populations, they must satisfy the conditions $x \geq 0$ and $y \geq 0$.

Example 2

Find the equilibrium points for the Lotka–Volterra equations (15) for rabbit and fox populations.

Solution

Using Procedure 1, we need to solve the equation $\mathbf{u}(x, y) = \mathbf{0}$, which becomes

$$\begin{bmatrix} kx \left(1 - \dfrac{y}{Y}\right) \\ -hy \left(1 - \dfrac{x}{X}\right) \end{bmatrix} = \begin{bmatrix} 0 \\ 0 \end{bmatrix}.$$

This gives the simultaneous equations

$$kx \left(1 - \frac{y}{Y}\right) = 0,$$

$$-hy \left(1 - \frac{x}{X}\right) = 0.$$

As stated earlier, h, k, X and Y are *positive* constants.

From the first equation, we deduce that either $x = 0$ or $y = Y$.

If $x = 0$, the second equation reduces to $-hy = 0$, so $y = 0$ and hence $(0, 0)$ is an equilibrium point.

If $y = Y$, the second equation becomes $-hY(1 - x/X) = 0$, so $x = X$ and hence (X, Y) is an equilibrium point.

This explains our choice of constants X and Y in Subsection 1.4.

Thus there are two possible equilibrium points for the pair of populations. The first has both the rabbit and fox populations as zero, i.e. the equilibrium point is at $(0, 0)$; there are no births or deaths – nothing happens. However, the other equilibrium point occurs when there are X rabbits and Y foxes, i.e. the equilibrium point is at (X, Y), when the births and deaths exactly cancel out and both populations remain constant.

Exercise 8

Suppose that the population x of a prey animal and the population y of a predator animal evolve according to the system of differential equations

$$\dot{x} = 0.1x - 0.005xy, \quad \dot{y} = -0.2y + 0.0004xy \quad (x \geq 0, \ y \geq 0).$$

Find the equilibrium points of the system. Put these equations in the standard form of the Lotka–Volterra equations.

Exercise 9

Suppose that two interacting populations x and y evolve according to the system of differential equations

$$\dot{x} = x(20 - y), \quad \dot{y} = y(10 - y)(10 - x) \quad (x \geq 0, \ y \geq 0).$$

Find the equilibrium points of the system.

These are *not* Lotka–Volterra equations.

2.2 Dynamics close to equilibrium

In a real ecosystem it is unlikely that predator and prey populations are in perfect harmony. What if equilibrium is disturbed by a small deviation caused perhaps by a severe winter or hunting? If the number of rabbits is reduced, there would be a decreased food supply for the foxes, and the population of foxes could decrease to zero as a consequence. On the other hand, if the number of foxes is reduced, the birth rate for rabbits would then exceed their death rate, and the number of rabbits could increase (perhaps without limit in a simplified model).

If a small change or *perturbation* in the populations of rabbits and foxes from their equilibrium values, for no matter what reason, results in subsequent populations that remain close to their equilibrium values, then we say that the equilibrium point is **stable**. On the other hand, if a perturbation results in a radical change, with, for example, the population of foxes or rabbits increasing without limit, then we say that the equilibrium point is **unstable**.

If you look at the phase diagram in Figure 12, where the origin is a sink, you can see that any slight perturbation from the origin will result in a phase point that returns to the origin as time increases. So the point $(0,0)$ is a *stable* equilibrium point.

On the other hand, the origin in the phase diagram shown in Figure 6 is an *unstable* equilibrium point. Any perturbation away from the origin will result in the phase point travelling further and further away from the origin with time. Similarly, the origin in the phase diagram shown in Figure 8 is an *unstable* equilibrium point. Apart from increases or decreases in y with x unchanged, any perturbation will result in a point that travels further and further away from the origin with time.

Figure 12 Phase paths close to a sink, which is a stable equilibrium point

The stability of equilibrium points

Suppose that the system of differential equations

$$\dot{\mathbf{x}} = \mathbf{u}(x, y)$$

has an equilibrium point at $x = x_e$, $y = y_e$. The equilibrium point is said to be:

- **stable** if all points in the neighbourhood of the equilibrium point remain in the neighbourhood of the equilibrium point as time increases

- **unstable** otherwise.

Exercise 10

Classify the equilibrium points $(0, 0)$ shown in the following phase diagrams as stable or unstable.

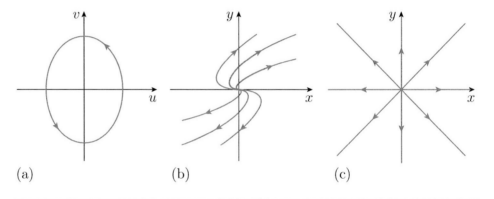

(a)　　　　　　　(b)　　　　　　　(c)

2.3   Linearised equations of motion

In general, non-linear systems of differential equations are hard to solve, and it may be impossible to find exact solutions. However, we are often interested in situations where the system is close to an equilibrium point. In this case, it is sensible to approximate the non-linear equations by a suitable set of *linear* differential equations, which can be analysed by the methods of Unit 6.

We have another motive for finding linear approximations. In the next section you will see that there is a systematic way of investigating whether equilibrium points are stable or unstable. This method applies most directly to linear systems of equations. For a non-linear system, such as the Lotka–Volterra equations, a preliminary step is needed: we must first find linear approximations to the non-linear system that apply close to the equilibrium points. This subsection explains how this is done.

If (x_e, y_e) is an equilibrium point, consider small perturbations p and q from x_e and y_e, giving new values x and y defined by

$$x = x_e + p, \quad y = y_e + q. \tag{17}$$

We can find the time development of the small perturbations p and q by **linearising** the differential equation $\dot{\mathbf{x}} = \mathbf{u}(x, y)$. We will make use of Taylor polynomials to achieve this.

In order to do so, we must write each component of the vector field $\mathbf{u}(x, y)$ as a function of the two variables x and y:

$$\mathbf{u}(x, y) = \begin{bmatrix} u(x, y) \\ v(x, y) \end{bmatrix}.$$

At the equilibrium point (x_e, y_e), we have $\mathbf{u}(x_e, y_e) = \mathbf{0}$, i.e.

$$u(x_e, y_e) = 0 \quad \text{and} \quad v(x_e, y_e) = 0.$$

Now, for small perturbations p and q, we can use the linear Taylor polynomial for functions of two variables to approximate each of $u(x, y)$ and $v(x, y)$ near the equilibrium point (x_e, y_e). We have

$$u(x_e + p, y_e + q) \simeq u(x_e, y_e) + p\,\frac{\partial u}{\partial x}(x_e, y_e) + q\,\frac{\partial u}{\partial y}(x_e, y_e)$$
$$= p\,\frac{\partial u}{\partial x}(x_e, y_e) + q\,\frac{\partial u}{\partial y}(x_e, y_e),$$

since $u(x_e, y_e) = 0$. Also,

$$v(x_e + p, y_e + q) \simeq v(x_e, y_e) + p\,\frac{\partial v}{\partial x}(x_e, y_e) + q\,\frac{\partial v}{\partial y}(x_e, y_e)$$
$$= p\,\frac{\partial v}{\partial x}(x_e, y_e) + q\,\frac{\partial v}{\partial y}(x_e, y_e),$$

since $v(x_e, y_e) = 0$.

The above two equations may appear rather unwieldy, but are much more succinctly represented in matrix form:

$$\begin{bmatrix} u(x, y) \\ v(x, y) \end{bmatrix} = \begin{bmatrix} \dfrac{\partial u}{\partial x}(x_e, y_e) & \dfrac{\partial u}{\partial y}(x_e, y_e) \\ \dfrac{\partial v}{\partial x}(x_e, y_e) & \dfrac{\partial v}{\partial y}(x_e, y_e) \end{bmatrix} \begin{bmatrix} p \\ q \end{bmatrix}.$$

Since $x(t) = x_e + p(t)$ and $y(t) = y_e + q(t)$, we also have

$$\dot{x} = \dot{p}, \quad \dot{y} = \dot{q}.$$

Putting the pieces together, by substituting in $\dot{\mathbf{x}} = \mathbf{u}(x, y)$, gives a system of *linear* differential equations for the perturbations p and q:

$$\begin{bmatrix} \dot{p} \\ \dot{q} \end{bmatrix} = \begin{bmatrix} \dfrac{\partial u}{\partial x}(x_e, y_e) & \dfrac{\partial u}{\partial y}(x_e, y_e) \\ \dfrac{\partial v}{\partial x}(x_e, y_e) & \dfrac{\partial v}{\partial y}(x_e, y_e) \end{bmatrix} \begin{bmatrix} p \\ q \end{bmatrix}. \tag{18}$$

An example will help to make this clear.

Although a population x or y cannot be negative, a perturbation p or q can (usually) be negative if the population is less than the equilibrium value.

Note that $\dfrac{\partial u}{\partial x}(x_e, y_e)$ means the same thing as $\dfrac{\partial u}{\partial x}\bigg|_{x=x_e,\ y=y_e}$, i.e. it is the partial derivative $\partial u / \partial x$ evaluated at the point $(x, y) = (x_e, y_e)$.

Example 3

For the Lotka–Volterra equations (15), determine the linearised equations that describe perturbations p and q from the equilibrium point (X, Y).

Solution

For the Lotka–Volterra equations we have

$$u(x, y) = kx \left(1 - \frac{y}{Y} \right),$$

$$v(x, y) = -hy \left(1 - \frac{x}{X} \right).$$

First we compute the partial derivatives, obtaining

$$\frac{\partial u}{\partial x} = k \left(1 - \frac{y}{Y} \right), \quad \frac{\partial u}{\partial y} = -\frac{kx}{Y},$$

$$\frac{\partial v}{\partial x} = \frac{hy}{X}, \quad \frac{\partial v}{\partial y} = -h \left(1 - \frac{x}{X} \right).$$

Evaluating these at the point (X, Y) gives

$$\frac{\partial u}{\partial x}(X, Y) = 0, \quad \frac{\partial u}{\partial y}(X, Y) = -\frac{kX}{Y},$$

$$\frac{\partial v}{\partial x}(X, Y) = \frac{hY}{X}, \quad \frac{\partial v}{\partial y}(X, Y) = 0.$$

Thus the required system of linear differential equations is

$$\begin{bmatrix} \dot{p} \\ \dot{q} \end{bmatrix} = \begin{bmatrix} 0 & -kX/Y \\ hY/X & 0 \end{bmatrix} \begin{bmatrix} p \\ q \end{bmatrix}, \tag{19}$$

which can be written as the pair of equations

$$\dot{p} = -\frac{kX}{Y} q, \quad \dot{q} = \frac{hY}{X} p.$$

We have replaced a system of non-linear equations, for which we have no explicit solution, with a pair of *linear* equations that can be solved using methods introduced in Unit 6. We should expect the solutions of equation (19) to provide a good approximation to the original system when p and q are small (i.e. when the system is close to the equilibrium point (X, Y)).

The matrix

$$\mathbf{J}(x, y) = \begin{bmatrix} \dfrac{\partial u}{\partial x} & \dfrac{\partial u}{\partial y} \\ \dfrac{\partial v}{\partial x} & \dfrac{\partial v}{\partial y} \end{bmatrix}$$

is called the **Jacobian matrix** of the vector field

$$\mathbf{u}(x, y) = \begin{bmatrix} u(x, y) \\ v(x, y) \end{bmatrix}.$$

The 2×2 matrix on the right-hand side of equation (18) is this Jacobian matrix evaluated at the equilibrium point (x_e, y_e), so equation (18) can be written succinctly as

$$\dot{\mathbf{p}} = \mathbf{J}(x_e, y_e)\, \mathbf{p},$$

where $\mathbf{p} = [p \quad q]^T$ is the perturbation from the equilibrium point (x_e, y_e).

Procedure 2   Linearising near an equilibrium point

Suppose that the system of differential equations

$$\dot{\mathbf{x}} = \mathbf{u}(x, y) = \begin{bmatrix} u(x,y) \\ v(x,y) \end{bmatrix}$$

has an equilibrium point at $x = x_e$, $y = y_e$.

1.   Find the Jacobian matrix

$$\mathbf{J}(x, y) = \begin{bmatrix} \dfrac{\partial u}{\partial x} & \dfrac{\partial u}{\partial y} \\ \dfrac{\partial v}{\partial x} & \dfrac{\partial v}{\partial y} \end{bmatrix}.$$

2.   In the neighbourhood of the equilibrium point (x_e, y_e), the differential equations can be approximated by the linearised form

$$\begin{bmatrix} \dot{p} \\ \dot{q} \end{bmatrix} = \begin{bmatrix} \dfrac{\partial u}{\partial x}(x_e, y_e) & \dfrac{\partial u}{\partial y}(x_e, y_e) \\ \dfrac{\partial v}{\partial x}(x_e, y_e) & \dfrac{\partial v}{\partial y}(x_e, y_e) \end{bmatrix} \begin{bmatrix} p \\ q \end{bmatrix},$$

where $x(t) = x_e + p(t)$ and $y(t) = y_e + q(t)$.

The Jacobian matrix, evaluated at the equilibrium point, is the *matrix of coefficients* of the linearised system.

Exercise 11

Write down the linear approximations to the Lotka–Volterra equations (15) near the equilibrium point $(0,0)$.

Exercise 12

Consider two populations modelled by the equations

$$\dot{x} = x(20 - y), \quad \dot{y} = y(10 - y)(10 - x) \quad (x \geq 0, \ y \geq 0).$$

Find the linear approximations to these equations near the equilibrium point $(10, 20)$.

These equations were considered in Exercise 9.

We have reduced the discussion of the behaviour of a pair of differential equations near an equilibrium point to an examination of the behaviour of a pair of *linear* differential equations. In the next section we will use the techniques from Unit 6 to solve these differential equations.

Find the equilibrium point (x_e, y_e) of the system of differential equations

$$\dot{x} = 3x + 2y - 8,$$
$$\dot{y} = x + 4y - 6.$$

Find a system of linear differential equations satisfied by small perturbations p and q from the equilibrium point.

Exercise 14

Suppose that a pair of populations x and y can be modelled by the system of differential equations

$$\dot{x} = 0.5x - 0.000\,05x^2,$$
$$\dot{y} = -0.1y + 0.0004xy - 0.01y^2 \quad (x \geq 0, \ y \geq 0).$$

(a) Find the three equilibrium points of the system.

(b) Find the Jacobian matrix of the system.

(c) For each of the three equilibrium points, find the matrix form of the linear differential equations that give the approximate behaviour of the system near the equilibrium point.

3 Classifying equilibrium points

In the previous section you saw how a system of non-linear differential equations $\dot{\mathbf{x}} = \mathbf{u}(x, y)$ may be approximated near an equilibrium point by a linear system $\dot{\mathbf{p}} = \mathbf{A}\mathbf{p}$, where $\mathbf{A}$ is the Jacobian matrix

$$\mathbf{A} = \mathbf{J}(x_e, y_e).$$

In this section we develop an algebraic method of classification, based on the eigenvalues of this Jacobian matrix. The procedure for classifying an equilibrium point of a non-linear system will then be as follows.

Classifying equilibrium points

- Near an equilibrium point, approximate the non-linear system by a linear system.

- Find the eigenvalues of the Jacobian matrix for these linearised equations.

- Classify the equilibrium point of the linearised system using these eigenvalues.

- Deduce (where possible) the behaviour of the original system in the neighbourhood of the equilibrium point.

The linearised system of differential equations, which approximates the behaviour of the non-linear system in the neighbourhood of the equilibrium point, has the form

$$\begin{bmatrix} \dot{p} \\ \dot{q} \end{bmatrix} = \begin{bmatrix} a & b \\ c & d \end{bmatrix} \begin{bmatrix} p \\ q \end{bmatrix},$$

where p and q are perturbations from the equilibrium point, and a, b, c and d are constants. This is equivalent to the set of equations

$$\dot{p} = ap + bq,$$
$$\dot{q} = cp + dq.$$

The perturbations p and q can usually take negative, as well as positive, values.

From Unit 6, we know that the general solutions of such equations are determined by the eigenvalues and eigenvectors of the matrix of coefficients, which in the present context is the Jacobian matrix evaluated at the equilibrium point. We will illustrate various kinds of behaviour that can arise, by examining some examples. First, we look at matrices with real eigenvalues of various signs, then we consider matrices with complex eigenvalues. A summary of all these cases is given in Subsection 3.3.

3.1   Matrices with two real eigenvalues

Let us first consider the linear system of differential equations $\dot{\mathbf{p}} = \mathbf{A}\mathbf{p}$ where

$$\mathbf{A} = \begin{bmatrix} 2 & 0 \\ 0 & 3 \end{bmatrix}. \tag{20}$$

For a linear system of differential equations, the Jacobian matrix is the matrix of coefficients, and the equilibrium point is at $p = 0$, $q = 0$.

(This system is very similar to the one considered in Example 1.) The matrix $\mathbf{A}$ is diagonal, so its eigenvalues are 2 and 3. The corresponding eigenvectors are $[1 \quad 0]^T$ and $[0 \quad 1]^T$, respectively. Following the method given in Unit 6, the general solution is constructed from these eigenvalues and eigenvectors, and is given by

$$\begin{bmatrix} p(t) \\ q(t) \end{bmatrix} = C \begin{bmatrix} 1 \\ 0 \end{bmatrix} e^{2t} + D \begin{bmatrix} 0 \\ 1 \end{bmatrix} e^{3t},$$

where C and D are arbitrary constants. Equivalently, we have

$$p(t) = Ce^{2t}, \quad q(t) = De^{3t}.$$

We are interested in the behaviour of phase paths near the equilibrium point at $p = 0$, $q = 0$. Consider, for example, the paths with $D = 0$ (and $C \neq 0$). On these paths we have $p(t) = Ce^{2t}$ and $q(t) = 0$, so the point $(p(t), q(t))$ moves away from the origin along the p-axis as t increases.

On the other hand, consider the paths with $C = 0$ (and $D \neq 0$). On these paths we have $p(t) = 0$ and $q(t) = De^{3t}$, so the point $(p(t), q(t))$ moves away from the origin along the q-axis as t increases. Hence we have seen that there are phase paths along the axes, corresponding to the eigenvectors $[1 \quad 0]^T$ and $[0 \quad 1]^T$. As t increases, a point on either of these axes moves away from the origin.

In this case, we can show that the paths are $q = K|p|^{3/2}$, as in Example 1, but in this section we are interested in the qualitative behaviour.

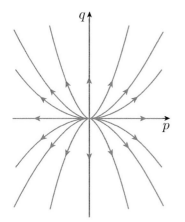

Figure 13   A source (unstable)

For general values of C and D, where neither $C = 0$ nor $D = 0$, the point (Ce^{2t}, De^{3t}) still moves away from the origin as t increases, but not along a straight line. On the other hand, as t decreases, the exponential functions e^{2t} and e^{3t} decrease (and tend to zero as t tends to $-\infty$). So the point (Ce^{2t}, De^{3t}) approaches the origin as t decreases, and all paths radiate from the origin. This is illustrated in Figure 13, where we have incorporated the fact that the only straight-line paths are the two axes, which correspond to the two eigenvectors of the matrix $\mathbf{A}$.

An equilibrium point with this type of qualitative behaviour in its neighbourhood is a **source**, and is unstable. This behaviour occurs for any linear system $\dot{\mathbf{p}} = \mathbf{A}\mathbf{p}$ where the Jacobian matrix $\mathbf{A}$ has *positive distinct eigenvalues*. The only straight-line paths are in the directions of the eigenvectors of the matrix $\mathbf{A}$, although these will not, in general, be along the axes.

Exercise 15

Consider the linear system of differential equations
$$\begin{bmatrix} \dot{p} \\ \dot{q} \end{bmatrix} = \begin{bmatrix} 3 & 0 \\ 2 & 1 \end{bmatrix} \begin{bmatrix} p \\ q \end{bmatrix}.$$

(a) Find the eigenvalues of the Jacobian matrix.

(b) Classify the equilibrium point $p = 0$, $q = 0$ of the system.

Now consider the system of differential equations $\dot{\mathbf{p}} = \mathbf{A}\mathbf{p}$ where
$$\mathbf{A} = \begin{bmatrix} -2 & 0 \\ 0 & -3 \end{bmatrix}. \tag{21}$$

The change in sign for matrix $\mathbf{A}$ from equation (20) to equation (21) changes the solution from one involving positive exponentials to one involving negative exponentials. You can think of this as replacing t by $-t$, so the solutions describe the same paths, but traversed in opposite directions. This changes the direction of the arrows along the paths in Figure 13.

So if the Jacobian matrix for a linear system has *negative distinct eigenvalues*, then the equilibrium point is a **sink**, and is stable. The only straight-line paths are along the directions of the eigenvectors of the Jacobian matrix.

Exercise 16

Consider the linear system of differential equations
$$\begin{bmatrix} \dot{p} \\ \dot{q} \end{bmatrix} = \begin{bmatrix} 0 & -1 \\ 2 & -3 \end{bmatrix} \begin{bmatrix} p \\ q \end{bmatrix}.$$

(a) Find the eigenvalues of the Jacobian matrix.

(b) Classify the equilibrium point $p = 0$, $q = 0$ of the system.

These conclusions are modified slightly when the two eigenvalues happen to be equal, as the following exercise illustrates.

We include here the case where both eigenvalues are equal, but we will always assume that there are two linearly independent eigenvectors.

Exercise 17

Consider the linear system of differential equations

$$\begin{bmatrix} \dot{p} \\ \dot{q} \end{bmatrix} = \begin{bmatrix} 2 & 0 \\ 0 & 2 \end{bmatrix} \begin{bmatrix} p \\ q \end{bmatrix},$$

which has eigenvalues 2 and 2, and eigenvectors $[1 \ \ 0]^T$ and $[0 \ \ 1]^T$.

(a) Find the general solution of the system of differential equations.

(b) By eliminating t, find the equations of the paths, and describe them.

(c) Is the equilibrium point $p = 0$, $q = 0$ stable or unstable?

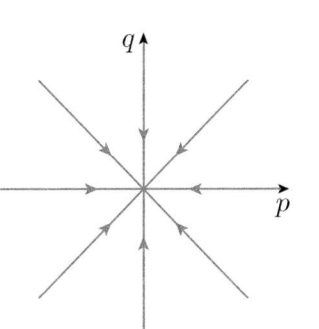

In Exercise 17, you saw that when the Jacobian matrix has two real *identical positive eigenvalues* (but there are still *two linearly independent eigenvectors*), all the paths are straight lines radiating away from the origin, as shown in Figure 14. The equilibrium point at $p = 0$, $q = 0$ is then called a **star source** (and is unstable).

Figure 14 A star source (unstable)

If there are two real *identical negative eigenvalues* (but there are still *two linearly independent eigenvectors*), then the arrows on the paths in Figure 14 are reversed, and the equilibrium point at $p = 0$, $q = 0$ is called a **star sink**, which is stable. This is illustrated in Figure 15.

So far in this section we have considered the case where the Jacobian matrix has two positive eigenvalues and the case where the matrix has two negative eigenvalues. We now consider the case where the matrix has *one positive eigenvalue and one negative eigenvalue*. For example, consider the matrix

$$\mathbf{A} = \begin{bmatrix} 1 & 4 \\ 1 & -2 \end{bmatrix},$$

Figure 15 A star sink (stable)

which has eigenvalues 2 and -3, and corresponding eigenvectors $[4 \ \ 1]^T$ and $[1 \ \ -1]^T$. The general solution of the linear system of differential equations $\dot{\mathbf{p}} = \mathbf{A}\mathbf{p}$ is therefore

$$\begin{bmatrix} p \\ q \end{bmatrix} = C \begin{bmatrix} 4 \\ 1 \end{bmatrix} e^{2t} + D \begin{bmatrix} 1 \\ -1 \end{bmatrix} e^{-3t}. \tag{22}$$

When $D = 0$ (and $C \neq 0$), we have $p(t) = 4Ce^{2t}$ and $q(t) = Ce^{2t}$, and the point $(p(t), q(t))$ moves away from the origin along the straight-line path $q = \frac{1}{4}p$ as t increases. On the other hand, when $C = 0$ (and $D \neq 0$), the solution is $p(t) = De^{-3t}$, $q(t) = -De^{-3t}$, so the point $(p(t), q(t))$ approaches the origin along the straight-line path $q = -p$ as t increases.

Hence we have seen that there are two straight-line paths. On the line $q = \frac{1}{4}p$ (which corresponds to the eigenvector $[4 \ \ 1]^T$), the point moves away from the origin as t increases. However, on the line $q = -p$ (which corresponds to the eigenvector $[1 \ \ -1]^T$), the point moves towards the origin as t increases.

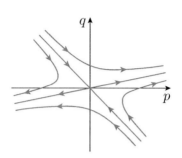

Figure 16   A saddle (unstable)

Now we will consider the behaviour of a general point $(p(t), q(t))$, where $p(t)$ and $q(t)$ are given by equation (22), and neither C nor D is zero. For large positive values of t, the terms involving e^{2t} dominate, so $p(t) \simeq 4Ce^{2t}$ and $q(t) \simeq Ce^{2t}$. So for large positive values of t, the general path approaches the line $q = \frac{1}{4}p$. On the other hand, for large negative values of t, the terms involving e^{-3t} dominate, so $p(t) \simeq De^{-3t}$ and $q(t) \simeq -De^{-3t}$. So for large negative values of t, the general path approaches the line $q = -p$. Using this information we can construct the paths in phase space, illustrated in Figure 16.

An equilibrium point with this type of behaviour is called a **saddle**. It occurs when the Jacobian matrix has *one positive eigenvalue and one negative eigenvalue*. Again, the two straight-line paths are in the directions of the eigenvectors of the matrix.

Exercise 18

Consider the linear system of differential equations

$$\begin{bmatrix} \dot{p} \\ \dot{q} \end{bmatrix} = \begin{bmatrix} 1 & 2 \\ 2 & -2 \end{bmatrix} \begin{bmatrix} p \\ q \end{bmatrix}.$$

(a) Find the eigenvalues and corresponding eigenvectors of the Jacobian matrix.

(b) Classify the equilibrium point $p = 0$, $q = 0$.

(c) Sketch the phase paths of the solutions of the differential equations.

3.2   Matrices with complex eigenvalues

In Unit 5 you saw that some matrices with real matrix elements have *complex* eigenvalues and eigenvectors. However, in Unit 6 you saw that these complex quantities can be used to construct the *real* solutions of the corresponding system of linear differential equations. Our next example involves such a system.

Example 4

Consider the linear system of differential equations

$$\begin{bmatrix} \dot{p} \\ \dot{q} \end{bmatrix} = \begin{bmatrix} 0 & -1 \\ 4 & 0 \end{bmatrix} \begin{bmatrix} p \\ q \end{bmatrix}.$$

(a) Find the eigenvalues and corresponding eigenvectors of the Jacobian matrix.

(b) Hence obtain the general solution of the system of differential equations.

(c) Show that the phase paths for these differential equations are the ellipses

$$p^2 + \tfrac{1}{4}q^2 = K,$$

where K is a positive constant.

The standard equation for an ellipse is

$$\frac{x^2}{a^2} + \frac{y^2}{b^2} = 1,$$

where a and b are constants.

Solution

(a) The matrix has the characteristic equation

$$\begin{vmatrix} -\lambda & -1 \\ 4 & -\lambda \end{vmatrix} = 0,$$

i.e. $\lambda^2 + 4 = 0$. So the eigenvalues are $\lambda = 2i$ and $\lambda = -2i$.

When $\lambda = 2i$, the eigenvector $[a \quad b]^T$ satisfies the equation

$$\begin{bmatrix} -2i & -1 \\ 4 & -2i \end{bmatrix} \begin{bmatrix} a \\ b \end{bmatrix} = \begin{bmatrix} 0 \\ 0 \end{bmatrix},$$

so $-2ia - b = 0$, which gives $b = -2ia$. Hence an eigenvector corresponding to the eigenvalue $\lambda = 2i$ is $[1 \quad -2i]^T$.

Similarly, an eigenvector corresponding to the eigenvalue $\lambda = -2i$ is $[1 \quad 2i]^T$.

(b) The general solution of the system can be found by the method explained in Unit 6. This involves finding the real and imaginary parts of $\mathbf{v}e^{\lambda t}$, where λ and $\mathbf{v}$ are an eigenvalue–eigenvector pair. Using the eigenvalue $2i$ and the corresponding eigenvector $[1 \quad -2i]^T$, we get

It does not matter which of the two eigenvalue–eigenvector pairs we choose, as they are complex conjugates of one another.

$$\begin{bmatrix} 1 \\ -2i \end{bmatrix} e^{2it} = \begin{bmatrix} 1 \\ -2i \end{bmatrix} (\cos 2t + i \sin 2t)$$

$$= \begin{bmatrix} \cos 2t \\ 2\sin 2t \end{bmatrix} + i \begin{bmatrix} \sin 2t \\ -2\cos 2t \end{bmatrix}.$$

The general solution can then be written down as

See Procedure 2 and Example 5 of Unit 6.

$$\begin{bmatrix} p \\ q \end{bmatrix} = C \begin{bmatrix} \cos 2t \\ 2\sin 2t \end{bmatrix} + D \begin{bmatrix} \sin 2t \\ -2\cos 2t \end{bmatrix},$$

where C and D are arbitrary constants.

(c) We have

$$p(t) = C \cos 2t + D \sin 2t,$$
$$q(t) = 2C \sin 2t - 2D \cos 2t,$$

so

$$\begin{aligned}
p^2 + \tfrac{1}{4}q^2 &= (C\cos 2t + D\sin 2t)^2 + (C\sin 2t - D\cos 2t)^2 \\
&= (C^2 \cos^2 2t + 2CD\cos 2t \sin 2t + D^2 \sin^2 2t) \\
&\quad + (C^2 \sin^2 2t - 2CD\cos 2t \sin 2t + D^2 \cos^2 2t) \\
&= C^2(\cos^2 2t + \sin^2 2t) + D^2(\cos^2 2t + \sin^2 2t) \\
&= C^2 + D^2 = K,
\end{aligned}$$

where $K = C^2 + D^2$.

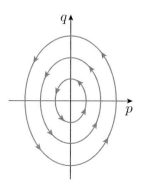

Figure 17   A centre (stable)

So the phase paths are ellipses, as shown in Figure 17. The direction of the arrows can be deduced from the original differential equations. For example, in the first quadrant, $\dot{p} = -q < 0$ and $\dot{q} = 4p > 0$.

In Example 4, you saw that the phase paths are ellipses. This type of behaviour corresponds to any linear system of differential equations where the eigenvalues of the Jacobian matrix are *purely imaginary*. An equilibrium point that has this behaviour in its neighbourhood is called a *centre*, and is stable. More generally, if all the phase paths in the vicinity of an equilibrium point are *closed curves*, then the equilibrium point is stable and is called a **centre**.

Exercise 19

Consider the linear system of differential equations

$$\begin{bmatrix} \dot{p} \\ \dot{q} \end{bmatrix} = \begin{bmatrix} 2 & -1 \\ 5 & -2 \end{bmatrix} \begin{bmatrix} p \\ q \end{bmatrix}.$$

(a) Find the eigenvalues of the Jacobian matrix.

(b) Classify the equilibrium point $p = 0$, $q = 0$.

In general, when the eigenvalues of a matrix are complex, they are not purely imaginary but also contain a real part. This has a significant effect on the solution of the corresponding system, as you will see in the following example.

Example 5

Find the general solution of the system of equations $\dot{\mathbf{p}} = \mathbf{A}\mathbf{p}$, where

$$\mathbf{A} = \begin{bmatrix} -2 & -3 \\ 3 & -2 \end{bmatrix}.$$

Sketch some phase paths corresponding to the solutions of the system.

Solution

The characteristic equation of the Jacobian matrix is $(2 + \lambda)^2 + 9 = 0$, so the eigenvalues are $-2 + 3i$ and $-2 - 3i$. The corresponding eigenvectors are $\begin{bmatrix} 1 & -i \end{bmatrix}^T$ and $\begin{bmatrix} 1 & i \end{bmatrix}^T$, respectively. To construct the general solution, we need to find the real and imaginary parts of $\begin{bmatrix} 1 & -i \end{bmatrix}^T e^{(-2+3i)t}$. We get

$$e^{-2t} e^{3it} \begin{bmatrix} 1 \\ -i \end{bmatrix} = e^{-2t}(\cos 3t + i \sin 3t) \begin{bmatrix} 1 \\ -i \end{bmatrix}$$

$$= e^{-2t} \begin{bmatrix} \cos 3t \\ \sin 3t \end{bmatrix} + ie^{-2t} \begin{bmatrix} \sin 3t \\ -\cos 3t \end{bmatrix}.$$

So the general solution is

$$\begin{bmatrix} p \\ q \end{bmatrix} = Ce^{-2t} \begin{bmatrix} \cos 3t \\ \sin 3t \end{bmatrix} + De^{-2t} \begin{bmatrix} \sin 3t \\ -\cos 3t \end{bmatrix},$$

where C and D are arbitrary constants.

If we neglect, for the time being, the e^{-2t} factors, the solution is

$$p = C\cos 3t + D\sin 3t,$$
$$q = C\sin 3t - D\cos 3t,$$

from which it follows that

$$p^2 + q^2 = C^2 + D^2$$

(the argument is similar to that given in the solution to Example 4).

So, in the absence of the e^{-2t} terms, the paths would be circles centred on the origin. The effect of the e^{-2t} terms on these paths is to reduce the radius of the circles gradually. In other words, the paths spiral in towards the origin as t increases, as shown in Figure 18.

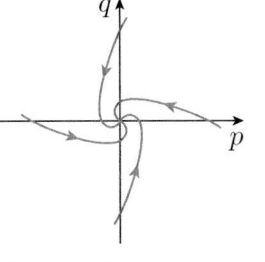

Figure 18   A spiral sink (stable)

In Example 5 the paths spiral in towards the origin, so the origin is a sink (which is called a **spiral sink**) and therefore is a *stable* equilibrium point. If the paths spiralled away from the origin, we would have a **spiral source** (Figure 19) with the equilibrium point *unstable*. The stability is determined by the sign of the real part of the complex eigenvalues. If the real part is positive, then the general solution involves e^{kt} terms (where k is positive) and the equilibrium point is an unstable spiral source; if the real part is negative, then the general solution involves e^{-kt} terms and the equilibrium point is a stable spiral sink.

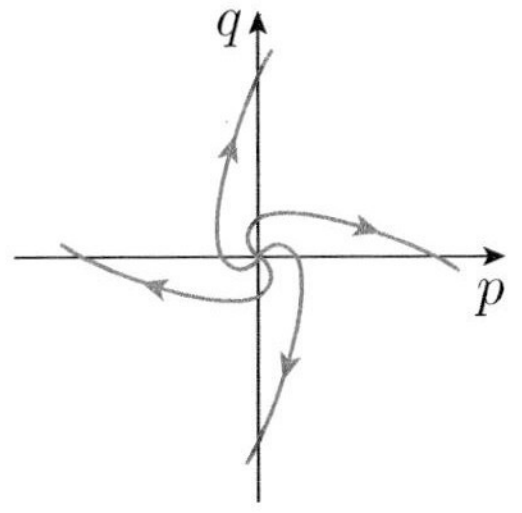

Figure 19   A spiral source (unstable)

Exercise 20

Consider the linear system of differential equations

$$\begin{bmatrix} \dot{p} \\ \dot{q} \end{bmatrix} = \begin{bmatrix} 1 & 1 \\ -1 & 1 \end{bmatrix} \begin{bmatrix} p \\ q \end{bmatrix}.$$

(a) Find the eigenvalues of the Jacobian matrix.

(b) Classify the equilibrium point $p = 0$, $q = 0$.

3.3   Classifying equilibrium points of linear systems

We now summarise the results of the previous three subsections. The phase diagrams are collected together in Figure 20.

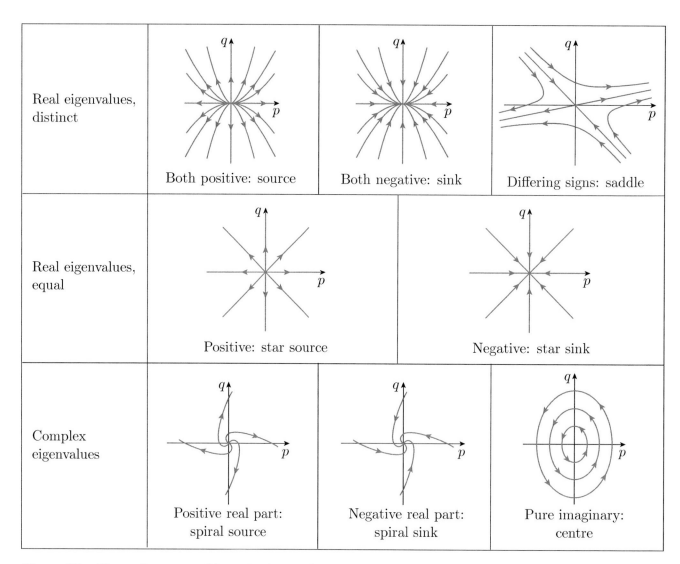

Real eigenvalues, distinct	Both positive: source	Both negative: sink	Differing signs: saddle
Real eigenvalues, equal	Positive: star source		Negative: star sink
Complex eigenvalues	Positive real part: spiral source	Negative real part: spiral sink	Pure imaginary: centre

Figure 20 Phase diagrams of linearised equations

Procedure 3   Classification of the equilibrium points of a linear system

Consider the linear system $\dot{\mathbf{p}} = \mathbf{A}\mathbf{p}$, for a 2×2 matrix $\mathbf{A}$. The nature of the equilibrium point at $p = 0$, $q = 0$ is determined by the eigenvalues and eigenvectors of $\mathbf{A}$.

1.   If the eigenvalues are **real and distinct**, then:

   • if both eigenvalues are positive, the equilibrium point is a *source* (and is unstable)

   • if both eigenvalues are negative, the equilibrium point is a *sink* (and is stable)

   • if one of the eigenvalues is positive and the other is negative, the equilibrium point is a *saddle* (and is unstable).

2.   If the eigenvalues are **real and equal** (and there are *two linearly independent eigenvectors*), then:

- if the eigenvalues are positive, the equilibrium point is a *star source* (and is unstable)

- if the eigenvalues are negative, the equilibrium point is a *star sink* (and is stable).

3.   If the eigenvalues are **complex**, then:

- if the eigenvalues are purely imaginary, the equilibrium point is a *centre* (and is stable)

- if the eigenvalues have a positive real part, the equilibrium point is a *spiral source* (and is unstable)

- if the eigenvalues have a negative real part, the equilibrium point is a *spiral sink* (and is stable).

Procedure 3 is not exhaustive; for example, it does not include a number of special cases, such as where one of the eigenvalues is zero.

Exercise 21

(a) Suppose that all you are told about a given equilibrium point is that both the eigenvalues of its Jacobian matrix are positive, or have a positive real part. What are the possible types of equilibrium point that fit this description?

(b) Suppose that all you are told about a given equilibrium point is that both the eigenvalues of its Jacobian matrix are negative, or have a negative real part. What are the possible types of equilibrium point that fit this description?

Exercise 22

In Example 3 you saw that the Lotka–Volterra equations can be approximated by the system of linear differential equations

$$\begin{bmatrix} \dot{p} \\ \dot{q} \end{bmatrix} = \begin{bmatrix} 0 & -kX/Y \\ hY/X & 0 \end{bmatrix} \begin{bmatrix} p \\ q \end{bmatrix} \quad (k > 0 \text{ and } h > 0)$$

in the neighbourhood of the equilibrium point (X, Y). Find the eigenvalues of the Jacobian matrix, and hence classify the equilibrium point $p = 0$, $q = 0$ for the linearised system around (X, Y).

Exercise 23

In Exercise 11 you saw that the Lotka–Volterra equations can be approximated by the system of linear differential equations

$$\begin{bmatrix} \dot{p} \\ \dot{q} \end{bmatrix} = \begin{bmatrix} k & 0 \\ 0 & -h \end{bmatrix} \begin{bmatrix} p \\ q \end{bmatrix}$$

in the neighbourhood of the equilibrium point $(0,0)$. Find the eigenvalues of the Jacobian matrix, and hence classify the equilibrium point $p = 0$, $q = 0$ for the linearised system around $(0,0)$.

3.4 Classifying equilibrium points of non-linear systems

In Section 2 you saw how to find the equilibrium points of non-linear systems of differential equations $\dot{\mathbf{x}} = \mathbf{u}(\mathbf{x})$, and how to find the linear system $\dot{\mathbf{p}} = \mathbf{A}\mathbf{p}$ that approximates the system in the neighbourhood of an equilibrium point. In this section you have seen how to classify an equilibrium point of the linear system by finding the eigenvalues and eigenvectors of the matrix $\mathbf{A}$. But is the behaviour of the non-linear system near the equilibrium point the same as the behaviour of the linear system that approximates it? It can be shown that, not surprisingly, the answer is yes, *except* when the equilibrium point of the approximating linear system is a centre.

Near a centre, the paths of the approximating linear system are circular or elliptical. However, the paths of the original non-linear system may spiral towards or away from the equilibrium point, or they may be closed curves. In such cases, we can say only that the paths are approximately circular or elliptical; we can say nothing about their actual behaviour without further examination. Thus, if the linear approximation has a centre, we cannot immediately deduce the nature of the equilibrium point of the original non-linear system: it may be a stable centre, a stable spiral sink or an unstable spiral source.

> **Procedure 4   Classification of the equilibrium points of a non-linear system**
>
> To classify the equilibrium points of the non-linear system of differential equations
>
> $$\dot{\mathbf{x}} = \mathbf{u}(x, y),$$
>
> do the following.

1. Find the equilibrium points by using Procedure 1.

2. Use Procedure 2 to find the linear system

   $$\dot{\mathbf{p}} = \mathbf{A}\mathbf{p}$$

   that approximates the original non-linear system in the neighbourhood of each equilibrium point.

3. For each equilibrium point, use Procedure 3 to classify the linear system.

The behaviour of the original non-linear system near an equilibrium point is the same as that of the linear approximation, except when the linear system has a centre. If the linear system has a centre, the equilibrium point of the original non-linear system may be a centre (stable), a spiral sink (stable) or a spiral source (unstable).

In the case of the Lotka–Volterra equations (15), in Exercise 23 you have seen that the linear system of differential equations that approximates the non-linear system in the neighbourhood of the equilibrium point $(0,0)$ has an (unstable) *saddle* at the equilibrium point. So the (non-linear) Lotka–Volterra equations also have an (unstable) *saddle* at the equilibrium point $(0,0)$.

You also saw in Exercise 22 that the linear system of differential equations that approximates the Lotka–Volterra equations in the neighbourhood of the equilibrium point (X,Y) has a (stable) *centre* at the equilibrium point. This means that we cannot immediately say anything about the classification of this equilibrium point of the original (non-linear) system of differential equations – it could be a centre, a spiral sink or a spiral source. However, further investigation (using a method that will be introduced in Subsection 3.5) shows that with the exception of the equilibrium points and the coordinate axes, *every* phase path of the Lotka–Volterra equations is a closed path. (These closed paths are not ellipses, however.) So the equilibrium point (X,Y) of the Lotka–Volterra equations *is* a (stable) *centre*, as shown in Figure 21.

The following important example illustrates the steps involved in locating and classifying equilibrium points.

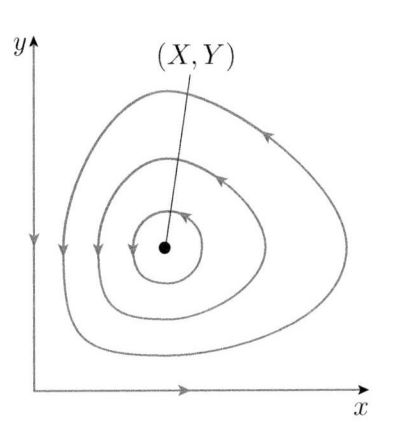

Figure 21 Phase diagram for the Lotka–Volterra equations, showing closed phase paths and a centre at (X,Y)

Example 6

Consider the non-linear system of differential equations

$$\dot{x} = -4y + 2xy - 8,$$
$$\dot{y} = 4y^2 - x^2.$$

(a) Find the equilibrium points of the system.

(b) Compute the Jacobian matrix of the system.

(c) In the neighbourhood of each equilibrium point:

- linearise the system of differential equations
- classify the equilibrium point of the linearised system.

(d) What can you say about the classification of the equilibrium points of the original (non-linear) system of differential equations?

Solution

(a) The equilibrium points are given by

$$-4y + 2xy - 8 = 0,$$
$$4y^2 - x^2 = 0.$$

The second equation gives

$$x = \pm 2y.$$

When $x = 2y$, substitution into the first equation gives

$$-4y + 4y^2 - 8 = 0,$$

or $y^2 - y - 2 = 0$, which factorises to give

$$(y - 2)(y + 1) = 0.$$

Hence

$$y = 2 \quad \text{or} \quad y = -1.$$

When $y = 2$, $x = 2y = 4$. When $y = -1$, $x = 2y = -2$. So we have found two equilibrium points, namely $(4, 2)$ and $(-2, -1)$.

When $x = -2y$, substitution into the first equation gives

$$-4y - 4y^2 - 8 = 0,$$

or $y^2 + y + 2 = 0$. This quadratic equation has no real solutions, so there are no more equilibrium points.

(b) With the usual notation,

$$u(x, y) = -4y + 2xy - 8,$$
$$v(x, y) = 4y^2 - x^2.$$

So the Jacobian matrix is

$$\begin{bmatrix} \dfrac{\partial u}{\partial x} & \dfrac{\partial u}{\partial y} \\ \dfrac{\partial v}{\partial x} & \dfrac{\partial v}{\partial y} \end{bmatrix} = \begin{bmatrix} 2y & 2x - 4 \\ -2x & 8y \end{bmatrix}.$$

(c) At the equilibrium point $(4, 2)$, the Jacobian matrix is

$$\begin{bmatrix} 4 & 4 \\ -8 & 16 \end{bmatrix}.$$

The characteristic equation of this Jacobian matrix is

$$(4 - \lambda)(16 - \lambda) + 32 = 0,$$

or $\lambda^2 - 20\lambda + 96 = 0$, which factorises to give

$$(\lambda - 8)(\lambda - 12) = 0,$$

so the eigenvalues are

$$\lambda = 8 \quad \text{and} \quad \lambda = 12.$$

The two eigenvalues are positive and distinct, so the equilibrium point $p = 0$, $q = 0$ is a *source*, which is unstable.

At the equilibrium point $(-2, -1)$, the Jacobian matrix is

$$\begin{bmatrix} -2 & -8 \\ 4 & -8 \end{bmatrix}.$$

The characteristic equation of this Jacobian matrix is

$$(-2 - \lambda)(-8 - \lambda) + 32 = 0,$$

which simplifies to

$$\lambda^2 + 10\lambda + 48 = 0.$$

The roots of this quadratic equation are

$$\lambda = \frac{-10 \pm \sqrt{100 - 192}}{2} = -5 \pm i\sqrt{23},$$

so the eigenvalues are complex with a negative real part. Hence the equilibrium point $p = 0$, $q = 0$ is a *spiral sink*, which is stable.

(d) As neither of the equilibrium points found in part (c) is a centre, the non-linear system has an equilibrium point $(4, 2)$ that is a source (unstable), and an equilibrium point $(-2, -1)$ that is a spiral sink (stable).

Exercise 24

Find the eigenvalues and eigenvectors of the matrix

$$\mathbf{A} = \begin{bmatrix} 2 & -3 \\ 3 & 2 \end{bmatrix},$$

and hence find the general solution of the system $\dot{\mathbf{p}} = \mathbf{A}\mathbf{p}$. Classify the equilibrium point $p = 0$, $q = 0$.

If this system is the linear approximation to a non-linear system $\dot{\mathbf{x}} = \mathbf{u}(x, y)$ in the neighbourhood of an equilibrium point, what can you say about this equilibrium point of the non-linear system?

Exercise 25

Consider the non-linear system of differential equations

$$\dot{x} = (1 + x - 2y)x,$$
$$\dot{y} = (x - 1)y.$$

(a) Find the equilibrium points of the system.

(b) Find the Jacobian matrix of the system.

(c) In the neighbourhood of each equilibrium point:

- find the linear system of differential equations that gives the approximate behaviour of the system near the equilibrium point

- find the eigenvalues of the Jacobian matrix

- use the eigenvalues to classify the equilibrium point of the linearised system.

(d) What can you say about the classification of the equilibrium points of the original non-linear system of differential equations?

3.5 Constants of motion

You saw in Exercise 22 that the (non-linear) Lotka–Volterra equations can be linearised about the equilibrium point (X, Y), and that this point is a (stable) centre for the linearised system. However, this is not enough to show that (X, Y) is a stable equilibrium point of the original non-linear equations. In fact, (X, Y) *is* a stable centre of the Lotka–Volterra equations, as shown in Figure 21, but how can we establish this fact?

The trick is to show that there is a **constant of motion**. This is a function $K(x, y)$ that remains constant as we follow any given phase path. To see what this means, consider a function $K(x, y)$ as x and y trace out a path in phase space. Then the rate of change of $K(x, y)$ with respect to t is obtained by applying the chain rule of Unit 7. We have

$$\frac{dK}{dt} = \frac{\partial K}{\partial x}\frac{dx}{dt} + \frac{\partial K}{\partial y}\frac{dy}{dt}, \tag{23}$$

where $dx/dt = \dot{x}$ and $dy/dt = \dot{y}$ are the components of the velocity of the phase point in phase space: in this context, these are given by the Lotka–Volterra equations (15). The function $K(x, y)$ is a constant of motion if $dK/dt = 0$, and this can be tested by checking that the right-hand side of equation (23) vanishes for all x and y.

If we can find a function $K(x, y)$ that is a constant of motion for a given set of equations, it follows that K remains constant as we trace out any given phase path. This means that the phase paths are coincident with the contour lines of $K(x, y)$, which can be investigated quite easily.

Even if a constant of motion exists for a given system of differential equations, finding the appropriate function $K(x,y)$ is not easy and often requires informed guesswork. You will not be asked to do this, but you may be asked to verify that a given function is a constant of motion, using equation (23).

In the case of the Lotka–Volterra equations, it turns out that there is a constant of motion, namely

$$K(x,y) = h \ln x + k \ln y - \frac{h}{X}x - \frac{k}{Y}y, \qquad (24)$$

where h and k are positive constants. The contour lines of this scalar field are plotted in Figure 22; they are closed curves and have the same shape as the phase paths plotted earlier, in Figure 21. Depending on the initial conditions, the phase point orbits around a particular contour, so that the motion of the Lotka–Volterra model is always periodic in time. The period depends on which contour is followed.

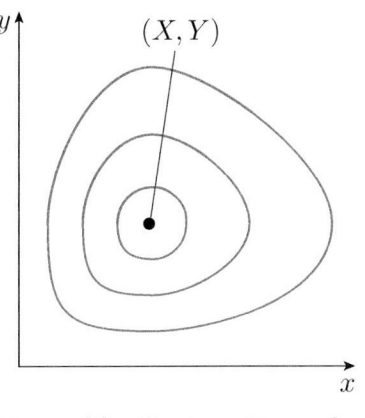

Figure 22 Contour lines of the scalar field $K(x,y)$ for the Lotka–Volterra equations

---

Example 7

Show that

$$K(x,y) = h \ln x + k \ln y - \frac{h}{X}x - \frac{k}{Y}y$$

is a constant of motion for the Lotka–Volterra equations.

Solution

The partial derivatives are

$$\frac{\partial K}{\partial x} = \frac{h}{x} - \frac{h}{X} = \frac{h(X-x)}{xX},$$

$$\frac{\partial K}{\partial y} = \frac{k}{y} - \frac{k}{Y} = \frac{k(Y-y)}{yY}.$$

From the Lotka–Volterra equations (15), the velocity components are

$$\dot{x} = \frac{kx(Y-y)}{Y} \quad \text{and} \quad \dot{y} = \frac{-hy(X-x)}{X}.$$

The rate of change of K is therefore

$$\frac{dK}{dt} = \frac{hk}{XY}\big[(X-x)(Y-y) - (Y-y)(X-x)\big] = 0.$$

A more general understanding of phase paths

We have addressed behaviour in the immediate vicinity of an equilibrium point. But what happens more generally?

If there is a constant of motion, then the path follows its contours: these could be closed curves (as for the Lotka–Volterra equations), or they could be open curves, which run off to infinity.

But having a constant of motion is a special case; for 'most' choices of the functions $u(x, y)$ and $v(x, y)$ in equations (1), there is no constant of motion. In order to appreciate what can happen in the general case, we need to describe a behaviour that we have not yet encountered. This is where paths converge towards a single closed curve, which is called a **limit cycle**.

Figure 23 illustrates the distinction between the spiralling paths around a limit cycle (part (a)) and the closed paths that arise when there is a constant of motion (part (b)). Around a limit cycle, paths corresponding to different initial conditions all approach the *same* closed curve (the limit cycle) as $t \to \infty$. When there is a constant of motion with closed contour lines, we have a set of *distinct* closed paths, each characterised by different initial conditions.

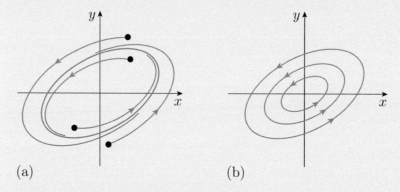

(a)   (b)

Figure 23   Contrasting phase paths around (a) a limit cycle (in blue) and (b) a centre

So what happens in the typical case, where there is no constant of motion? The first systematic study was made in the 1880s by Henri Poincaré (Figure 24), who showed that most two-dimensional, autonomous systems have paths that do one of three things:

- approach a stable equilibrium point
- approach a limit cycle
- run off to infinity.

The chaotic behaviour illustrated in Figure 1 is not consistent with the path approaching a limit cycle. Poincaré appreciated that chaotic motion could exist, but that it requires at least three coupled equations (in the case of autonomous systems).

Figure 24   Henri Poincaré (1854–1912) and his flamboyant signature. He pioneered the geometric analysis of systems of differential equations, along with important contributions to many other topics in mathematics, physics and engineering.

4 Motion of a rigid pendulum

In the Introduction we mentioned that non-linear differential equations arise in the description of mechanical systems. We will present a brief discussion of just one mechanical system, taking its equation of motion as given. This is included because it illustrates a useful general principle: higher-order differential equations are often written as systems of first-order equations in a larger number of variables. There are various advantages in this approach. Here we emphasise that it leads to a graphical representation of the motion in phase space. This helps us to give qualitative descriptions of differential equations that we cannot solve exactly.

The derivation of equations of motion often requires special techniques, such as those of *Lagrangian mechanics*, and is beyond the scope of this module.

4.1   Equations of motion for a rigid pendulum

We consider the motion of a rigid pendulum, illustrated in Figure 25. There is a mass m at the end of a rigid rod, which moves freely in a fixed vertical plane. Let θ (measured in radians) be the angular displacement from the downward vertical in an anticlockwise direction. When frictional forces can be neglected, the equation of motion for θ as a function of time t is the **rigid pendulum equation** or **undamped pendulum equation**

$$\ddot{\theta} = -\omega^2 \sin\theta, \tag{25}$$

where ω is a positive constant. You can think of this as a form of Newton's second law where the force is proportional to $\sin\theta$, but a satisfactory derivation requires a relatively sophisticated approach. Note that the force is zero when $\theta = \pi$, as well as when $\theta = 0$. This is a consequence of the fact that the rigid pendulum can, in principle, be balanced so that the mass is vertically above the pivot.

We also mention two closely-related equations.

If the displacement of the pendulum is small, you can use the approximation $\sin\theta \simeq \theta$, and the equation of motion (25) is replaced by an equation that we refer to as the **simple pendulum equation**

$$\ddot{\theta} = -\omega^2 \theta. \tag{26}$$

This equation has the advantage that it is linear, but the disadvantage that it is a good approximation only for small oscillations. Of course, it is the same as the equation for simple harmonic motion, which was discussed in Unit 3.

We also consider the **damped pendulum equation**

$$\ddot{\theta} = -\omega^2 \sin\theta - \varepsilon\dot{\theta}, \tag{27}$$

where ε is a positive constant. This equation is very similar to the equation for the damped harmonic oscillator, also considered in Unit 3: the term proportional to $\dot{\theta} = d\theta/dt$ represents the effect of a frictional force that resists the movement of the rod.

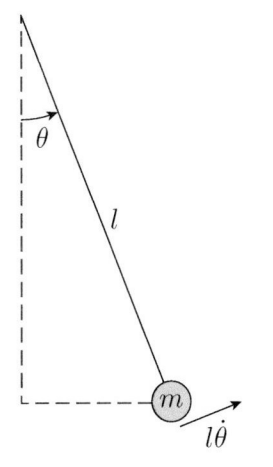

Figure 25   A rigid pendulum consisting of a mass (sometimes called a bob) at the end of a pivoted rigid rod

4.2 The phase plane for a pendulum

In the Introduction we mentioned that the second-order differential equation (25) can be written as two first-order equations. Here we return to look at this point in greater depth.

Although the differential equations (25), (26) and (27) in the previous subsection are of second order, we can rewrite each of them as a *pair* of first-order differential equations; this will enable us to use the techniques from earlier in the unit. More precisely, we will replace θ by x and $\dot{\theta}$ by y, so that

$$y = \dot{x} = \dot{\theta}$$

and

$$\dot{y} = \ddot{x} = \ddot{\theta}.$$

So, for example, equation (25) can be rewritten as the system of first-order differential equations

$$\dot{x} = y,$$
$$\dot{y} = -\omega^2 \sin x,$$

which can be rewritten in terms of a vector field as

$$\dot{\mathbf{x}} = \mathbf{u}(x, y), \tag{28}$$

where

$$\mathbf{u}(x, y) = \begin{bmatrix} y \\ -\omega^2 \sin x \end{bmatrix}.$$

Let us consider the significance of equation (28). Starting from (25), which is a second-order differential equation in a single variable θ, we transformed this into (28), which is a first-order differential equation describing the motion of a point in a two-dimensional phase space, where the coordinates are the angle $x = \theta$ and its rate of change $y = \dot{\theta}$.

Exercise 26

Using the technique employed above, rewrite equation (27) as a system of first-order differential equations.

So the two models introduced in Subsection 4.1 for the motion of a pendulum when the oscillations can be large give rise to two pairs of first-order differential equations.

The pendulum equations

- For arbitrarily large oscillations and no friction, we have

$$\dot{x} = y, \quad \dot{y} = -\omega^2 \sin x, \tag{29}$$

arising from the *undamped pendulum equation.*

- For arbitrarily large oscillations and a frictional force, we have

$$\dot{x} = y, \quad \dot{y} = -\omega^2 \sin x - \varepsilon y, \tag{30}$$

arising from the *damped pendulum equation*.

The analogy with our previous discussion of two interacting populations should be immediately obvious, but here the variables x and y are even more closely related than before, since one is the derivative of the other. A phase point representing a solution of equations (29) or (30) at a given time would tell us not only the position of the pendulum bob, but also its velocity.

For a pendulum, the variable $x = \theta$ represents an angle measured in radians, so the points $(x + 2\pi, y)$ and (x, y) represent the same state of the system. We could restrict the range of x to $-\pi < x \leq \pi$, although we could use any interval of length 2π, such as $0 \leq x < 2\pi$, for example.

Although we can solve the simple pendulum equation (26), we cannot find simple analytical solutions of the undamped and damped pendulum equations (25) and (27). However, we can use the techniques developed in Sections 1–3 of this unit to investigate the qualitative behaviour of the solutions of these equations.

Exercise 27

(a) Find the equilibrium points of the system described by equations (29), i.e.

$$\dot{x} = y,$$
$$\dot{y} = -\omega^2 \sin x \quad (-\pi < x \leq \pi),$$

which is the system of differential equations arising from the undamped pendulum equation.

(b) Describe physically the two equilibrium points that you found in part (a). On physical grounds, would you expect these equilibrium points to be stable or unstable?

Exercise 28

(a) Find the equilibrium points of the system described by equations (30), i.e.

$$\dot{x} = y,$$
$$\dot{y} = -\omega^2 \sin x - \varepsilon y \quad (-\pi < x \leq \pi),$$

which is the system of differential equations arising from the damped pendulum equation.

(b) Describe physically the two equilibrium points that you found in part (a). On physical grounds, would you expect these equilibrium points to be stable or unstable?

In Exercise 27, you showed that the undamped pendulum has two equilibrium points. The first equilibrium point is the origin $x = 0$, $y = 0$, which corresponds to the pendulum hanging vertically downwards at rest, and physically we expect this to be stable. The second equilibrium point is $x = \pi$, $y = 0$, which corresponds to a stationary pendulum pointing vertically upwards, which we would not expect to be stable. To classify these equilibrium points mathematically we must first consider the corresponding linearised equations.

Exercise 29

Consider the non-linear system of differential equations

$$\dot{x} = y,$$
$$\dot{y} = -\omega^2 \sin x,$$

which is the system of differential equations arising from the undamped pendulum equation.

(a) Find the Jacobian matrix of the system.

(b) In the neighbourhood of each of the equilibrium points $(0, 0)$ and $(\pi, 0)$:

   • find the linear system of differential equations that gives the approximate behaviour of the non-linear system near the equilibrium point

   • find the eigenvalues of the Jacobian matrix

   • use the eigenvalues to classify the equilibrium point of the linearised system.

We have seen that an undamped rigid pendulum has two equilibrium points, at $x = \pi$, $y = 0$ (corresponding to a stationary pendulum pointing vertically upwards) and at $x = 0$, $y = 0$ (corresponding to a stationary pendulum hanging vertically downwards. In the approximation of linearised equations, the point at $x = \pi$, $y = 0$ is a saddle (which is unstable) and the point at $x = 0$, $y = 0$ is a centre (which is stable).

For the non-linear rigid pendulum equations, we can again conclude that the equilibrium point at $x = \pi$, $y = 0$ is a saddle (which is unstable). However, the equilibrium point at $x = 0$, $y = 0$ may be either a centre (stable), or a spiral sink (stable) or a spiral source (unstable). This uncertainty can be resolved by noting that the non-linear rigid pendulum equations have a constant of motion. An argument similar to that given in Subsection 3.5 can then be used to show that the $x = 0$, $y = 0$ equilibrium point is a centre and is therefore stable. This makes good sense physically: the pendulum undergoes periodic motion as it swings to and fro.

Exercise 30

Use the equations of motion for an undamped pendulum, equations (29), to show that

$$E(x, y) = \tfrac{1}{2}y^2 + \omega^2(1 - \cos x)$$

is a constant of motion for the undamped pendulum. (If you have studied mechanics, you may recognise that this is proportional to the sum of the kinetic energy and the gravitational potential energy.)

So far we have investigated the motion of the pendulum in the neighbourhood of the equilibrium points. But what about the motions that are not close to the equilibrium points? We can investigate these by considering the *vector field*, which is shown in Figure 26 along with the associated phase paths. Two of the paths shown represent the pendulum continuously circling the support in the same direction, with the value of $x\ (=\theta)$ always increasing or decreasing, so that the bob passes repeatedly through the vertical. The path $EFGH$ describes an anticlockwise rotation of the bob, and $IJKL$ describes a clockwise rotation. These paths do not look closed on the diagram, but they really are because points for which x differs by 2π are equivalent.

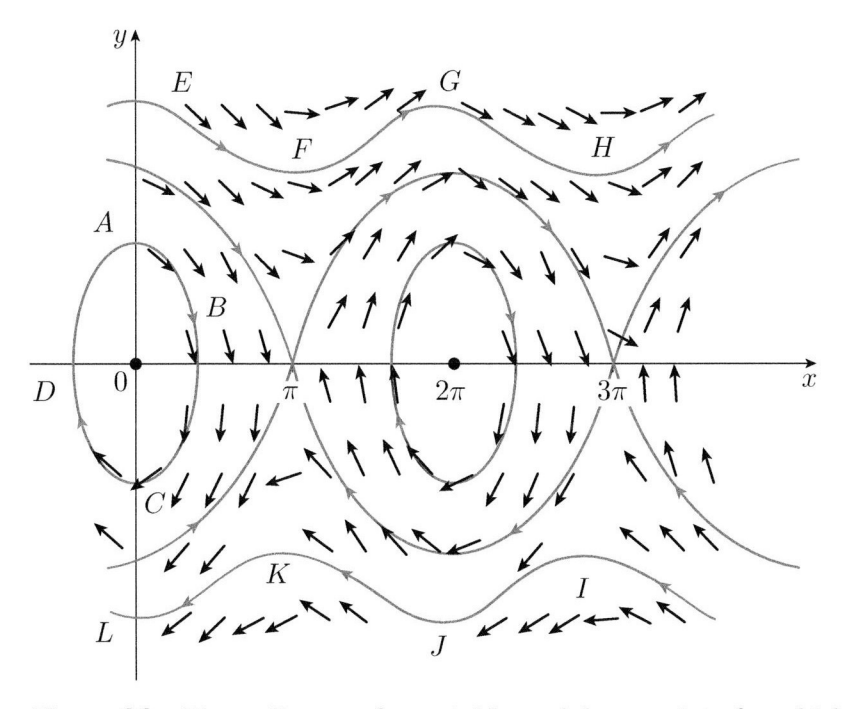

Figure 26 Phase diagram for a rigid pendulum; points for which x differs by 2π are equivalent

Figure 26 also shows a path that is a closed curve $ABCD$: this corresponds to a swinging motion of the pendulum, where there is a maximum angle of deflection and where the sign of the angular velocity can be positive or negative. Finally, the figure also shows a special phase curve where the pendulum reaches $x = \pi$ and $x = 3\pi$ with zero angular velocity $(y = \dot{\theta} = 0)$. This curve, which divides the rotational and vibrational motions, is called the *separatrix*.

In the following exercises, we investigate the behaviour of the damped pendulum.

Exercise 31

Consider the non-linear system of differential equations

$$\dot{x} = y,$$
$$\dot{y} = -\omega^2 \sin x - \varepsilon y,$$

arising from the damped pendulum equation.

(a) Find the Jacobian matrix of the system.

(b) In the neighbourhood of each of the equilibrium points $(0,0)$ and $(\pi,0)$:

- find the linear system of differential equations that gives the approximate behaviour of the non-linear system near the equilibrium point

- find the eigenvalues of the Jacobian matrix

- use the eigenvalues to classify the equilibrium point of the linearised system.

Note: For the equilibrium point $(0,0)$, you will need to treat the cases $0 < \varepsilon < 2\omega$ and $\varepsilon > 2\omega$ separately. You may ignore the possibility $\varepsilon = 2\omega$.

Exercise 32

The figure below shows the vector field for equations (30), which arise from the damped pendulum equation for $0 < \varepsilon < 2\omega$. Describe the behaviour of the pendulum as it follows the path $ABCD$.

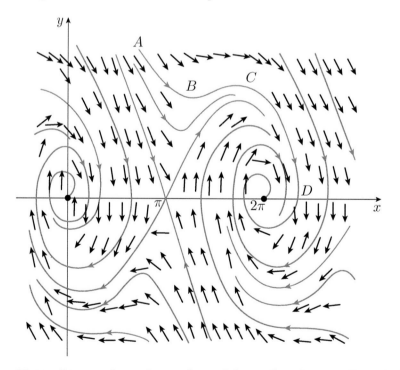

Phase diagram for a damped pendulum; the phase paths spiral towards the equilibrium point $(\theta, \dot{\theta}) = (0, 0)$, where the bob hangs downwards

An overview of non-linear differential equations

Non-linear differential equations can describe a vast range of phenomena, and you will find a bewildering number of techniques for treating them discussed in textbooks. But there are three basic approaches that a mathematically trained scientist tries when confronted with non-linear differential equations. These are:

- Consider the equilibrium points of the equations and their stability.
- Try to use geometrical insights, perhaps by making a sketch of the phase paths.
- Use a computer to calculate solutions using numerical methods.

The first two of these approaches have been discussed at length in this unit. Let us make a few comments about how computers are used to solve non-linear equations. The usual tactic is to reduce the problem to a system of first-order differential equations, using the approach discussed in this section. In Unit 2 we explained how first-order differential equations may be solved by using Euler's method, programming a computer to do the repetitive tasks. Euler's method (and the more sophisticated variants that are used in practice) is easily extended to deal with systems of coupled first-order equations.

Of course, there are many approaches tailored to work with particular types of differential equation. But the three approaches mentioned above are the powerful general-purpose tools.

Postscript: what is chaos?

In the Introduction we mentioned that systems described by non-linear differential equations can show a property called 'chaos', which is present in the trajectory shown in Figure 1. We are now able to give a clearer description of what this term means.

In Sections 2 and 3 we discussed the stability of equilibrium points. This idea can be extended to consider the stability of trajectories. Consider a trajectory of a system of equations, represented by a vector $\mathbf{r}(t) = (x(t), y(t), z(t))$. Compare this with a nearby trajectory $\mathbf{r}(t) + \delta\mathbf{r}(t)$, where $\delta\mathbf{r}$ is very small when $t = 0$. We can ask how the separation $s(t) = \delta|\mathbf{r}(t)|$ of two nearby trajectories grows as a function of time t.

It turns out that there are systems where the separation $s(t)$ of trajectories grows like an exponential function of time: $s(t) \simeq S\exp(\lambda t)$, for some positive constants S and λ. A system is said to be *chaotic* if it has this property of '*exponential instability*'.

Chaos is commonly found in systems that have more than two variables, such as the very complicated equations that determine the weather. In 1961 one of the pioneers of this field, Edward Lorenz (1917–2008), was using a computer to model a weather prediction. When, as a shortcut, he entered some data as 0.506 instead of the more precise 0.506 127, he found that the program gave an entirely different prediction. A tiny shift of the starting point of a trajectory had grown into a large separation. He made a very elegant statement of the significance of this discovery: one of his conference presentations (in 1972) was given the title 'Predictability: does the flap of a butterfly's wings in Brazil set off a tornado in Texas?'.

The early papers on chaos theory from the 1960s do not assume much more mathematical knowledge than you have gained from studying this module. And more generally, if you continue to study quantitative sciences, you will find that the topics treated in this module can take you a long way. We hope that you will find some of the material useful, wherever your curiosity takes you in the future.

Learning outcomes

After studying this unit, you should be able to do the following.

- Use a vector field to describe a pair of first-order non-linear differential equations, and use phase paths to represent the solutions.

- Understand the Lotka–Volterra equations modelling the populations of predators and prey, and interpret their solution using phase paths.

- Interpret points and paths in the phase plane.

- Determine whether an equilibrium point is stable or unstable by sketching paths near it.

- Find the equilibrium points for a system of non-linear differential equations.

- Find linear equations that approximate the behaviour of a system of non-linear differential equations near an equilibrium point.

- Use the eigenvalues and eigenvectors of the Jacobian matrix to classify an equilibrium point for a system of linearised equations. Where possible, use this information to classify equilibrium points of the corresponding non-linear equations.

- Describe, using vector fields and phase paths, the qualitative behaviour of the undamped pendulum and the damped pendulum.

- Check that a given quantity is a constant of motion.

Solutions to exercises

Solution to Exercise 1

The growth rate is proportional to the current population when every individual has an equal opportunity to survive and reproduce, and there are no external factors, such as a shortage of food, that might limit growth. This is generally true when the population is relatively small (although when the population is very small, its growth could be limited by difficulties in finding a mate).

Solution to Exercise 2

Assuming a positive constant proportionate growth rate means that no matter how large the population becomes, the proportionate birth rate exceeds the proportionate death rate by the same amount. The population goes on increasing exponentially. This can never be completely realistic for animals in the wild: for example, at some point the food supply that sustains the population must begin to be exhausted. The difference between the proportionate birth and death rates must then fall.

Solution to Exercise 3

The solution of the differential equation $\dot{y} = -hy$ is $y = y_0 e^{-ht}$, where y_0 represents the initial fox population at $t = 0$. So the number of foxes is declining exponentially (because $h > 0$). This decrease is what we would expect as the foxes have no access to their assumed sole source of food, namely rabbits.

Solution to Exercise 4

The system of differential equations is

$$\dot{x} = x, \quad \dot{y} = -y.$$

The general solution is

$$x(t) = x_0 e^{t}, \quad y(t) = y_0 e^{-t},$$

where x_0 and y_0 are arbitrary constants. Eliminating t gives $xy = A$, so

$$y = \frac{A}{x},$$

for some constant A. Curves of this form are called *hyperbolas*.

Some paths corresponding to these hyperbolas are shown in the figure in the margin.

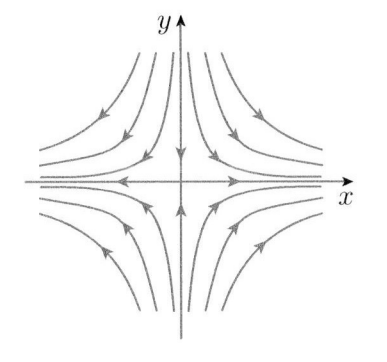

Paths with $x_0 = 0$ and $y_0 \neq 0$ approach the origin as $t \to \infty$, but strictly speaking they never reach it. The only path that includes the origin is the one with $x_0 = y_0 = 0$, which starts at the origin and does not move away from it.

Solution to Exercise 5

Rearranging equation (13), we obtain

$$\frac{\dot{x}}{x} = k - \frac{k}{Y}y,$$

which is the equation of a straight line, as shown below.

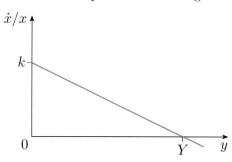

The proportionate growth rate $\dot{x}/x$ of rabbits decreases as the population y of foxes increases, becoming zero when $y = Y$. The population x of rabbits will increase if the population y of foxes is less than Y, but it will decrease if $y > Y$.

Similarly, rearranging equation (14), we obtain

$$\frac{\dot{y}}{y} = -h + \frac{hx}{X}.$$

This is also the equation of a straight line, as shown below.

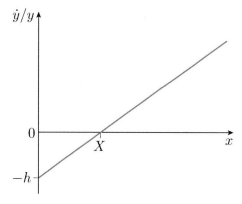

The proportionate growth rate $\dot{y}/y$ of foxes increases linearly as the population x of rabbits increases. The fox population y will decrease if the population x of rabbits is less than X, but it will increase if $x > X$.

Solution to Exercise 6

(a) $[0 \quad 0]^T$ (Note that $\mathbf{u}(0,0) = \mathbf{0}$.)

(b) $[0 \quad -10]^T$

(c) $[0 \quad -5]^T$

(d) $[50 \quad 0]^T$

(e) $[0 \quad 0]^T$ (Note that $\mathbf{u}(1000, 100) = \mathbf{0}$.)

(f) $[0 \quad 5]^T$

(g) $[25 \quad 0]^T$

(h) $[-25 \quad 0]^T$

Solution to Exercise 7

(a) (i) The differential equations under consideration are

$$\dot{x} = 0.05x \left(1 - \frac{y}{100}\right), \quad \dot{y} = -0.1y \left(1 - \frac{x}{1000}\right),$$

with $x \geq 0$ and $y \geq 0$.

In this case, $\dot{x} = 0$ when $x = 0$ or when $y = 100$.

(ii) $\dot{x} > 0$ when $x > 0$ and $0 \leq y < 100$.

(iii) $\dot{x} < 0$ when $x > 0$ and $y > 100$.

We ignore solutions with $x < 0$ or $y < 0$ because populations cannot be negative.

(b) (i) $\dot{y} = 0$ when $x = 1000$ or when $y = 0$.

(ii) $\dot{y} > 0$ when $x > 1000$ and $y > 0$.

(iii) $\dot{y} < 0$ when $0 \leq x < 1000$ and $y > 0$.

(c) Using the results above together with Figures 9 and 10, typical paths representing solutions are shown below.

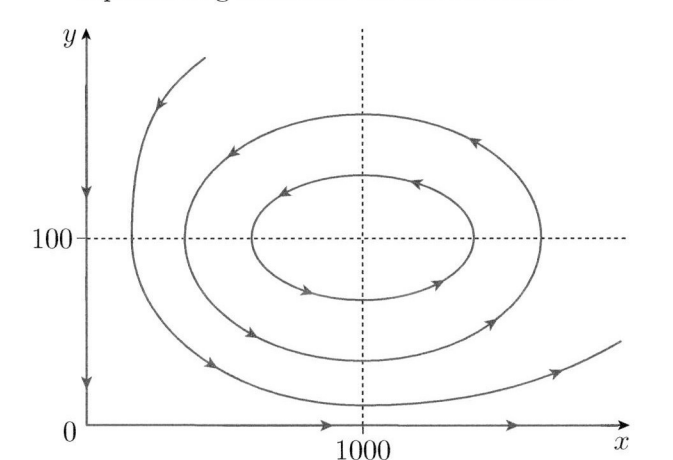

This figure shows a path down the positive y-axis, a path to the right along the positive x-axis, and various cycles about the point $(1000, 100)$. The path down the y-axis describes a population of foxes decreasing to zero in the absence of rabbits. The path to the right along the x-axis describes a population of rabbits increasing without limit in the absence of foxes. It will be shown later (in Subsection 3.5) that the cycles are closed (as shown in the diagram), rather than spirals.

Solution to Exercise 8

Using Procedure 1, we have to solve the pair of simultaneous equations

$$0.1x - 0.005xy = 0,$$
$$-0.2y + 0.0004xy = 0.$$

Factorising these equations gives

$$0.1x(1 - 0.05y) = 0,$$
$$-0.2y(1 - 0.002x) = 0.$$

From the first equation, either $x = 0$ or $y = 20$.

If $x = 0$, the second equation gives $y = 0$, hence $(0,0)$ is an equilibrium point. If $y = 20$, the second equation gives $x = 500$, so $(500, 20)$ is another equilibrium point.

Therefore the only equilibrium points are when there are no animals or when there is a balance between 500 prey and 20 predators. Using the values for this second equilibrium point, the equations can be put in the standard Lotka–Volterra form

$$\dot{x} = 0.1x\left(1 - \frac{y}{20}\right), \quad \dot{y} = -0.2y\left(1 - \frac{x}{500}\right).$$

Solution to Exercise 9

Procedure 1 leads to the pair of simultaneous equations

$$x(20 - y) = 0,$$
$$y(10 - y)(10 - x) = 0.$$

From the first equation, either $x = 0$ or $y = 20$.

If $x = 0$, the second equation gives $y = 0$ or $y = 10$. If $y = 20$, the second equation gives $x = 10$.

Hence the equilibrium points are $(0,0)$, $(0,10)$ and $(10,20)$.

Solution to Exercise 10

(a) Stable.   (b) Unstable.   (c) Unstable.

Solution to Exercise 11

We evaluate the various partial derivatives given in the solution to Example 3. At the equilibrium point $(0,0)$, we obtain

$$\frac{\partial u}{\partial x}(0,0) = k, \quad \frac{\partial u}{\partial y}(0,0) = 0,$$
$$\frac{\partial v}{\partial x}(0,0) = 0, \quad \frac{\partial v}{\partial y}(0,0) = -h.$$

Thus the required linear approximation is

$$\begin{bmatrix} \dot{p} \\ \dot{q} \end{bmatrix} = \begin{bmatrix} k & 0 \\ 0 & -h \end{bmatrix} \begin{bmatrix} p \\ q \end{bmatrix},$$

giving the pair of equations

$$\dot{p} = kp, \quad \dot{q} = -hq.$$

(These are the equations studied in Subsection 1.3.)

Solution to Exercise 12

Here we have

$$u(x, y) = x(20 - y),$$
$$v(x, y) = y(10 - y)(10 - x),$$

giving partial derivatives

$$\frac{\partial u}{\partial x} = 20 - y, \quad \frac{\partial u}{\partial y} = -x,$$

$$\frac{\partial v}{\partial x} = -y(10 - y), \quad \frac{\partial v}{\partial y} = (10 - y)(10 - x) - y(10 - x) = 2(5 - y)(10 - x).$$

So the Jacobian matrix of the vector field $\mathbf{u}(x, y)$ is

$$\mathbf{J}(x, y) = \begin{bmatrix} 20 - y & -x \\ -y(10 - y) & 2(5 - y)(10 - x) \end{bmatrix}.$$

At the equilibrium point $(10, 20)$, we have

$$\mathbf{J}(10, 20) = \begin{bmatrix} 0 & -10 \\ 200 & 0 \end{bmatrix},$$

so the linear approximation is

$$\begin{bmatrix} \dot{p} \\ \dot{q} \end{bmatrix} = \begin{bmatrix} 0 & -10 \\ 200 & 0 \end{bmatrix} \begin{bmatrix} p \\ q \end{bmatrix},$$

giving the pair of equations

$$\dot{p} = -10q, \quad \dot{q} = 200p.$$

Solution to Exercise 13

Solving the equations

$$3x + 2y - 8 = 0,$$
$$x + 4y - 6 = 0,$$

we obtain the equilibrium point $x_e = 2$, $y_e = 1$.

The Jacobian matrix is

$$\begin{bmatrix} \dfrac{\partial u}{\partial x} & \dfrac{\partial u}{\partial y} \\ \dfrac{\partial v}{\partial x} & \dfrac{\partial v}{\partial y} \end{bmatrix} = \begin{bmatrix} 3 & 2 \\ 1 & 4 \end{bmatrix}.$$

In this case, the elements of the Jacobian matrix are all constants, so putting $x = 2 + p$ and $y = 1 + q$, we obtain the matrix equation

$$\begin{bmatrix} \dot{p} \\ \dot{q} \end{bmatrix} = \begin{bmatrix} 3 & 2 \\ 1 & 4 \end{bmatrix} \begin{bmatrix} p \\ q \end{bmatrix}.$$

The corresponding system of equations is

$$\dot{p} = 3p + 2q,$$
$$\dot{q} = p + 4q.$$

Solution to Exercise 14

(a) To find the equilibrium points, we solve the simultaneous equations

$$0.5x - 0.000\,05x^2 = 0,$$
$$-0.1y + 0.0004xy - 0.01y^2 = 0.$$

Factorising these equations gives

$$0.5x(1 - 0.0001x) = 0,$$
$$-0.1y(1 - 0.004x + 0.1y) = 0.$$

The first equation gives

$$x = 0 \quad \text{or} \quad x = 10\,000.$$

If $x = 0$, the second equation is

$$-0.1y(1 + 0.1y) = 0,$$

which gives $y = 0$ or $y = -10$. As $y \geq 0$, only the first solution is possible. This leads to the equilibrium point $(0, 0)$.

If $x = 10\,000$, the second equation is

$$-0.1y(-39 + 0.1y) = 0,$$

which gives $y = 0$ or $y = 390$. So we have found two more equilibrium points, namely $(10\,000, 0)$ and $(10\,000, 390)$.

(b) We have

$$u(x, y) = 0.5x - 0.000\,05x^2,$$
$$v(x, y) = -0.1y + 0.0004xy - 0.01y^2.$$

So the Jacobian matrix is

$$\mathbf{J}(x, y) = \begin{bmatrix} 0.5 - 0.0001x & 0 \\ 0.0004y & -0.1 + 0.0004x - 0.02y \end{bmatrix}.$$

(c) At the equilibrium point $(0, 0)$,

$$\mathbf{J}(0, 0) = \begin{bmatrix} 0.5 & 0 \\ 0 & -0.1 \end{bmatrix},$$

and the linearised approximations to the differential equations in the neighbourhood of this equilibrium point are

$$\begin{bmatrix} \dot{p} \\ \dot{q} \end{bmatrix} = \begin{bmatrix} 0.5 & 0 \\ 0 & -0.1 \end{bmatrix} \begin{bmatrix} p \\ q \end{bmatrix}.$$

At the equilibrium point $(10\,000, 0)$,

$$\mathbf{J}(10\,000, 0) = \begin{bmatrix} -0.5 & 0 \\ 0 & 3.9 \end{bmatrix},$$

and the linearised approximations to the differential equations near this equilibrium point are

$$\begin{bmatrix} \dot{p} \\ \dot{q} \end{bmatrix} = \begin{bmatrix} -0.5 & 0 \\ 0 & 3.9 \end{bmatrix} \begin{bmatrix} p \\ q \end{bmatrix}.$$

Finally, at the equilibrium point $(10\,000, 390)$,

$$\mathbf{J}(10\,000, 390) = \begin{bmatrix} -0.5 & 0 \\ 0.156 & -3.9 \end{bmatrix},$$

and the linearised approximations to the differential equations near the equilibrium point are

$$\begin{bmatrix} \dot{p} \\ \dot{q} \end{bmatrix} = \begin{bmatrix} -0.5 & 0 \\ 0.156 & -3.9 \end{bmatrix} \begin{bmatrix} p \\ q \end{bmatrix}.$$

Solution to Exercise 15

(a) The characteristic equation of the Jacobian matrix is

$$(3 - \lambda)(1 - \lambda) = 0,$$

so the eigenvalues are $\lambda = 3$ and $\lambda = 1$.

(b) As the eigenvalues are positive and distinct, the equilibrium point is a *source*, and is unstable.

Solution to Exercise 16

(a) The characteristic equation of the Jacobian matrix is

$$-\lambda(-3 - \lambda) + 2 = 0,$$

i.e. $\lambda^2 + 3\lambda + 2 = 0$, which factorises to give

$$(\lambda + 1)(\lambda + 2) = 0,$$

so the eigenvalues are $\lambda = -1$ and $\lambda = -2$.

(b) As the eigenvalues are negative and distinct, the equilibrium point is a *sink* (which is stable).

Solution to Exercise 17

(a) The differential equations are

$$\dot{p} = 2p,$$
$$\dot{q} = 2q,$$

which have general solution

$$p(t) = Ce^{2t}, \quad q(t) = De^{2t},$$

where C and D are arbitrary constants.

(b) Eliminating t from the general solution, the equations of the paths are

$$q = \frac{D}{C}p = Kp,$$

where $K = D/C$ is also an arbitrary constant. So the paths are all straight lines passing through the origin.

The above analysis has neglected the possibility $C = 0$. In this case the path is $p = 0$, which is also a straight line passing through the origin, namely the q-axis.

(c) The magnitudes of both $p(t)$ and $q(t)$ are increasing functions of time, so the point $(p(t), q(t))$ moves away from the origin as t increases. So the equilibrium point is *unstable*.

Solution to Exercise 18

(a) The characteristic equation of the matrix is

$$(1 - \lambda)(-2 - \lambda) - 4 = 0,$$

i.e. $\lambda^2 + \lambda - 6 = 0$, which factorises to give

$$(\lambda - 2)(\lambda + 3) = 0,$$

so the eigenvalues are $\lambda = 2$ and $\lambda = -3$.

The eigenvector $[a \quad b]^T$ corresponding to $\lambda = 2$ satisfies the equation

$$\begin{bmatrix} -1 & 2 \\ 2 & -4 \end{bmatrix} \begin{bmatrix} a \\ b \end{bmatrix} = \begin{bmatrix} 0 \\ 0 \end{bmatrix},$$

so $-a + 2b = 0$, and an eigenvector corresponding to the positive eigenvalue $\lambda = 2$ is $[2 \quad 1]^T$. Other eigenvectors corresponding to $\lambda = 2$ are multiples of this; all these eigenvectors are along the line $q = \frac{1}{2}p$.

The eigenvector $[a \quad b]^T$ corresponding to $\lambda = -3$ satisfies the equation

$$\begin{bmatrix} 4 & 2 \\ 2 & 1 \end{bmatrix} \begin{bmatrix} a \\ b \end{bmatrix} = \begin{bmatrix} 0 \\ 0 \end{bmatrix},$$

so $4a + 2b = 0$, and an eigenvector corresponding to the negative eigenvalue $\lambda = -3$ is $[1 \quad -2]^T$; all these eigenvectors are along the line $q = -2p$.

(b) The matrix has one positive and one negative eigenvalue, so the (unstable) equilibrium point is a *saddle*.

(c) There are two straight-line paths, namely $q = \frac{1}{2}p$ and $q = -2p$, corresponding to the two eigenvectors. On the line $q = \frac{1}{2}p$, the point $(p(t), q(t))$ moves away from the origin as t increases, because the corresponding eigenvalue is *positive*. On the line $q = -2p$, the point approaches the origin as t increases, because the corresponding eigenvalue is *negative*. This information, together with the knowledge that the equilibrium point is a saddle, allows us to sketch the phase diagram in the margin.

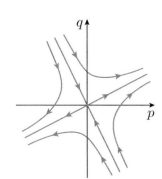

Solution to Exercise 19

(a) The characteristic equation of the Jacobian matrix is

$$(2 - \lambda)(-2 - \lambda) + 5 = 0,$$

i.e. $\lambda^2 + 1 = 0$, so the eigenvalues are $\lambda = i$ and $\lambda = -i$.

(b) As both of the eigenvalues are imaginary, the equilibrium point is a *centre*, which is stable.

Solution to Exercise 20

(a) The characteristic equation of the Jacobian matrix is

$$(1 - \lambda)^2 + 1 = 0,$$

i.e. $\lambda^2 - 2\lambda + 2 = 0$, which has complex roots $\lambda = 1 + i$ and $\lambda = 1 - i$.

(b) As the eigenvalues are complex with positive real part, the equilibrium point is a *spiral source* (and is unstable).

Solution to Exercise 21

(a) The point could be a source, a star source or a spiral source (all of which are unstable).

(b) The point could be a sink, a star sink or a spiral sink (all of which are stable)

Solution to Exercise 22

The Jacobian matrix is
$$\mathbf{J} = \begin{bmatrix} 0 & -kX/Y \\ hY/X & 0 \end{bmatrix},$$

which has the characteristic equation
$$\lambda^2 + hk = 0.$$

The eigenvalues are $\lambda = \pm i\sqrt{hk}$, which are purely imaginary, so the equilibrium point is a *centre*, which is stable.

Solution to Exercise 23

The eigenvalues of the Jacobian matrix are $\lambda = k$ and $\lambda = -h$, which are real and have opposite signs because $k > 0$ and $h > 0$. So the equilibrium point is a *saddle*. (In fact, in this case we have to restrict p and q to non-negative values, but this does not affect our conclusion.)

Solution to Exercise 24

The characteristic equation is $(2 - \lambda)(2 - \lambda) + 9 = 0$, which gives
$$\lambda^2 - 4\lambda + 13 = 0.$$

The eigenvalues are
$$\lambda = \frac{4 \pm \sqrt{16 - 52}}{2} = 2 \pm 3i.$$

The eigenvector $\begin{bmatrix} a & b \end{bmatrix}^T$ corresponding to the eigenvalue $2 + 3i$ satisfies
$$\begin{bmatrix} -3i & -3 \\ 3 & -3i \end{bmatrix} \begin{bmatrix} a \\ b \end{bmatrix} = \begin{bmatrix} 0 \\ 0 \end{bmatrix},$$

so $-3ia - 3b = 0$. Hence an eigenvector corresponding to $2 + 3i$ is $\begin{bmatrix} 1 & -i \end{bmatrix}^T$. (In a similar way, an eigenvector corresponding to $2 - 3i$ is $\begin{bmatrix} 1 & i \end{bmatrix}^T$.)

To find the general solution of the system of differential equations, we need to find the real and imaginary parts of $\begin{bmatrix} 1 & -i \end{bmatrix}^T e^{(2+3i)t}$. We get
$$e^{2t}e^{3it} \begin{bmatrix} 1 \\ -i \end{bmatrix} = e^{2t}(\cos 3t + i\sin 3t) \begin{bmatrix} 1 \\ -i \end{bmatrix}$$
$$= e^{2t} \begin{bmatrix} \cos 3t \\ \sin 3t \end{bmatrix} + ie^{2t} \begin{bmatrix} \sin 3t \\ -\cos 3t \end{bmatrix}.$$

The general solution is

$$\begin{bmatrix} p \\ q \end{bmatrix} = Ce^{2t} \begin{bmatrix} \cos 3t \\ \sin 3t \end{bmatrix} + De^{2t} \begin{bmatrix} \sin 3t \\ -\cos 3t \end{bmatrix}.$$

As the eigenvalues are complex with a positive real component, the equilibrium point $p = 0$, $q = 0$ is a *spiral source*, which is unstable (see Figure 19).

As the equilibrium point of the linear approximation is not a centre, the corresponding equilibrium point of the non-linear system is also a spiral source.

Solution to Exercise 25

(a) The equilibrium points are given by

$$(1 + x - 2y)x = 0,$$
$$(x - 1)y = 0.$$

The second equation gives

$$x = 1 \quad \text{or} \quad y = 0.$$

When $x = 1$, substituting into the first equation gives

$$2 - 2y = 0,$$

which leads to $y = 1$. So $(1, 1)$ is an equilibrium point.

When $y = 0$, substituting into the first equation gives

$$(1 + x)x = 0,$$

hence $x = 0$ or $x = -1$. So we have found two further equilibrium points, namely $(0, 0)$ and $(-1, 0)$.

(b) With the usual notation,

$$u(x, y) = (1 + x - 2y)x = x + x^2 - 2xy,$$
$$v(x, y) = (x - 1)y = xy - y.$$

So the Jacobian matrix is

$$\begin{bmatrix} \dfrac{\partial u}{\partial x} & \dfrac{\partial u}{\partial y} \\ \dfrac{\partial v}{\partial x} & \dfrac{\partial v}{\partial y} \end{bmatrix} = \begin{bmatrix} 1 + 2x - 2y & -2x \\ y & x - 1 \end{bmatrix}.$$

(c) At the point $(0, 0)$, the Jacobian matrix is

$$\begin{bmatrix} 1 & 0 \\ 0 & -1 \end{bmatrix},$$

so the linearised system is

$$\begin{bmatrix} \dot{p} \\ \dot{q} \end{bmatrix} = \begin{bmatrix} 1 & 0 \\ 0 & -1 \end{bmatrix} \begin{bmatrix} p \\ q \end{bmatrix}.$$

The eigenvalues of the Jacobian matrix are $\lambda = 1$ and $\lambda = -1$. As one of the eigenvalues is positive and the other is negative, the equilibrium point of the linearised system is a *saddle*.

At the point $(-1, 0)$, the Jacobian matrix is

$$\begin{bmatrix} -1 & 2 \\ 0 & -2 \end{bmatrix},$$

so the linearised system is

$$\begin{bmatrix} \dot{p} \\ \dot{q} \end{bmatrix} = \begin{bmatrix} -1 & 2 \\ 0 & -2 \end{bmatrix} \begin{bmatrix} p \\ q \end{bmatrix}.$$

The characteristic equation of the Jacobian matrix is $(-1 - \lambda)(-2 - \lambda) = 0$, so the eigenvalues are $\lambda = -1$ and $\lambda = -2$. As these eigenvalues are negative and distinct, the equilibrium point of the linearised system is a *sink*.

At the point $(1, 1)$, the Jacobian matrix is

$$\begin{bmatrix} 1 & -2 \\ 1 & 0 \end{bmatrix},$$

so the linearised system is

$$\begin{bmatrix} \dot{p} \\ \dot{q} \end{bmatrix} = \begin{bmatrix} 1 & -2 \\ 1 & 0 \end{bmatrix} \begin{bmatrix} p \\ q \end{bmatrix}.$$

The characteristic equation of the Jacobian matrix is

$$(1 - \lambda)(-\lambda) + 2 = \lambda^2 - \lambda + 2 = 0.$$

The roots of this quadratic equation are

$$\lambda = \tfrac{1}{2}(1 \pm i\sqrt{7}),$$

so the eigenvalues are complex with a positive real part.

Hence the equilibrium point of the linearised system is a *spiral source*.

(d) As none of the equilibrium points of the linearised systems found in part (c) are centres, the behaviour of the original non-linear system near the equilibrium points is the same as that of the linear approximations. In other words,

$(0, 0)$ is a *saddle*, which is unstable,
$(-1, 0)$ is a *sink*, which is stable,
$(1, 1)$ is a *spiral source*, which is unstable.

Solution to Exercise 26

If we replace θ by x and let $y = \dot{x} = \dot{\theta}$, then we have

$$\dot{y} = \ddot{x} = \ddot{\theta} = -\omega^2 \sin\theta - \varepsilon\dot{\theta} = -\omega^2 \sin x - \varepsilon y.$$

So the system of first-order differential equations that is equivalent to equation (27) is

$$\dot{x} = y,$$
$$\dot{y} = -\omega^2 \sin x - \varepsilon y.$$

The associated vector field is

$$\mathbf{u}(x, y) = \begin{bmatrix} y \\ -\omega^2 \sin x - \varepsilon y \end{bmatrix}.$$

Solution to Exercise 27

(a) To find the equilibrium points, we use Procedure 1 and put
$\mathbf{u}(x, y) = \mathbf{0}$. This gives

$$y = 0,$$
$$-\omega^2 \sin x = 0.$$

So there are two equilibrium points in the range $-\pi < x \le \pi$, namely
$(0, 0)$ and $(\pi, 0)$.

(b) The equilibrium point $(0, 0)$ corresponds to $x = 0$, $\dot{x} = 0$. Physically,
this corresponds to a stationary pendulum hanging vertically
downwards. From experience, we know that a small disturbance from
this equilibrium point will result in small oscillations about the
downwards vertical. So we would expect this equilibrium point to be
stable.

The equilibrium point $(\pi, 0)$ corresponds to $x = \pi$, $\dot{x} = 0$, which is a
pendulum pointing vertically upwards at rest. (Not easy to achieve in
practice!) A small disturbance from this equilibrium point will result
in the pendulum moving away from the upwards vertical and speeding
up until it is vertically downwards. It will then move through its
lowest position and continue to move in the same direction, slowing
down and heading towards the highest point. So we would expect this
equilibrium point to be *unstable*.

Solution to Exercise 28

(a) As in the solution to Exercise 27(a), to find the equilibrium points we
need to find the solutions of

$$y = 0,$$
$$-\omega^2 \sin x - \varepsilon y = 0.$$

Substituting $y = 0$ from the first equation into the second equation
leads to $x = 0$ or $x = \pi$. So there are two equilibrium points in the
range $-\pi < x \le \pi$, namely $(0, 0)$ and $(\pi, 0)$.

(b) Using reasoning similar to that used in the solution to Exercise 27(b),
the equilibrium point $(0, 0)$ corresponds to a pendulum hanging
vertically downwards at rest. We expect this equilibrium point to be
stable. The equilibrium point $(\pi, 0)$ corresponds to a stationary
pendulum pointing vertically upwards. As in Exercise 27, we expect
this equilibrium point to be unstable.

Solution to Exercise 29

(a) Using the usual notation,

$$u(x, y) = y,$$
$$v(x, y) = -\omega^2 \sin x.$$

So the Jacobian matrix is

$$\mathbf{J} = \begin{bmatrix} \dfrac{\partial u}{\partial x} & \dfrac{\partial u}{\partial y} \\ \dfrac{\partial v}{\partial x} & \dfrac{\partial v}{\partial y} \end{bmatrix} = \begin{bmatrix} 0 & 1 \\ -\omega^2 \cos x & 0 \end{bmatrix}.$$

(b) Using Procedure 2, in the neighbourhood of the equilibrium point $(0,0)$, the linear system of differential equations that approximates the non-linear system is

$$\begin{bmatrix} \dot{p} \\ \dot{q} \end{bmatrix} = \begin{bmatrix} 0 & 1 \\ -\omega^2 & 0 \end{bmatrix} \begin{bmatrix} p \\ q \end{bmatrix}.$$

The characteristic equation of the Jacobian matrix is

$$\lambda^2 + \omega^2 = 0,$$

so the eigenvalues are $\lambda = \pm i\omega$.

Hence the equilibrium point $(0,0)$ is a *stable centre* of the linearised system.

The linearised system of differential equations in the neighbourhood of the equilibrium point $(\pi, 0)$ is

$$\begin{bmatrix} \dot{p} \\ \dot{q} \end{bmatrix} = \begin{bmatrix} 0 & 1 \\ \omega^2 & 0 \end{bmatrix} \begin{bmatrix} p \\ q \end{bmatrix}.$$

The eigenvalues of the Jacobian matrix are $\lambda = \pm\omega$.

The eigenvalues have opposite signs, so the equilibrium point $(\pi, 0)$ is a *saddle* of the linearised system.

Solution to Exercise 30

The equations of motion are $\dot{x} = y$, $\dot{y} = -\omega^2 \sin x$, and we have

$$\frac{\partial E}{\partial x} = \omega^2 \sin x, \qquad \frac{\partial E}{\partial y} = y,$$

so equation (23) gives

$$\frac{dE}{dt} = \frac{\partial E}{\partial x} \dot{x} + \frac{\partial E}{\partial y} \dot{y} = \omega^2 \sin x \dot{x} + y\dot{y}$$
$$= \omega^2 (\sin x)y - y\omega^2 \sin x = 0.$$

So $E(t) = E(x(t), y(t))$ is indeed a constant of motion.

Solution to Exercise 31

(a) Using the usual notation,

$$u(x, y) = y,$$
$$v(x, y) = -\omega^2 \sin x - \varepsilon y.$$

So the Jacobian matrix is

$$\mathbf{J} = \begin{bmatrix} 0 & 1 \\ -\omega^2 \cos x & -\varepsilon \end{bmatrix}.$$

(b) The linear system of differential equations that approximates the system near the equilibrium point $(0,0)$ is

$$\begin{bmatrix} \dot{p} \\ \dot{q} \end{bmatrix} = \begin{bmatrix} 0 & 1 \\ -\omega^2 & -\varepsilon \end{bmatrix} \begin{bmatrix} p \\ q \end{bmatrix}.$$

The characteristic equation of the Jacobian matrix is

$$-\lambda(-\varepsilon - \lambda) + \omega^2 = \lambda^2 + \varepsilon\lambda + \omega^2 = 0.$$

For $0 < \varepsilon < 2\omega$, the eigenvalues are

$$\lambda = \tfrac{1}{2}\left(-\varepsilon \pm i\sqrt{4\omega^2 - \varepsilon^2}\right),$$

so the equilibrium point is a *spiral sink* (which is stable).

For $\varepsilon > 2\omega$, the eigenvalues are

$$\lambda = \tfrac{1}{2}\left(-\varepsilon \pm \sqrt{\varepsilon^2 - 4\omega^2}\right).$$

Both the eigenvalues are negative, so $(0,0)$ is a *sink* (which is stable).

The linearised system of differential equations in the neighbourhood of the equilibrium point $(\pi, 0)$ is

$$\begin{bmatrix} \dot{p} \\ \dot{q} \end{bmatrix} = \begin{bmatrix} 0 & 1 \\ \omega^2 & -\varepsilon \end{bmatrix} \begin{bmatrix} p \\ q \end{bmatrix}.$$

The characteristic equation of the Jacobian matrix is

$$-\lambda(-\varepsilon - \lambda) - \omega^2 = \lambda^2 + \varepsilon\lambda - \omega^2 = 0,$$

so the eigenvalues are

$$\lambda = \tfrac{1}{2}\left(-\varepsilon \pm \sqrt{\varepsilon^2 + 4\omega^2}\right).$$

One of these eigenvalues is positive, whereas the other is negative, so the equilibrium point $(\pi, 0)$ is a *saddle* (which is unstable).

Solution to Exercise 32

At A, $y = \dot{\theta} > 0$ so the pendulum is moving in an anticlockwise direction and it is approaching its highest point $(x = \pi)$. It slows down as it passes through this point, and continues to slow down until a little after the highest point at B. It then continues to move in an anticlockwise direction, and speeds up until it reaches C. It moves through its lowest position $(x = 2\pi)$, still moving anticlockwise, and heads towards its highest point again – but does not reach it. At D it stops, then falls back and oscillates about its lowest point with ever-decreasing amplitude.

Acknowledgements

Grateful acknowledgement is made to the following source:

Figure 1: Taken from www.zvjezdarnica.com/ps_photo/1190068473/normal_1208549484.jpg.

Every effort has been made to contact copyright holders. If any have been inadvertently overlooked, the publishers will be pleased to make the necessary arrangements at the first opportunity.

Index

trigonometric Fourier series 22
trivial solution 93
truncated Fourier series 25
Tukey, John 53

undamped pendulum equation 183, 184
    constant of motion 187
unstable equilibrium point 161, 162, 168–170, 173

vector field 149

Volterra, Vito 156

water wave on the surface of the sea 129
wave equation 84, 87
    d'Alembert's solution 128
    general solution 99, 128
    without boundaries 126
wave speed 84, 87, 127
wavelength 127
Wilbraham, Henry 44